GAS CHROMATOGRAPHY IN ADSORPTION AND CATALYSIS

ELLIS HORWOOD SERIES IN PHYSICAL CHEMISTRY

Editor: Professor T. J. Kemp, Department of Chemistry and Molecular Science, University of Warwick

Ball, M. A. and Strachan, A. N. — Chemistry and Reactivity of Solids
Bodor, G. — The Structural Investigation of Polymers
Buxton, G. V. and Salmon, G. A. — Pulse Radiolysis and its Applications in Chemistry
Cook, D. B. — Structures and Approximations for Electrons in Molecules
Coyle, J. D. — Organic Photochemistry
Devonshire, R. — Physical Photochemistry
Gray, G. W. and Winsor, P. A. — Liquid and Plastic Crystals, Vols. I and II
Harriman, A. — Inorganic Photochemistry
Horvath, A. L. — Handbook of Aqueous Electrolyte Solutions
Ignatowicz, S. and Kobendza, A. — Semiconducting Thin Films of $A^{II}B^{VI}$ Compounds
Jaycock, M. J. and Parfitt, G. D. — Chemistry of Interfaces
Jaycock, M. J. and Parfitt, G. D. — Chemistry of Colloids
Ladd, M. F. C. — Structure and Bonding in Solid State Chemistry
Ladd, M. F. C. — Symmetry in Molecules and Crystals
Mills, A. and Darwent, J. R. — Photochemical and Photoelectrical Conversion of Solar Energy
Ościk, J. — Adsorption
Paryjczak, T. — Gas Chromatography in Adsorption and Catalysis
Rest, I. R. and Dunkin, A. J. — Cryogenic Photochemistry
Snatzke, G. — Optical Rotary Dispersion and Circular Dichroism
Southampton Electrochemistry Group — Instrumental Methods in Electrochemistry
Wan, J. K. S. and Depew, M. C. — Polarization and Magnetic Effects in Chemistry
Wiseman, P. — Petrochemicals

GAS CHROMATOGRAPHY IN ADSORPTION AND CATALYSIS

TADEUSZ PARYJCZAK

Professor of Chemistry,
Institute of General Chemistry,
Technical University of Łódź

ELLIS HORWOOD LIMITED
Publishers · Chichester

Halsted Press: a division of
JOHN WILEY & SONS
New York · Chichester · Brisbane · Toronto

PWN—Polish Scientific Publishers
Warszawa

CHEMISTRY

English edition first published in 1986 in coedition between
ELLIS HORWOOD LIMITED
Market Cross House, Cooper Street, Chichester, West Sussex, PO19 1EB, England
and
PWN — POLISH SCIENTIFIC PUBLISHERS
Warsaw, Poland
The Horwood publisher's colophon is reproduced from James Gillison's drawing of the ancient Market Cross, Chichester
Translated by Peter Senn from the Polish
Chromatografia gazowa w badaniach adsorpcji i katalizy, Państwowe Wydawnictwo Naukowe, Warszawa 1975; subsequently subjected to minor revision

DISTRIBUTORS:
Australia, New Zealand, South-east Asia:
JACARANDA WILEY LTD
G.P.O. Box 859, Brisbane, Queensland 4001, Australia
Canada:
JOHN WILEY & SONS CANADA LIMITED
22 Worcester Road, Rexdale, Ontario, Canada
Europe, Africa:
JOHN WILEY & SONS LIMITED
Baffines Lane, Chichester, West Sussex, England
Albania, Bulgaria, Cuba, Czechoslovakia, German Democratic Republic, Hungary, Korean People's Democratic Republic, Mongolia, People's Republic of China, Poland, Romania, the U.S.S.R., Vietnam, Yugoslavia:
ARS POLONA — Foreign Trade Enterprise
Krakowskie Przedmieście 7, 00-068 Warszawa, Poland
North and South America and the rest of the world:
Halsted Press: a division of
JOHN WILEY & SONS
605 Third Avenue, New York, N.Y. 10158, U.S.A.

British Library Cataloguing Publication Data
Paryjczak, T.
Gas chromatography in adsorption and catalysis. —
(Ellis Horwood series in physical chemistry)
1. Gas chromatography 2. Chemistry, Physical and theoretical
I. Title II. Chromatografia gazowa w badaniach
adsorpcji i katalizy. *English*
541.3′028 QD79. C45
ISBN 0-85312-219-9 (Ellis Horwood Limited)
ISBN 0-470-20131-2 (Halsted Press)
LIBRARY OF CONGRESS Card No. 85-936

Printed in Poland

Contents

List of the More Important Symbols

a — quantity of adsorbed substance
a_A, a_B — quantity of adsorbed component A and B
a_m — quantity of substance adsorbed in the monolayer — the monolayer capacity
a_{mg} — quantity of poison required to cover the catalyst surface with a monolayer
A — constant characterizing the eddy diffusion coefficient in the van Deemter equation
A_0 — activity of an unpoisoned catalyst
A_g — activity of a poisoned catalyst
b_g — adsorption coefficient of a poison at active sites
B — constant characterizing the molecular diffusion coefficient in the van Deemter equation
B — the distance between atomic centres or groups of atoms and the centre of surface atoms of graphite under equilibrium conditions
B_{11} — second virial coefficient for the sorbate
B_{12} — second virial coefficient of sorbate vapour (1) and carrier gas (2)
c — concentration of adsorbate in the mobile phase
c_A^0, c_B^0 — initial concentrations of components A and B in the gaseous mixture
c_A, c_B — concentrations of components A and B in the gaseous phase
c_x — mole fraction of adsorbate in the carrier gas
c_s — concentration of adsorbate in the adsorption layer

c_{av} — average concentration of adsorbate in the gaseous phase
c_g — resistance to mass transfer in the gaseous phase
c_k — expression characterizing the kinetics of adsorption
C — constant characterizing the resistance to mass transfer in the van Deemter equation
C — constant in the BET equation
C_k — constant C in the van Deemter equation after having taken the "wall" effect into account
d — density
d_p — average diameter of particles in the column packing
d_e — edge of metal crystallite
d_ε — dispersion of metal
D_g — molecular diffusion coefficient of adsorbate in the carrier gas
D_l — diffusion coefficient in the liquid phase
D_{ef} — effective diffusion coefficient
D_K — Knudsen diffusion coefficient
D_s — surface diffusion coefficient
E — activation energy
E_d — activation energy of desorption
E_p — porosity of column packing particles
E_{pack} — porosity of column packing
F_c — volumetric flow rate of carrier gas through the column
F_c^0 — volumetric flow rate of carrier gas corrected to normal conditions
F_m — volumetric flow rate of gas through the flow-meter
F_{cal} — volumetric flow rate of gas during calibration
F_{ads} — volumetric flow rate of adsorbate
F_{cx} — average volumetric flow rate of the mobile phase in the presence of adsorbate
G_0 — quantity of substance introduced into the reactor
$\Delta G^\ominus$ — change in the standard energy of a system during adsorption
$\hbar$ — Planck's constant
h — height measured (perpendicular to the time axis) from the baseline to a point on the chromatogram
H — height equivalent to a theoretical plate (HETP)
H_M — peak height at maximum c_g
$\Delta H^\ominus$ — change in the standard enthalpy during adsorption

j — pressure gradient correction factor
k — detector constant
$\bar{k}$ — Boltzmann constant
k_a — adsorption rate constant
k_d — desorption rate constant
k_n — rate constant for irreversible activated adsorption
k_f — coefficient of mass transfer from gas to particle surface
k_1, k_2 — rate constants of reactions
k_{ef} — effective rate constant of a reaction
k_{hom} — rate constant of a homogeneous reaction
$K, K_{a,p}, K_{a,c}$ — Henry's constant
K_0 — Henry's constant during the adsorption of a molecule not forming a complex on the surface of a solid
K_A, K_B, K_C — adsorption equilibrium constants
K_A^{ef} — effective Henry's constant for substrate A
K_v — volume partition coefficient
K_p — partition coefficient
K_s — adsorption coefficient at the solid-liquid partition boundary
K_L — adsorption coefficient at the liquid–gas partition boundary
K_{AB} — stability constant of a complex
l_0 — length of recorder tape from the instant of sample injection to the outflow of carrier gas
l_h — length of recorder tape from the instant of sample injection to the outflow of adsorbate at concentration c (to the appropriate deflection h)
L — length of column
m — mass of adsorbent or catalyst in the column
m_L — mass of a unit length of adsorbent layer
Δm_A — quantity of reacted substance A in the microreactor
m_g — quantity of poison introduced into the microreactor
m_{st} — mass of standard
Me_s — surface atoms of a metal which are available for chemisorption
M — molecular weight (relative molecular mass)
n — order of reaction
n_a — number of atoms or chemisorbed molecules on the surface of a metal

n_s — number of moles of adsorbate in the sample
n_L — number of moles of test substance in the liquid phase
n_g — number of moles of test substance in the gaseous phase
N — number of theoretical plates in the column
N_a — number of active sites
N_A — Avogadro's number
N_g — number of adsorbate molecules in the gas space of the column
N_0 — constant dependent on the number of active sites per unit of surface
N_L — number of moles of stationary liquid phase per unit of volume
N_t — number of adsorbed molecules
N_∞ — monolayer capacity
p — vapour pressure of adsorbate at the temperature of measurement
p_s — saturated vapour pressure of adsorbate at the temperature of measurement
p_i — column inlet pressure
p_o — column outlet pressure
p_c — mean column pressure
p_b — barometric pressure
p_m — gas pressure in the flow-meter
p_A, p_B — partial pressures of components A and B
p_{eq} — equilibrium pressure
q — cross-sectional area of the column
q_{st} — isosteric heat of adsorption
$q_{st\,A}$ — isosteric heat of adsorption of substance A
q_{int} — integral heat of adsorption
q_d — differential heat of adsorption
q_0 — differential heat of adsorption at zero packing of adsorbent surface
Q_1 — heat of adsorption in the first layer
Q_c — heat of condensation of adsorbate
r — column radius
R — gas constant
S — specific surface area
S_{st} — specific surface area of standard
S_{ads} — adsorption surface area

S_{peak} — peak area
$S_{peak\,st}$ — peak area of standard
S_v — surface area of sorbent per unit volume of column
$\Delta S^{\ominus}$ — change in standard entropy during adsorption
t — time
t_R — uncorrected retention time
t_M — carrier gas retention time
t'_R — adjusted retention time
t_0 — duration of a pulse of gas at concentration c_0 being adsorbed
T_c — column temperature
T_m — temperature of gas in the flow-meter
T_{ch} — characteristic temperature at $u_A = u_p$
$t'_{R\,alkene}$, $t'_{R\,alkane}$ — adjusted retention times of an alkene and an alkane
t_{max} — time required for complete catalyst regeneration
u — linear velocity of carrier gas
u_c — linear migration velocity of adsorbate at concentration c along the column
u_A — linear velocity of substance A along the column
u_{opt} — optimum linear velocity
u_p — rate of temperature field shift (thermodesorption)
$\bar{u}_{mol}$ — average thermal velocity of adsorbate molecules
u'_1 — first moment
u_2 — second central moment
V — volume of mobile phase per unit length of column
V'_s — volume of adsorption layer per unit length of column
V_{cat} — volume of catalyst
V_R — uncorrected retention volume
V'_R — adjusted retention volume
V_N — net retention volume
V^0_R — corrected retention volume
V_M — retention volume of unsorbed gas (gas hold-up)
V_g — specific retention volume
$V_{g(c)}$ — specific retention volume for adsorbate concentration c
V_s — "net retention volume" — V_g/S
V_m — volume of adsorbate equivalent to a monolayer
V'_{R_A} — adjusted retention volume of substance A if there is no chemical reaction

Introduction

Physical and chemical processes taking place at phase boundaries play an important part in nature and in chemical technology.

In recent years they have become particularly important in all branches of scientific research, though especially in chemistry and biochemistry. From both the practical and theoretical points of view, adsorption and heterogeneous catalysis are outstanding examples of surface phenomena. A knowledge of the effects occurring at the surfaces of solids is essential if one is to explain the mechanisms of processes taking place there. Thus there is a constant need for further study of these processes, and for newer, simpler, quicker and more accurate methods of determining the physicochemical properties of a solid surface. Widespread use is now made of methods based on various physical phenomena. These include X-ray radiography, neutron radiography, electron radiography, IR and Raman spectroscopy, ESR spectroscopy, NMR spectroscopy, Mössbauer spectroscopy, Auger spectroscopy, ESCA electron spectroscopy, ion field microscopy, and electron field microscopy. Gas chromatography (GC) also has a number of applications in this field [1–10].

Rapid advances in GC in the last 25 years have led to the development of new methods in the study of solid surfaces, catalysis and adsorption processes.

The applications of GC in the study of various phenomena in gases, solutions and on solid surfaces are set out in Table 1.

This book deals primarily with the non-analytical applications of gas–solid chromatography. It aims to describe the present stage of investigations on certain physicochemical properties of boundary phases and the possibilities of studying the elementary processes taking place in the chromatographic column.

Some of the properties of the adsorbent–adsorbate system can be defined by comparing the functions of input and output signals; alterna-

Table 1 APPLICATIONS OF GAS CHROMATOGRAPHY

	Non-analytical applications — determination of physicochemical quantities	*Analytical applications*
Gas–liquid chromatography	Determination of the thermodynamic functions of sorption on the basis of the liquid ⇌ gas equilibrium: activity, partition and adsorption coefficients, isotherms and heats of solution, stability constants of complexes. Determination of the properties of gases and liquids: vapour pressure, boiling point of a liquid, dipole moments, extraction properties of solvents, thermal conductivity of vapours and gases. Reaction kinetics of the gas–liquid system.	analysis of organic compounds
Gas–solid chromatography	Study of the kinetics and equilibrium of the gas ⇌ solid system. Determination of the adsorption isotherm, adsorption and desorption coefficients, thermodynamic functions of adsorption, surface adsorption potential, heterogeneity of energetic surface, surface acidity, total and selective surface, diffusion, kinetics of adsorption and chemisorption. Study of adsorbent–adsorbate and adsorbate–adsorbate molecular interactions. Study of reactions occurring at the surface of a solid. Study of catalytic processes.	analysis of gases and very volatile compounds

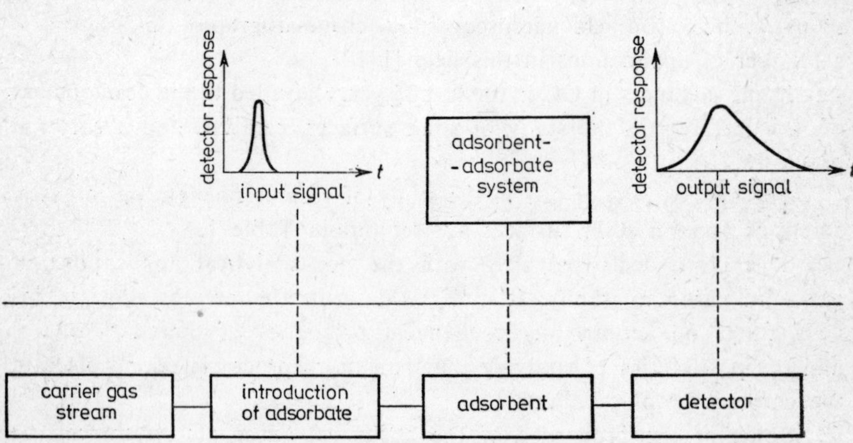

Fig. 1 Diagram illustrating the principle of gas chromatographic measurement.

Table 2 Possible chromatographic determinations

Known function	*Required function*	*Application*	*Example*
Input signal and output signal	properties of the adsorbent–adsorbate system	non-analytical	kinetics and equilibrium of sorption and catalytic processes (qualitatively and quantitatively)
Output signal and adsorbent–adsorbate system	input signal	analytical	chemical analysis, selection of column for separation
Input signal and adsorbent–adsorbate system	output signal		

tively, knowing the properties of the adsorbent–adsorbate system and the function of one of the signals, we can define the other signal (Fig. 1). Thus there are three possible cases (Table 2).

In analytical GC particular emphasis is laid on the good separation of the mixture into its components which are recorded on the chromatogram as a series of peaks or steps. On the other hand, where GC is merely a physicochemical research tool, we are usually interested only in a single peak and how this alters within the system we are testing with changes in the experimental conditions. The task is therefore to determine the effect of elementary processes taking place in the column on the shape of the output curve, and conversely, the possibility of identifying the course of elementary processes in the column on the basis of a given output curve. The shape of this curve is considerably affected by diffusion and kinetic processes, especially in the case of porous adsorbents. The principles of obtaining information from non-analytical chromatography are outlined in Table 3.

Investigation of the different physicochemical properties of the adsorbent–adsorbate systems by GC is now common. However, the development of all the potential applications of GC is still distant and requires further intensive research. The chromatographic method of investigating surface phenomena has a great advantage over the other physical and physicochemical methods mentioned above because of its universal application.

Table 3 Information in non-analytical gas chromatography; adsorbent–adsorbate system in equilibrium in the chromatographic column

Elementary process	*Sorption*		*Reaction at a surface*	*Flow in the gaseous phase*
Primary information	isotherm	sorption rate constant, order of sorption	type, order, rate constant	diffusion in a gas, diffusion in pores

It allows investigations of various phenomena in the same relatively simple apparatus, whereas other methods, much more costly, usually permit the study of only one process. However, the complete elucidation of complex surface phenomena often requires the application of various methods, among which GC is extremely useful. Recent years have seen the rapid development of methods combining GC with other physico-chemical analytical techniques [11, 12], for example, mass spectroscopy, nuclear and electron resonance, infra-red, radiochemical and derivatographic spectrophotometry.

In this book I would like to present the possible applications of gas–solid chromatography to studies of adsorption and catalysis and, above all, to stress the methodological principles, which should be of interest to research groups dealing experimentally with adsorption and catalysis. A number of valuable monographs on GC have appeared recently [1–6, 13], so I have accordingly reduced the scope of certain chapters. This edition has been thoroughly revised and the section on the applications of GC in studies of adsorption and catalysis has been considerably extended.

The first chapter contains a short introduction to the study of adsorption and catalysis using chromatography. I have set down all the essential elementary information about GC which a reader not directly involved with this method will require in order to take full advantage of the remainder of this monograph. I have then gone on to discuss the methods of determining the adsorption isotherm; there is also a detailed presentation of the techniques for determining the specific surface area of a solid, the selective surface area of metals deposited on supports, and the acidity of a surface. The book continues with an examination of the possible uses of GC to determine the thermodynamic functions of adsorption, and to study molecular interactions in the adsorbate–adsorbent and adsorbate–adsorbate adsorption layer. In the final part of the book I have presented the current state of research into the use of chromatography as a tool in the study of catalytic processes. It should be stressed that chromatography is especially useful in investigations into catalysis as in this way one can make measurements in conditions approaching those found in real catalytic reactions in industry.

Chromatographic techniques have nowadays become almost classical and have many merits: the apparatus is simple, they allow for rapid measurement, they are highly sensitive and accurate, and they permit testing over a wide range of temperature and pressure. Despite this, they are all too slowly attaining their rightful place in research and industrial laboratories. The information on the applications of GC in adsorption and catalysis obtained over a number of years is contained in source works and it is for this reason that GC is not exerting a sufficiently powerful influence on laboratory practice in this field. I have done my best to provide an exhaustive literature, although in a rapidly expanding field such as this, my task has proved difficult. It is therefore possible that I have omitted to mention some valuable papers, so here I offer their authors my apologies. I hope this book will draw the reader's attention to the enormous opportunities offered by GC methods in the investigation of surface effects, and in consequence contribute to their widespread use in research laboratories and in industry.

References

[1] Roginskii S. Z., Yanovskii M. I. and Berman A. D., *Osnovy primenenya khromatografii v katalize*, Izd. Nauka, Moskva, 1972.

[2] Vigdergauz M. S. and Izmaylov R. I., *Primenenie gazovoy khromatografii dlya opredelenya fizikokhimicheskikh svoystv veshchestv*, Izd. Nauka, Moskva, 1970.

[3] Kiselev A. V. and Yashin Ya. I., *Gas–Adsorption Chromatography*, Plenum Publ., New York, 1969.

[4] Conder J. R. and Young C. L., *Physicochemical Measurement by Gas Chromatography*, J. Wiley, New York, 1979.

[5] Laub R. J. and Pecsok R. L., *Physicochemical Applications of Gas Chromatography*, J. Wiley, New York, 1978.

[6] *Fizikokhimicheskie primenenie gazovoy khromatografii*, Izd. Khimya, Moskva, 1973.

[7] Hopfe V. and Marx G., *Z. Chemie*, **12**, 370 (1972).

[8] Szepesy L., *Gas Chromatography*, Akadémiai Kiadó, Budapest, 1970.

[9] Grob R. L. (Ed.), *Modern Practice of Gas Chromatography*, J. Wiley and Sons, Inc., New York, London, Sydney, Toronto, 1977.

[10] Purnell J. H., *Progress in Gas Chromatography*, Interscience Publishers, J. Wiley and Sons, New York, 1968.

[11] McFadden W. H., *Techniques of Combined Gas Chromatography/Mass Spectrometry*, J. Wiley-Interscience, New York, 1973.

[12] Steingaszner P., Ettre L. S. and McFadden W. H. (Eds.), *Ancillary Techniques of Gas Chromatography*, J. Wiley-Interscience, New York, 1969.

[13] Berezkin V. G., *Analytical Reaction Gas Chromatography*, Plenum Press, New York, 1968.

Chapter 1

Introduction to the Use of Gas Chromatography in Physicochemical Research

I would like to stress that in this chapter I will deal only with the theoretical and practical problems from the field of GC which are neccessary for using the book.

A fully-developed theory of chromatographic phenomena and techniques can be found in other general monographs [1–5].

1.1 General

When a gas or liquid (mobile phase) flows through a porous bed of adsorbent in a chromatographic column (stationary phase), various elementary processes take place. Each component of the mobile phase moves through the stationary phase at a characteristic rate which emerges from a number of coefficients of adsorption (gas–solid chromatography — GSC) or partition (gas–liquid chromatography — GLC). In this way, a homogeneous mixture is split into a series of bands. While migrating through the stationary phase, the components of the mobile phase are repeatedly adsorbed and desorbed. They thus become distributed between the two phases.

Figure 1.1 is a simplified diagram of a gas chromatograph which is also used for investigating the properties of catalysts. The carrier gas flows from the cylinder *1* through the needle valve *2*, the purification and dessication system *3*, the manometer *4*, and flow-meter *5* into the comparative katharometer cell *9*. Gaseous samples are fed in through tap *14*, liquids are introduced through the feeder *15*. If, say, we are testing the activity of a catalyst, the gas flow is introduced into the microreactor *7* and thence to the column *6*. The sample under test can be introduced in single doses or continuously. On leaving the column the gas flows through the katharometer cell. The content of the gas flow is detected continuously by means of the bridge *10* and recorder *11*. The volumetric flow rate at which the gas leaves the system is given by the flow-meter *12*. The substances being tested can be arrested in the freezer *13*. The column,

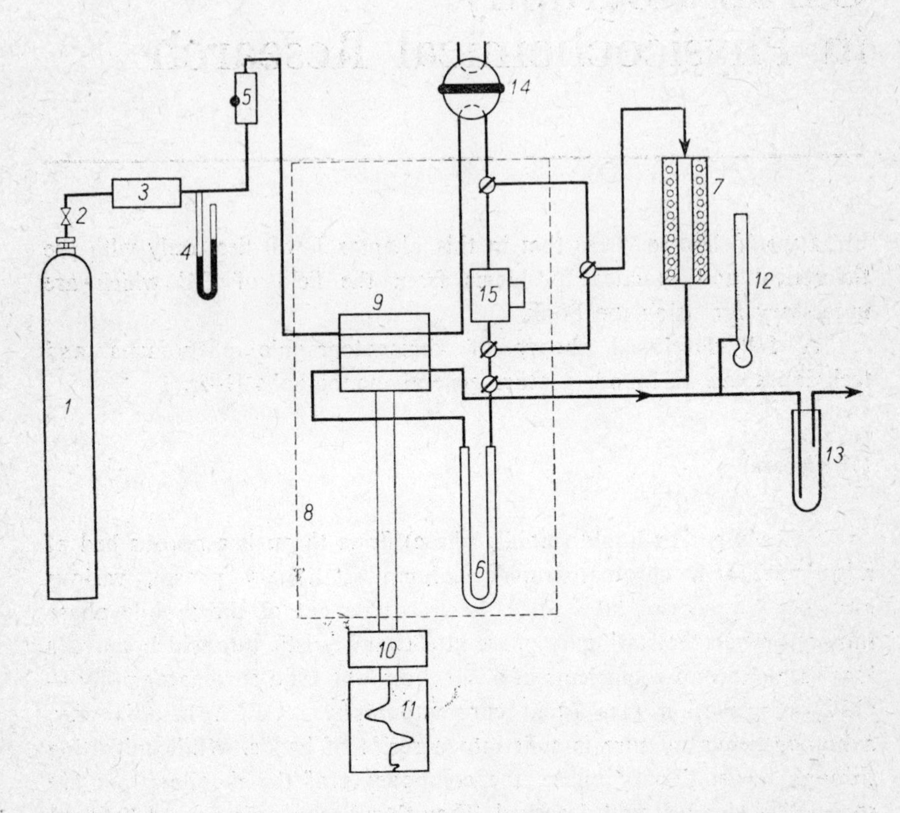

Fig. 1.1 Block diagram showing a gas chromatograph with connected microreactor: *1* — carrier gas supply, *2* — needle valve, *3* — purification system, *4* — manometer, *5* — flow-meter, *6* — column, *7* — microreactor in oven, *8* — thermostat, *9* — detector, *10* — bridge, *11* — recorder, *12* — flow-meter, *13* — freezer, *14* — gas feeder tap, *15* — liquid feeder.

katharometer and liquid sample feeder are all located in the thermostat. The microreactor 7 is heated separately in an electric oven whose temperature is regulated independently.

Chromatographic apparatus and additional equipment used in chromatographs have been described in detail in a number of monographs [1–7].

Attention should be drawn to the stringencies required of chromatographic apparatus used in physicochemical research [8]. (In ordinary analytical GC, these requirements are not so critical.) They include:

(1) accurate measurement of the carrier gas flow rate, high flow stability and a precise pressure check at the column inlet and outlet (any pressure gradient along the column should be reduced to an absolute minimum);

(2) accurate measurement of temperature, its stability in the thermostat and minimal temperature gradients along the column;

(3) the possibility of rapid, consecutive injections of very small samples;

(4) precise determination of retention times;

(5) the smallest possible volume of tubing between the sample injection point and the detector, i.e. the smallest possible dead space in the system;

(6) high detector and recorder sensitivity, and the greatest possible range of sensitivity.

Various companies produce different types of chromatographic apparatus for particular physicochemical research purposes. However, regardless of the type of apparatus and the problem to be solved using GC, the researcher has to choose a suitable carrier gas and its velocity, a technique of sample introduction and its size, an appropriate column of a suitable length, a detector and a chromatographic technique.

1.1.1 The Carrier Gas

The choice of carrier gas depends largely on the type of detector used and the process being studied. Hydrogen, helium, nitrogen and argon are the most commonly used carrier gases. If a thermoconductometric detector (katharometer) is being used, a carrier gas should be used whose thermal conductivity differs most from the thermal conductivity of the substance being tested. The coefficients of thermal conductivity of the above-mentioned gases at 273 K ($\lambda \times 10^5$ J/cm·s·K) are as follows: argon — 16.3; nitrogen — 23.8; helium — 143.7; hydrogen — 159.2. The high thermal conductivities of hydrogen and helium render them the most useful and make the katharometer more sensitive. In non-analytical GC one should use a carrier gas which is not adsorbed on to the surface of the solid, or which does not dissolve in the liquid in the case of GLC. Helium is usually the best for such purposes. Hydrogen can also be used, provided it does not react with the surface of the stationary phase or with the adsorbate under experimental conditions. However, the danger of explosion when using hydrogen and the high cost of helium restrict their use somewhat. For these reasons, nitrogen or argon are often used as carrier gases in highly sensitive katharometers. The diffusion coefficients of test substances are lower in nitrogen and argon than in hydrogen and helium, and in consequence, narrower peaks are obtained. These gases do, however, have disadvantages, namely, a considerable viscosity and low thermal conductivity. The effect of the carrier gas on heats of adsorption has been demonstrated [9, 10]. This is due to the non-ideality of real carrier gases, i.e. their compressibility, viscosity and partial adsorption on to the surface of the solid under test [11, 12].

High purity of the carrier gas is essential, since even trace amounts of a contaminant which may be adsorbed will, as a result of accumulation, completely distort the results. Trace contaminants can be removed from hydrogen and helium by adsorption on molecular sieves or on activated charcoal at the temperature of liquid nitrogen. To purify helium, use is also made of its diffusion properties through the walls of thin capillary tubes [13]. Pure hydrogen can be obtained from the electrolysis of water; any oxygen present is then removed over a platinum or palladium catalyst.

The purity of hydrogen or helium should always be checked, even by the simplified method of passing it for a certain time through a layer of molecular sieves cooled by liquid nitrogen.

After having heated the adsorber, any contaminants are desorbed, which the recording device will record as a deflection from the base line.

It is also extremely important to remove traces of oxygen from neutral carrier gases, especially from nitrogen and argon. A high degree of deoxygenation of 1 part oxygen to $10^{9.5}$ parts of carrier gas can be achieved on manganese oxide [14, 15]. In fact, the degree of deoxygenation of a neutral gas is even higher (theoretically $1 : 10^{35}$), the value given depending on the sensitivity of the detector. Carrier gases are usually dried on molecular sieves.

An extremely stable carrier gas flow rate is essential not only for the precise determination of the volumetric flow rate F_c, but also for obtaining significant and reproducible signals from most detectors.

Either the flow rate or the pressure can be regulated at the column inlet. In temperature-programmed desorption (TPD) investigations the flow rate changes, and disturbances in the base line are observed while working with, e.g. a katharometer.

In this case it is better to use flow rate regulator, devices which maintain a constant pressure drop owing to pneumatic resistance. The use of a flame-ionization detector (FID) allows a wide choice of carrier gas.

In physicochemical investigations nitrogen is often used because its retention times, much longer than for hydrogen and helium, can be determined more precisely.

The flow rate of the carrier gas at ambient temperature can be easily measured by means of a flow-meter containing a solution of soap to show any slight decrease in pressure.

However, using such a flow-meter results in saturation of the carrier gas with water vapour.

The molecular pressure in the flow-meter is, therefore, $p_m - p_w$. The volume velocity at the column outlet estimated for the column temperature T_c and the ambient pressure p_m is

$$F_c = F_m \frac{T_c}{T_m} \frac{p_m - p_w}{p_m}, \tag{1.1}$$

where p_w is the pressure of water vapour, taken from the tables for ambient temperature, F_m is the volume velocity of the carrier gas measured by means of a flow-meter, T_m is the ambient temperature.

1.1.2 Injection System

The investigated sample is injected and evaporated in the stream of carrier gas, as near as possible to the column inlet in order to avoid diffusion of the sample in the gaseous phase. For the same reason all the tubes joining the dosing point with the column inlet should be short and narrow with no rapid changes in the cross-section. The injector must be purpose-built. Liquid samples are usually injected with a microsyringe or other arrangement [16] through a silicone rubber septum resistant to high temperatures. Liquid samples must evaporate rapidly in the feed chamber to prevent peak broadening, tailing and a prolongation of the retention time [17]. It is not recommended to inject gaseous samples with a syringe as it is very difficult to remove the last traces of air from one; furthermore, results cannot be reproduced with an accuracy of greater than about 2%.

Samples are fed in through special multi-way valves. Results can be reproduced to within less than 0.5%. Some types of gas injector are used together with a vacuum system [18]. Gas injectors (capillary tubes of known volume) are usually made of stainless steel [19]. A number of systems for the automatic injection of samples at predetermined time intervals have been described [20–24]. Such apparatus is widely used in studies of adsorption and catalysis.

1.1.3 The Sample Size

The sample size depends on whether the investigations are carried out in the range of "infinite-dilution", or in the range of "finite-concentration". At infinite dilution, concentrations of the components in the carrier gas may be neglected and thus the gaseous phase may be considered ideal.

At finite concentration, a correction for retention calculations should be introduced, which makes them more complicated [86, 88, 89] (see Chapter 4).

It should be stressed that the effect of non-ideality in the gaseous phase is much smaller than that of non-ideality in the stationary phase. The physicochemical properties of the latter phase for the sample at infinite dilution are thus easily investigated.

In the range of infinite dilution, the principles of linear chromatography are applied. In the range of their application, the molecules of the introduced adsorbate samples behave independently of one another since no interactions take place.

All the equilibrium investigations of the mobile phase-stationary phase system require a linear course of the isotherm and so they should be carried out in the range of infinite dilution. Both the theoretical considerations and experimental techniques are much simpler in this concentration range.

The common application of GC over a small concentration range makes it particularly convenient for investigating interface equilibrium, including a solid surface-gas equilibrium.

The sample size in the range of infinite dilution is of 10^2 μg liquid in GLC, from 10^{-3} to 10 μg in GSC, and from 10^{-1} to 10 μg in gas-liquid interface investigations.

In physicochemical and also analytical investigations the range of infinite dilution is usually employed, but often investigations require higher concentrations (e.g. the determination of adsorption isotherms for a higher pressure range and some investigations of catalytic reactions). For higher concentrations the peak is widened and deformed, i.e. it becomes asymmetric and the retention time changes; it may increase or decrease (Chapter 4).

Deformation of the peaks may result from two independent phenomena:

(1) a sorption effect, resulting in a shorter retention time of the peak maximum. It is due to a local increase in the rate of the mobile phase while introducing a sample of a considerable size;

(2) an adsorption isotherm effect resulting from the change in adsorption coefficient accompanying the change in partial pressure.

Various chromatographic techniques are at present applied to investigations in this concentration range (Chapter 4, Section 1.2).

1.1.4 Columns

The column is the heart of the gas chromatograph since the investigated physicochemical processes occur in it. The factors which considerably affect the work of the columns are: the type and the size of packing grains, the way they have been packed, the working temperature and the column dimensions.

The columns used in chromatography are tubes of different shapes (U, W and spirals) and sizes (internal diameters 2–4 mm, length 0.5 to several meters). Chromatographic separation is largely influenced by the column length.

A column of suitable length is essential for analytical purposes, although here too one should avoid an excessive pressure gradient and retention time. A compromise has therefore to be found: simple columns are the best and they are often applied in adsorption and catalysis investigations.

Considering that the shape of a single peak and its changes with experimental conditions are the basis for physicochemical calculations of the properties of a given adsorbate–adsorbent system, we try to obtain good resolution of chromatographic peaks or fronts.

The optimum mass of adsorbent required for physicochemical studies depends on its specific surface area and on the measurement temperature. The higher the measurement temperature and the lower the specific surface area of the adsorbent, the more of it that needs to be used.

When investigating an adsorbent–adsorbate system over a wide range of temperatures, columns of various dimensions are used. At low temperatures, which are accompanied by a more marked physical adsorption, short columns are usually used, whereas at higher temperatures longer columns are the rule in order to obtain more precise determination of retention times. The mass of the adsorbent placed in the column also depends on its diameter. As the column diameter is increased one must take into account the simultaneously increasing eddy diffusion and wall effect. In order to maintain a uniform temperature in the column, its diameter should not exceed 8 mm.

The column should be packed evenly with adsorbent whose particles are of more or less equal dimensions, though no greater than 15–20% of the column diameter. Columns are usually manufactured from stainless steel or aluminium tubes [25]. However, these materials are not so inert as glass and for physicochemical investigations glass and quartz columns are recommended.

In physicochemical investigations micro-packed columns (packed capillaries) are also used. Such columns are prepared by stretching glass tubes (diameter — a few millimeters) packed with adsorbents or catalysts to get capillaries. The capillary diameter should be twice or three times as large as that of the adsorbent or catalyst grains.

1.1.5 Column Temperature Control

The column must be maintained at a constant temperature, such as may be obtained in air thermostats with circulation and thermoregulator temperature control. Programmed heating of columns is becoming more common in experiments on desorption processes (Section 6.7).

Where the temperature rise is programmed, the rate of temperature increase is normally from 0.5 to 25°/min, and sometimes even 40°/min. In practice, however, the rate of temperature increase does not exceed 15–20°/min owing to the difficulties involved in direct temperature control and, because of the low thermal conductivity of the sorbents, the considerable delay before the column packing heats up.

In much physicochemical research a greater stability and accuracy of temperature measurement is required than is provided by factory-produced chromatographs. Modern chromatographs are quite stable as regards column thermostatting: for instance, ±0.1–0.2° over a temperature range from about 293 to 573 K and ±0.2–0.3° from 573 to 773 K. Placing the column in a liquid vapour jacket or liquid bath ensures great stability of temperature and accuracy of its measurement.

If in the measurement of temperature we use a pair of quartz sensors with a resolution of $(1 \times 10^{-3})°$, we may, assuming the sensors to have been suitably placed, obtain a temperature constant to within 0.01° over a working period of 8–10 hours. High temperature stability is essential when determining net retention volumes. If the heater is not thyristor-controlled, one of suitable power must be selected with great care. The volume and shape of the thermostat chamber and the method of mixing are of great importance. Considerable temperature gradients may also exist along the length of the column.

The temperature stability is much enhanced if a cylindrical block of aluminium is placed inside a Dewar flask. The aluminium block is heated electrically. A longer column can be wound around the block; a shorter one, in the shape of a U-tube, can be placed inside it. The optimum temperature fluctuation along the column should then be less than ±0.1°. This is critical when determining net retention values.

In practice, when determining net retention values, the temperature fluctuations along the column should be reduced to under ±0.1°. However, when determining relative retention values, the column temperature can be set with a tolerance of 1 or even 1.5°.

1.1.6 Measurement of Retention Time

A very important question which directly affects the accuracy of chromatographic determinations is the actual measurement of the retention time [26]. Any error in measurement depends on the method of measurement adopted, and will be relatively greater for a substance with a short retention time giving an unsymmetrical peak or a symmetrical but very broad one.

The commonest techniques for measuring retention times include:

(a) using a stop-watch;

(b) using an electronic integrator;

(c) reading the distance from the sample injection to the peak maximum directly from the recorder tape;

(d) using special electronic equipment controlled by the detector signal.

This last method gives the best accuracy [26]. Regardless of the time measured, this equipment gives a standard deviation of only 0.02%. Where retention times are longer, of the order of 1000 s, an ordinary stop-watch gives results which are almost as good. If the retention times are of the same magnitude, reading the time directly from the recorder tape results in differences of around 0.2%.

The integrator is very useful for measuring peak areas but is much less so for retention times, especially if the peaks are broadened. The accuracy of retention time measurement can be improved by lengthening the column packing bed. However, as the length of packing increases, so does the pressure gradient, and the equilibrium conditions at the inlet and outlet of the column will thus be different. The effect of this on the values of the thermodynamic parameters being determined is considerable.

1.1.7 Detectors

Around 20 different types of detectors are used in GC, and their modes of operation make use of the various physicochemical properties of the mobile phase [20]. There are integral and differential detectors (Fig. 1.2).

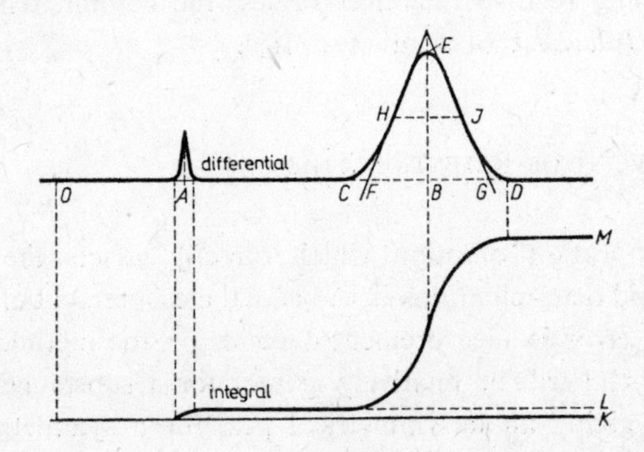

Fig. 1.2 Typical chromatogram for one component; above — the elution peak, (differential detector), below — the frontal chromatogram (integral detector):
0 — sample feed, A — appearance of carrier gas peak, B — appearance of adsorbate peak, FG — peak width, HJ — peak width at half the height, BE — peak height.

Integral detectors measure the quantity of component eluted and add to it the total quantity of components eluted earlier (Fig. 1.6). A series of steps appears on the chromatogram. The size of each step corresponds quantitatively to one component [27, 28].

Differential detectors show momentary changes in the properties of the gas leaving the column. They measure a given physical property of the test substance in the gas stream (e.g. thermal conductivity) or they detect the presence of the substance directly.

A good detector should be characterized by stability, high sensitivity and linearity of the signal. The stability concerns both the base line and the signal. The internal noise of the detector should be as low as possible.

When a given amount of the component is passed through the detector the signal should be as strong as possible (sensitivity) and proportional to that amount (linearity).

An important feature of a detector is the range of linear dependence of its indications on the concentration of the test substance. Outside this range the size of the peak area changes disproportionately in relation to the amount of adsorbate. If the detector needs to be worked non-linearly, quantitative determinations require very precise calibration of the detector in this concentration range. The threshold of detectability is the smallest amount of the component which will produce a signal, the amplitude of which is equal to or several times higher (usually twice as high) than the noise level.

Selective detectors are also used because of their very great sensitivity in relation to a given group of chemical compounds and nearly complete indifference to all other compounds (e.g. the electron capture detector is highly sensitive to halogen compounds).

In adsorption and catalysis investigations differential detectors are most often used. They are based on the measurement of gas conductivity — katharometers (with thermistor or metal fibre sensors [29]) and flame-ionization detectors.

Katharometer. A detector of this type measures changes in the thermal conductivity of the flowing gas. Thermal conductivities of gases vary greatly (Section 1.1.1) and the conductivities of gas mixtures are a function of their components.

Four thin metal fibres (tungsten, Pt–Ir alloys) or thermistors are included in a Wheatstone bridge system; two of them are placed in the pure carrier gas stream (comparative sections) and the two other ones in the stream of outlet gas from the column (measurement sections). The Wheatstone bridge is equilibrated only if pure carrier gas is flowing through the comparative and measurement sections.

The equilibrium is disturbed when a component outwashed from the column passes through the measurement section. This disturbance is amplified and recorded.

The sensitivity of katharometers depends mainly on the type of sensor, its resistance and temperature (the intensity of current), the type of carrier gas and the difference between the specific thermal conductivities of the carrier gas and test substance.

As mentioned in Section 1.1.1, hydrogen and helium are the most commonly used carrier gases with a katharometer because they have the highest thermal conductivities.

It should be noticed that the katharometer signal also depends on its conditions of use. For the same amount of test substance, the peak area is inversely proportional to the square root of the number of theoretical plates (Section 1.3.2) and to the reciprocal of the retention volume [90]. The signal is also inversely proportional to the gas flow rate in the detector. Detectors of this kind are very sensitive even to small alterations in temperature and pressure. They should be thermostatted at a temperature higher than that of the column so as to prevent the adsorbate from condensing in the detector.

Often the detector is placed in a separate thermostat. This ensures that any change in the column temperature does not affect the detector temperature.

Thermal conductivity detectors generally require a greater temperature stability (within the range ± 0.02–$0.05°$) than the chromatographic column because of interference.

Even though they are not very sensitive, katharometers are commonly used because of their universality and reliability.

Their main disadvantage is the possible corrosion of the sensors by certain corrodible compounds.

Flame-ionization detector. In the large group of α, β, and γ-ionization detectors [31, 32] a special position is occupied by the flame-ionization detector [30].

In a flame-ionization detector, ionization is caused by combustion of the test substance in an air–hydrogen or oxygen–hydrogen flame. Organic compounds are combusted in a hydrogen flame in which they are ionized to ions and electrons. The ions gather on the appropriately-charged electrode and the resulting current is multiplied and recorded.

This detector is particularly useful for physicochemical investigations at "infinite dilution" when introducing very small samples of organic compounds. Besides, relatively high concentrations of up to about 1% do not overload the detector.

It is almost insensitive to the presence of water vapour and air in the carrier gas. The use of hydrogen as a carrier gas is not necessary and its separate introduction to the detector is recommended.

Various gases may be used, as inorganic impurities are not harmful.

Flame-ionization detectors can operate satisfactorily without special thermostatting, though precautions do have to be taken to prevent the adsorbate from condensing between the column and the detector. Flame-ionization detectors are thousands of times more sensitive than detectors measuring differences in thermal conductivity. However, one of their disadvantages is their very low sensitivity towards many substances used in adsorption and catalysis studies, such as nitrogen, water vapour, oxygen, carbon dioxide, sulphur dioxide, ammonia, oxides of nitrogen and other simple inorganic gases. A helium detector is particularly useful for detecting these inorganic substances as it is very sensitive towards them [33, 34]. However, the helium has to be of the required standard of purity.

Ionization detectors do not ensure good results when very pure carrier gases are used, e.g. helium should, besides neon, contain at least 1 ppm of other impurities.

1.2 Techniques Used in Gas Chromatography

The following GC techniques are most frequently used in adsorption and catalysis studies:

(1) the elution technique;
(2) frontal analysis;
(3) the elution-on-a-plateau technique;
(4) the displacement technique;
(5) the thermodesorption technique.

1.2.1 The Elution Technique

In the elution technique, discrete samples of adsorbate are injected into the carrier gas stream flowing through the column. Since the adsorbate is alternately adsorbed on to the surface of the adsorbent and then desorbed a large number of times, the sample becomes distributed between the two phases. We obtain a more or less Gaussian elution chromatogram in the form of a peak (Fig. 1.3). Deviations of the peak from a Gaussian curve may be brought about by various factors. These will be discussed in Section 1.3.3 on the broadening of chromatographic peaks.

The fundamental parameter of the peak characterizing the quantity of analysed substance is the peak area (S_{peak}), delimited by the chromatographic curve *CDE* and the base line (Fig. 1.3).

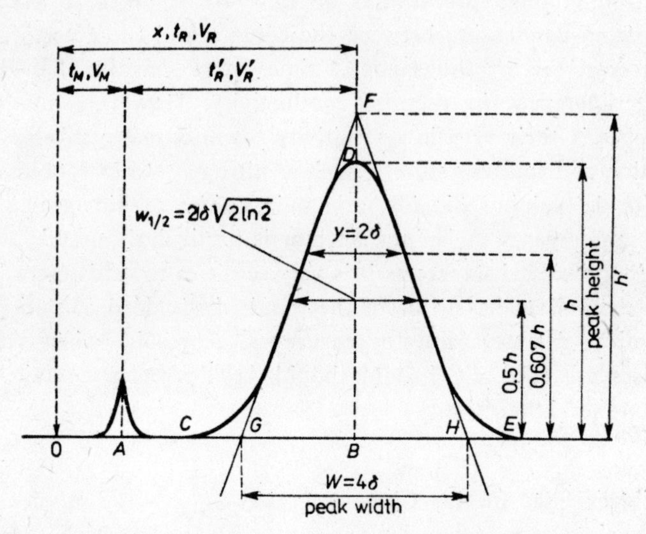

Fig. 1.3 Characteristic magnitudes of an elution peak taking the magnitude of retention into account:

0 — sample injection, *A* — appearance of carrier gas peak, *B* — appearance of adsorbate peak, δ — standard deviation, t_R, t'_R, t_M — retention times (t_R — uncorrected, t'_R — adjusted, t_M — carrier gas), V_R — retention volume, V'_R — adjusted retention volume, V_M — gas holdup, W — peak width at base.

Precise calculation of the peak area is not always possible (for example, where the separation of components is incomplete). In the quantitative analysis of peaks one also uses magnitudes proportional to the peak area, such as the peak height (h) and the product of the peak height and retention time (ht_R). However, the use of the peak height is wholly justified only if the peak is symmetrical. Likewise, using the product of peak height and retention time is permissible only when the peak width alters in proportion to the retention time. For physicochemical purposes the area of the peak, or its height in the case of narrow, symmetrical peaks, is generally determined.

Additional parameters characterizing the chromatographic peak include:

(1) the height of the triangle GFH (h') formed by the base line cutting the tangents to the curve at its inflexions;

(2) the width of the peak at base W (segment GH);

(3) the width of the peak at half the height $\omega_{1/2} = 2\delta\sqrt{2\ln 2}$.

If conditions permit a linear adsorption isotherm to be obtained, the peak is Gaussian. The standard deviation δ is a typical parameter determining a Gaussian curve. In chromatography it is regarded as an "elementary" parameter read directly from a chromatogram although the peak shapes do differ slightly from a Gaussian curve. The parameter is equal to 1/4 of the peak base width. In order to decide whether a peak is Gaussian or not, it is convenient to calculate the ratio of peak width at base W to the width at half the height ($\omega_{1/2}$). Under real GC conditions, one may assume to a first approximation that the peak is symmetrical (Gaussian) if $W/\omega_{1/2}$ lies within the range 1.67–1.73. For greater deviations from the Gaussian shape, the asymmetry of the peak is often assessed with the aid of the so-called asymmetry coefficient. This is the ratio of the distances between the peak height line of the peak and the front and rear profiles of the curve at half height. Figure 1.3 illustrates the characteristic magnitudes of an elution peak which are used, among other things, for determining the number of theoretical plates (see Section 1.3.2).

Under stable conditions, the output time of the peak is a magnitude characteristic of a given system — this is called the *retention time* t_R. It is the time elapsing from the moment the sample is injected to the appearance of the peak maximum (distance OB in Fig. 1.3). Any substance not being sorbed by the stationary phase (e.g. the carrier gas) leaves the column at point A. The distance OA is the retention time of a gas not being adsorbed, t_M, the *carrier gas retention time.*

The difference between the retention time of a given adsorbate and that of a neutral carrier gas is called the *adjusted retention time* of the adsorbate t'_R (distance $OB-OA$)

$$t'_R = t_R - t_M . \tag{1.2}$$

The magnitude of t'_R depends on the volumetric flow rate of carrier gas F_c (cm^3/min) at the column outlet (at column temperature and ambient pressure — formula (1.1)).

The product $t_R F_c$ gives the so-called *retention volume* V_R

$$V_R = t_R F_c . \tag{1.3}$$

The retention volume of a given adsorbate is the volume of carrier gas flowing through the column from the moment of sample injection to the appearance of the peak maximum. The *adjusted retention volume* (V'_R) is the volume of carrier gas flowing through the column when the adsorbate is in the stationary phase.

We can calculate the adjusted retention volume thus

$$V'_R = t'_R F_c = (t_R - t_M) F_c = V_R - V_M , \tag{1.4}$$

where $V_M = t_M F_c$ is the gas hold-up.

The boundary or corrected retention volume V^0_R is the retention volume when there is no pressure drop along the column (i.e. for zero flow). The value $j = V^0_R / V_R$ is less than 1 and decreases as the ratio of inlet pressure (p_i) to outlet pressure (p_o) in the column increases.

In order to calculate the retention volume, we have to correct the volumetric flow rate of the carrier gas F_m, measured at temperature T_m and pressure p_m to the column temperature T_c and pressure p_c.

The variable flow of gas through the column is due to the pressure gradient along the column. The mean pressure in the uniformly packed column can be determined by including a correction factor for this pressure gradient [35]

$$j = \frac{3}{2} \frac{(p_i/p_o)^2 - 1}{(p_i/p_o)^3 - 1} , \tag{1.5}$$

where p_i and p_o are the gas pressures at the column inlet and outlet respectively.

The *net retention volume* V_N is obtained as a result of a double correction of the uncorrected retention volume V_R

$$V_N = jV'_R = j(t_R - t_M) F_c . \tag{1.6}$$

Normally, values V_R, V'_R, V^0_R and V_M are measured at the column temperature T_c and at the outlet pressure p_o, and so F_c also requires correction for these conditions (formula (1.1)).

The net retention volume with respect to unit mass m of adsorbent (GSC) or liquid phase (GLC) calculated to 273 K gives the *specific retention volume* V_g

$$V_g = \frac{273}{T_c} \frac{V_N}{m} . \tag{1.7}$$

In GLC the specific retention volume is a physicochemical constant; in GSC, however, it depends on the magnitude of the specific surface area of the adsorbent. In this case, the physicochemical constant is the specific retention volume with respect to unit area S, also known as the net retention volume V_s [36–38], i.e.

$$V_s = \frac{V_g}{S}, \tag{1.8}$$

where S is the specific surface area of the adsorbent (m^2/g).

A number of physicochemical values can be determined from the specific retention volume — for instance, the specific surface area of adsorbents and catalysts, partition coefficients, adsorption or solution isotherms, thermodynamic functions of adsorption, and many others. The following equation gives the relationship between the specific retention volume and temperature [39]:

$$\log V_g = A + \frac{B}{T_c + C}, \tag{1.9}$$

where T_c is the column temperature, and A, B, C are constants.

The relationship between the relative change in retention volume with temperature is also given by [64]

$$\frac{\Delta V_g}{V_g} = \frac{Q}{RT_c} \cdot \frac{\Delta T}{T_c}, \tag{1.10}$$

where Q is the heat of adsorption (kJ/mol), and R is the gas constant.

Bearing in mind the fact that for most adsorbate–adsorbent systems the heat of physical adsorption ranges from 8.38 to 50.28 kJ/mol, the relative change in retention volume for a temperature change in the column of 1° is easily calculated. At 298 K these changes range from 1.7 to 6.7%, at 498 K from 0.6 to 2.4%.

For the same experimental conditions it is unnecessary in many cases to calculate the retention volume — retention times are quite sufficient.

1.2.2 Frontal Analysis

Frontal analysis is based on the continual introduction of adsorbate samples into the carrier gas stream which then become distributed in the column between the mobile and stationary phases. However, as the

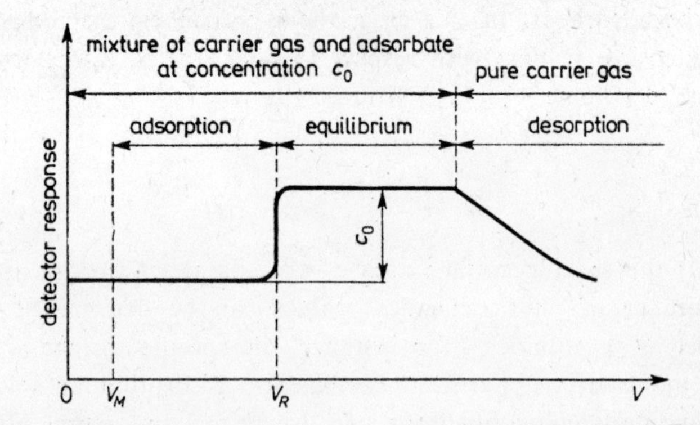

Fig. 1.4 Frontal chromatogram for a single component, showing the stages of adsorption, equilibrium and exit of the component from the column.

concentration of adsorbate in the mobile phase is maintained at a constant level, no peak develops [40, 41]. The concentration profile takes on the form of a plateau, preceded by an S-shaped front. Figure 1.4 illustrates a chromatogram for a single component.

1.2.3 The Elution-on-a-Plateau Technique

An effective and extremely useful technique, suggested by Reilley, Hildebrand and Ashley [42], is the combination of the elution technique with frontal analysis [43]. This method is especially convenient for the accurate determination of adsorption isotherms at high adsorbate partial pressure in the carrier gas. At first, one proceeds with the usual frontal technique for a given concentration of adsorbate in the mobile phase. Adsorption equilibrium having been established (plateau), a small sample of adsorbate or carrier gas is injected into the carrier gas stream. The samples pass through the column during the normal elution process, giving a positive peak for the adsorbate or a negative one for the carrier gas. Retention volumes of adsorbate are determined for a known concentration of it in the stationary phase. Samples of various quantities can be introduced any number of times. Studies on various concentrations of adsorbate on the surface of the stationary phase are easily carried out (Fig. 1.5). Apart from the simple determination of the adsorption isotherm gradient [44, 45], this method enables adsorbate–adsorbate and adsorbate–

adsorbent interactions in the adsorption layer to be studied. Worthy of mention is the fact that this technique can be used to study the properties of catalysts *in situ*.

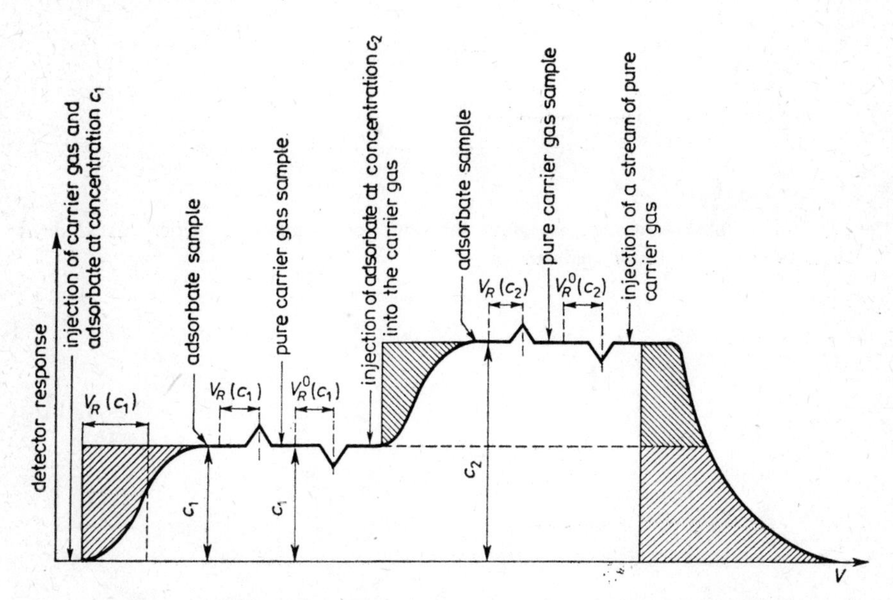

Fig. 1.5 Elution-frontal chromatogram (hatched areas indicate adsorption and desorption surfaces respectively for equilibrium concentrations c_1 and c_2; the gas hold-up is determined in separate experiments.

1.2.4 The Displacement Technique

In principle, the displacement technique is similar to the elution technique, except that the adsorbent is not eluted with pure carrier gas but with the aid of strongly adsorbable substances. Such a substance is injected at constant concentration into the carrier gas stream. It displaces the most strongly adsorbing component from the surface, this one in turn displaces another component whose adsorption capabilities are weaker, and so on. In this way, each component forms a band of constant concentration, which appears as a step on the chromatogram (Fig. 1.6).

The displacement technique is of great service when determining the sorption properties of the components of gaseous mixtures [46] — for example, of reagents on the surface of a catalyst [30, 31]. The method cannot, however, be applied if sorption is irreversible.

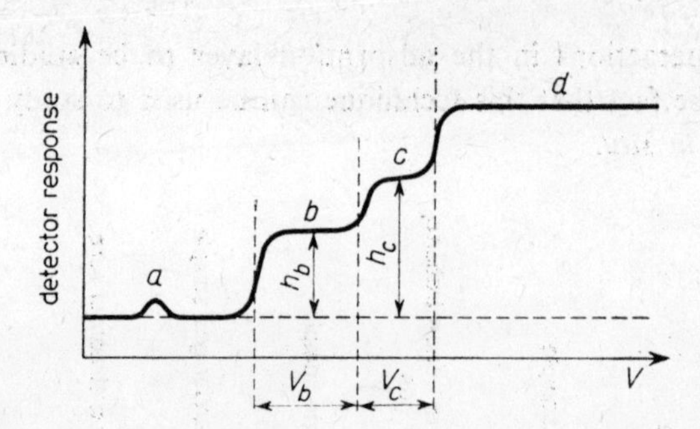

Fig. 1.6 Displacement chromatogram showing step height and carrier gas volumes required for quantitative analysis.

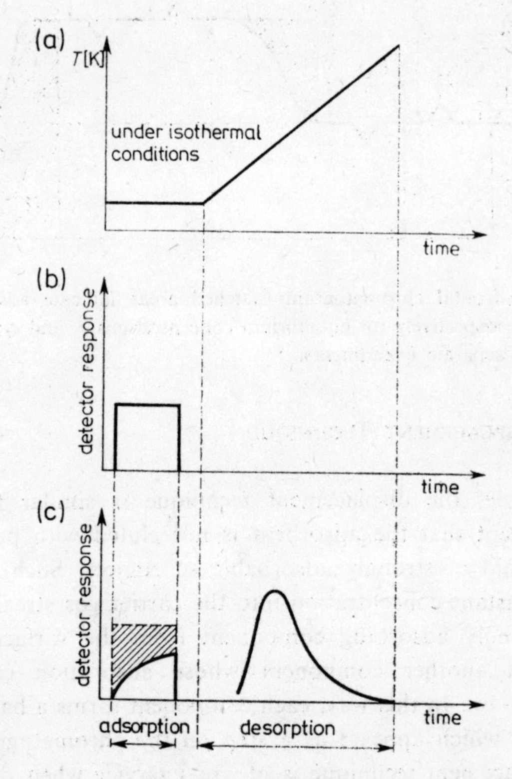

Fig. 1.7 Thermodesorption with programmed temperature increase: (a) adsorption under isothermal conditions and linear rate of change of temperature; (b) concentration of adsorbate before adsorption; (c) desorption peak; hatched area represents the quantity of substance adsorbed.

1.2.5 The Thermodesorption Technique

The principle of this method is as follows: adsorption from the gaseous phase takes place at a given temperature, followed by desorption into the carrier gas stream at a higher temperature.

The desorption temperature depends on the properties of the adsorbate–adsorbent system. It may exceed 873 K if the adsorbate undergoes powerful chemisorption on the surface of the solid.

This method has found application in studies of physical adsorption and chemisorption, e.g. in kinetic studies, and during the determination of surface activity and of the specific, total and selective surface areas of metals.

Thermodesorption is usually carried out with a programmed temperature increase (Fig. 1.7). In most cases the temperature increase programme is a linear one as it is easy to implement and control.

Figure 1.7 shows the processes of adsorption and desorption after having switched on the programmed heating. The area under the desorption curve corresponds to the quantity of desorbed adsorbate, and its shape provides information about the kinetics of desorption (see Chapter 9).

1.3 Elements of Theory

Theories of chromatography attempt to explain the process during which an adsorbate migrates through a mobile phase, and to establish the causes (diffusion and kinetic) of chromatographic band broadening. These problems have not yet been completely solved.

1.3.1 Theories

Depending on the conditions under which the chromatographic process takes place, the following types of chromatography can be differentiated [47, 48] (Fig. 1.8):

(a) ideal linear chromatography;
(b) ideal non-linear chromatography;
(c) non-ideal linear chromatography;
(d) non-ideal non-linear chromatography.

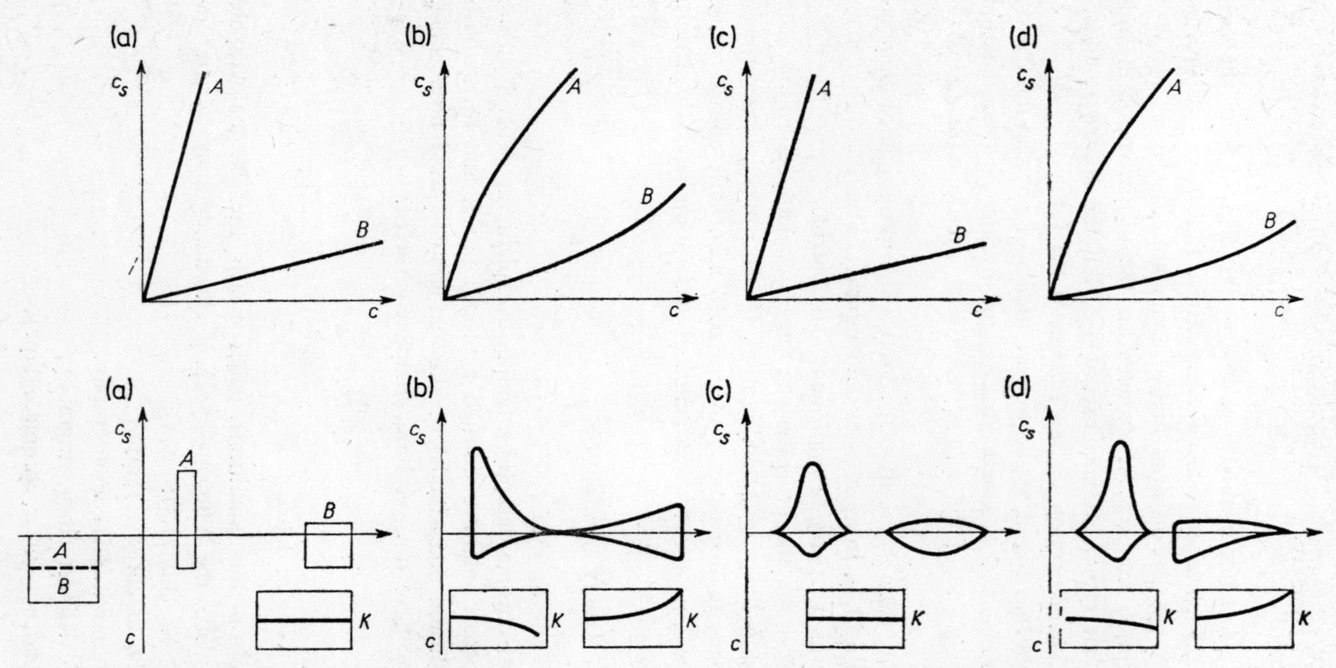

Fig. 1.8 Various chromatographic theories; the upper part of the figure shows the adsorption isotherms of substances A and B, below them the corresponding peak shapes and the change in partition or adsorption coefficient K with changing concentration: (a) ideal linear chromatography; (b) ideal non-linear chromatography; (c) non-ideal linear chromatography; (d) non-ideal non-linear chromatography (after A. K. Golberg and M. S. Vigdergauz [47]):

c_s — concentration of adsorbate in the adsorption layer, c — equilibrium concentration of adsorbate in the carrier gas.

The theory of ideal linear chromatography accounts for processes which take place in the column very rapidly and are thermodynamically reversible. The substance migrates through the column at a constant rate for various concentrations. The rate of migration depends on the partition coefficient (GLC) or the adsorption coefficient (GSC) (Fig. 1.8).

Chromatographic processes characterized by a concave or convex sorption isotherm with correspondingly asymmetrical peaks are described by the ideal non-linear chromatography theory.

In non-ideal linear chromatography, the peaks are symmetrical but may be much broadened. This is due to the slow exchange of adsorbate between the two phases. This type of chromatography is frequently met with in physicochemical investigations.

A process taking place in a real column and taking account of the rate at which equilibrium is reached is covered by the non-ideal non-linear chromatography theory.

The chromatographic process can be described by starting with the material balance and the migration of a single molecule along the mobile phase; this is the basis of the rate theory [48] and of the plate theory.

1.3.2 The Number of Theoretical Plates

The efficiency of the column is given by the height of a theoretical plate H

$$H = \frac{L}{N}, \tag{1.11}$$

where L is the length of the column, and N is the number of theoretical plates.

The value of H can be determined from the formula

$$H = \frac{L}{16}\left(\frac{W}{V_R}\right)^2, \tag{1.12}$$

where W is the peak width at base (Fig. 1.3) and V_R is the retention volume.

The assumption is made that interphasal equilibrium is established at every theoretical plate.

The more frequently equilibrium is established, the better the distribution along the column and the smaller the value of H.

The number of theoretical plates can be calculated from this formula (symbols as in Fig. 1.3)

$$N = 16\left(\frac{x}{W}\right)^2. \tag{1.13}$$

In practice, it is better to use the peak width at half the height, ω, as the possibility of error when drawing the tangents is less. Thus

$$N = 5.54\left(\frac{x}{\omega}\right)^2. \tag{1.14}$$

The theory of plates, despite considerable simplification, usefully links the height of a theoretical plate with the working parameters of the chromatographic process.

1.3.3 Broadening of Chromatographic Peaks

The problem of chromatographic peak broadening has not yet been satisfactorily solved, even though nearly all the processes causing broadening are known. A major step forward has been the application of the method of static moments to the investigation of theories of phenomena taking place in the chromatographic column [49–56].

Broadening of peaks is largely brought about by thermodynamic, diffusion and kinetic factors.

(a) *Thermodynamic factors*. Peak broadening in cases where diffusion factors are negligible is due basically to the deviation of the adsorption isotherm from Henry's law. It is made use of when determining the adsorption isotherm by chromatography (see Chapter 4). For a non-linear adsorption isotherm we get distorted peaks since the rate of adsorbate migration through the column alters with its concentration. The front profile becomes steeper and the tailing line spreads, or vice versa (Fig. 1.9).

One of the conditions for obtaining narrow symmetrical peaks is the linearity of the adsorption isotherm. This will be linear at sufficiently high temperatures and on non-porous or sufficiently wide-pored adsorbents.

(b) *Diffusion factors*. The diffusion processes taking place in a band moving along the column are highly complex. They cannot be removed in their entirety, only limited to a certain extent [48, 57, 58]. Peak broaden-

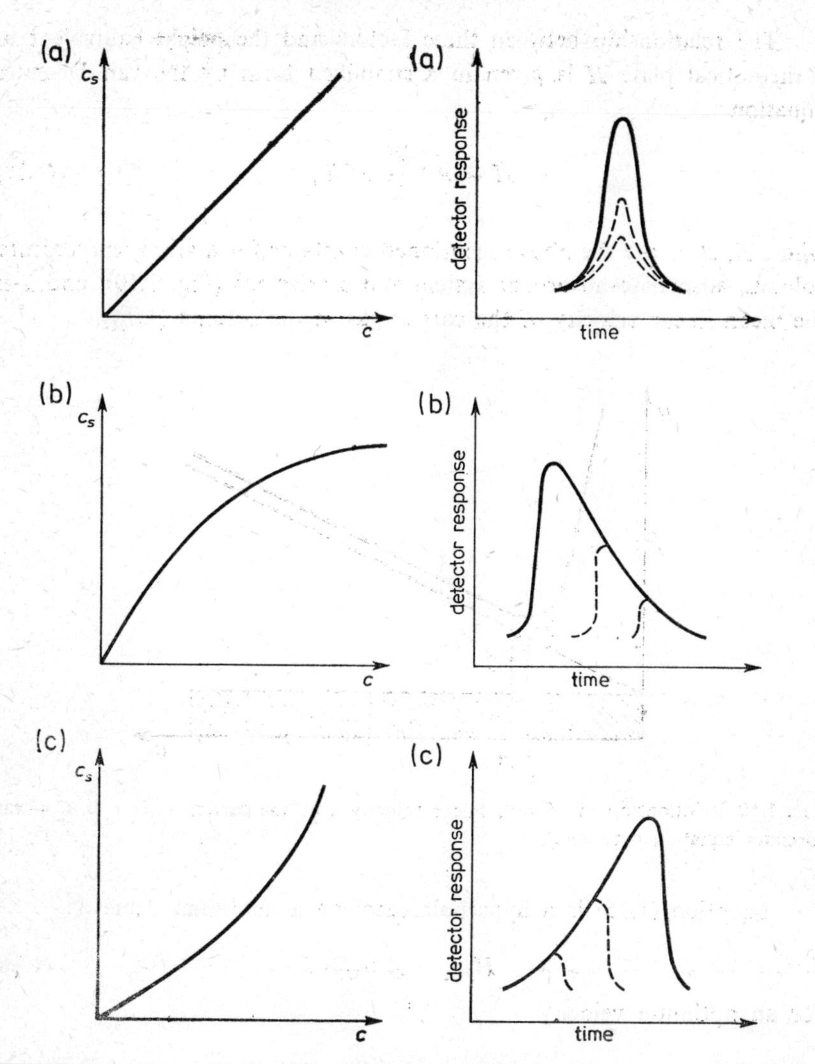

Fig. 1.9 Shapes of isotherms and their corresponding elution peaks: (a) linear adsorption isotherm — symmetrical peak with position of peak maximum constant; (b) convex adsorption isotherm — distorted peak, tailing line spread, position of peak maximum dependent on sample size; (c) concave adsorption isotherm — peak distorted, front profile spread, position of peak maximum dependent on sample size.

ing results largely from eddy diffusion A, molecular diffusion B and the resistance to mass transfer C since adsorption and desorption processes on the adsorbent surface take place fairly quickly.

The relationship between these factors and the height equivalent to a theoretical plate H is given in a simplified form by the van Deemter equation

$$H = A + \frac{B}{\bar{u}} + C\bar{u}\,, \qquad (1.15)$$

where A, B, C are the above-mentioned constants for a given temperature column, adsorbate–adsorbent system and carrier gas (Fig. 1.10), and $\bar{u}$ is the mean linear velocity of the carrier gas in the column (L/t_M).

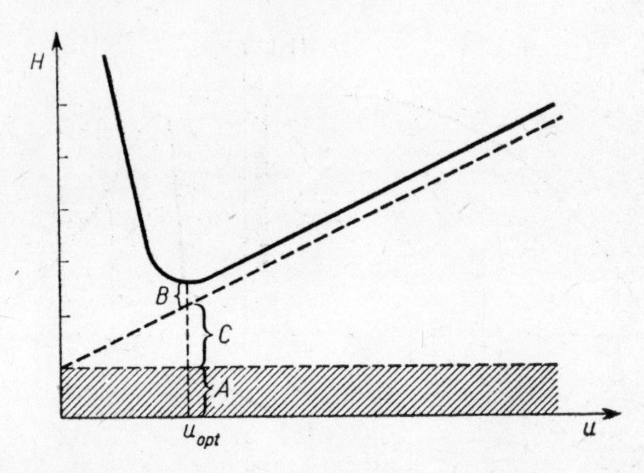

Fig. 1.10 Relationship of H with linear velocity u of the carrier gas (A, B, C — van Deemter equation constants).

Equation (1.15) is a hyperbole reaching a minimum value

$$H_{min} = A + \sqrt{BC} \qquad (1.16)$$

for an optimum velocity

$$u_{opt} = \sqrt{\frac{B}{C}}\,. \qquad (1.17)$$

Like most equations in GC theory, it is approximate, as the model upon which its calculation has been based is simpler than the processes taking place in reality.

If, for GSC, we take the so-called conjugated eddy diffusion into consideration and introduce the expression C_k characterizing the kinetics of adsorption in place of the resistance to mass transfer through the liquid phase C, the equation giving the value of H takes on the following form [59–61]:

$$H = \sum_{i=1}^{5} \frac{1}{\frac{1}{A_i} + \frac{1}{C_{gi}\bar{u}}} + \frac{B}{\bar{u}} + C_k\bar{u} + \text{other terms}\,, \tag{1.18}$$

where C_{gi} is an expression defining diffusion in the gaseous phase, and C_k an expression characterizing the kinetics of adsorption; A, B and $\bar{u}$ refer to the same factors as in equation (1.15).

Eddy diffusion A. The parameter A characterizes the column packing and is independent of the chemical properties of the adsorbate and adsorbent, flow rate and temperature:

$$A = 2\lambda d_p\,, \tag{1.19}$$

where λ is a constant characterizing the statistical heterogeneity of the column packing, and d_p is the average particle diameter.

Adsorbate molecules in the carrier gas move through the column packing along various routes; hence the time they spend there varies, and

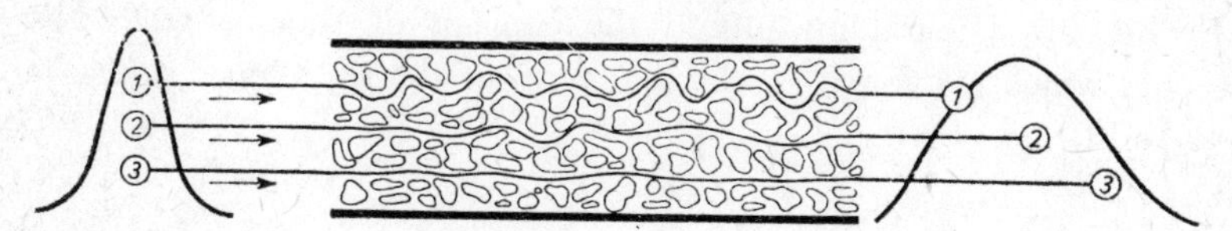

Fig. 1.11 Illustration of eddy diffusion.

the result is peak broadening. The velocity of local streams of gas between particles differs from the average velocity (Fig. 1.11).

In chromatographic columns one may also observe a wall effect: this is due to the fact that the resistance offered to the gas stream near the walls is less than that at the centre of a packed column. Eddying of the gas stream around the adsorbent particles, which leads to peak broadening, is commonly thought to take place as the stream flows through the column. The high efficiency of capillary columns is explained by the lack of the eddy diffusion which takes place during movement through a layer of granular material.

Peak broadening depends on the dimensions of the adsorbent particles, their shape, porosity, position in the column, and on the column diameter.

Not knowing the precise geometry of the column packing, it is difficult to explain the processes taking place in it by means of the molecular-kinetic theory.

One obvious way of reducing A is to use small adsorbent particles. However, bearing in mind the constant λ characterizing the method of packing the column, the particle diameter ought to be increased as it is easier to maintain a homogeneous packing of uniform, larger particles [58]. The large value of λ for particles of small size probably has something to do with the nature of the interparticle spaces in the column.

A second factor limiting the size of the adsorbent particles is the pressure gradient along the column. The smaller the particle size, the greater this is. A particle diameter of about 0.2 mm is regarded as optimal. Even if they are not of a uniform size (0.25–0.5 mm), wide-pore adsorbents will always ensure a good column efficiency.

Diffusion between streams of gas is substantial for rapidly diffusing adsorbates and slow flow rates, but is minimal for slowly diffusing substances and fast flow rates as there is no time for adsorbate molecules to diffuse from one stream to the next. Chromatographic band broadening as a result of adsorbate diffusion between slow-flowing streams is less than might be predicted from the eddy diffusion conception of the problem [59–61].

Giddings [59–61] introduced the concept of "conjugated eddy diffusion", which is defined by the first term of the right-hand side of equation (1.18), i.e.

$$A = \sum_{i=1}^{5} \frac{1}{\dfrac{1}{A_i} + \dfrac{1}{C_{gi}\bar{u}}}, \tag{1.20}$$

where $A_i = 2\lambda_i d_p$, $C_{gi} = \lambda_{\gamma i} d_p^2 / D_g$, $\lambda_{\gamma i}$ is a structural factor describing the various flow routes [47] — the labyrinth of gas channels in the column — and D_g is the coefficient of diffusion of the adsorbate in the carrier gas.

The values measured make up the sum of all the expressions in equation (1.20) describing the various possible flow geometries in the column.

For slow flow rates the expression $C_{gi}\bar{u}$ is small; its reciprocal is therefore large and so exerts an appropriate influence on the value of the denominator in equation (1.20). For fast flow rates, $1/A_i$ largely decides the value of the denominator, since the effect of $1/C_{gi}\bar{u}$ is now much diminished. The theory of conjugated diffusion explains much of the experimental data, especially for medium flow rates [64]; nevertheless, a number of researchers do not accept it [65, 66].

Molecular diffusion *B*. The molecular diffusion parameter B, often known as longitudinal diffusion, accounts for the diffusion of adsorbate in the carrier gas in the same direction as the flow or in the opposite direction, from a high concentration in the band of substance to the carrier gas not containing any molecules of the substance [67]:

$$B = \frac{2\gamma D_g}{u}, \tag{1.21}$$

where D_g is the diffusion coefficient of the adsorbate in the carrier gas, γ is a coefficient accounting for the labyrinth of gas channels in the column [63], and u is the linear velocity of the carrier gas measured at the column outlet.

The diffusion coefficient D_g is inversely proportional to the pressure and to the square root of the gas density, but is directly proportional to the temperature.

In laminar flow, mass exchange takes place only as a result of straightforward diffusion, whereas in turbulent flow forced mixing of the carrier gas takes place. At the carrier gas velocities normally used in columns, laminar flow is the rule in most cases; thus external exchange of mass takes place mainly by means of diffusion.

Molecular diffusion can be reduced by increasing the density of the carrier gas [67, 68]. It would thus appear to be more advantageous to use a higher-density carrier gas such as argon or nitrogen than hydrogen or helium. Nevertheless, bearing in mind other factors such as the sensitivity of the detector towards the carrier gas and retention times, light gases do seem more suitable.

A grainy column packing favours molecular diffusion. The coefficient γ increases with particle size and approaches unity. The factor B in equation (1.15) can be reduced if the linear velocity u is higher.

Resistance to mass transfer *C*. The final term in the van Deemter equation includes processes involved in the resistance to mass transfer. The resistance to mass transfer rises with the carrier gas flow velocity (Fig. 1.10), where C is the summed coefficient $C = C_g + C_k + C_c$. Each of these terms is proportional to $1/D_g$ (D_g is the diffusion coefficient of adsorbate in the carrier gas), $1/k_a$ (k_a is the kinetic coefficient of adsorption on the surface) and $1/D_c$ (D_c is the diffusion coefficient in the liquid phase) respectively.

In GSC, only the coefficients C_g and C_k can affect peak broadening.

The significance of the coefficient of resistance to mass transfer in the gaseous phase, C_g, was discussed earlier; C_k characterizes the kinetics of adsorption on the adsorbent surface. The delay in mass exchange from the adsorbent surface is due to the adsorption and desorption processes. In the general case, the rate of mass exchange depends not only on the nature of the adsorbate molecules and their kinetic energy, but also on the kind of carrier gas and its flow parameters. Furthermore, of fundamental importance to the kinetics of adsorption and desorption are the geometrical and electronic structure of the adsorbent surface (for specific adsorption), and the experimental temperature. There are three distinct stages in the adsorption process: the movement of adsorbate molecules towards the adsorbent surface (external diffusion), their penetration into the pores (internal diffusion in pores, surface diffusion) and the adsorption process proper. Physical adsorption itself takes place almost immediately. Mass exchange in the column, brought about by external and internal diffusion, decreases as the temperature is raised. A temperature increase raises the efficiency of the column, extends the area of small values of H and reduces the gradient of the kinetic branch of the van Deemter graph (Fig. 1.10 — right-hand side of the graph).

Despite certain inaccuracies, the van Deemter equation in both its simple and modified forms gives a good definition of the factors affecting the efficiency of the column and describes the chromatographic process mathematically, which makes it easier to comprehend and facilitates the choice of methods for increasing its efficiency.

Starting from the kinetic equation of mass exchange, Zhukhovitskii *et al.* [43] obtained an expression for the effective coefficient of longitudinal diffusion D_{ef}

$$D_{ef} = D_{eddy} + D_{mol} + \left(\frac{u^2}{\beta}\right)_{ext} + \left(\frac{u^2}{\beta}\right)_{int}, \tag{1.22}$$

where (u^2/β) denotes the kinetic coefficient characterizing the external and internal exchange of mass, whereas $(1/\beta)$ in the physical sense is the characteristic unit of time during which adsorption takes place.

The effect of all the physicochemical factors which lead to peak broadening is described, according to Zhukhovitskii, by the equation

$$H = A + \frac{\beta}{u} + Wu^{1/2} + Cu, \tag{1.23}$$

where W is the peak width.

The remaining symbols are as in equations (1.15) and (1.22).

Both equations (1.23) and (1.15) show that for low carrier gas velocities it is molecular diffusion that chiefly affects the value of H, and that as the carrier gas velocity increases, so does the significance of the other terms.

It is usually only the second and third terms of the equation that play a fundamental role in GSC. The fourth term, the internal exchange of mass, is mainly responsible for band broadening in GLC. Within the range of the hyperbolic minimum (Fig. 1.10), eddy diffusion is of particular importance in both GSC and GLC.

1.3.4 Correction of Peaks for Diffusion

There are a number of graphical methods of correcting peaks for diffusion [69–72]. This correction is often necessary when determining the adsorption surface (see Chapter 4). This is particularly important when the retention times of the chromatographed substance are short.

Figure 1.12 shows Bechtold's method for correcting peaks [71]. In this method, it is assumed (this is not fully justified) that the diffusion

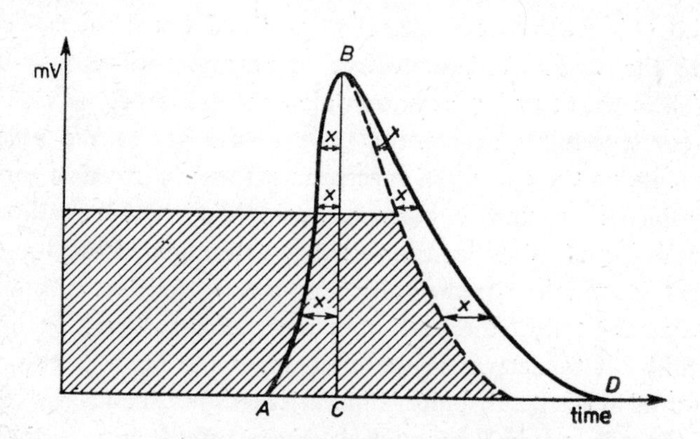

Fig. 1.12 Bechtold's method of correcting peaks for diffusion (after E. Bechtold [71]).

of the front profile of the peak is equal to the diffusion of the rear profile. Thus the non-diffusional profile of the peak can be used as a correction of the broadened profile. The line CB on Fig. 1.12 leaving the peak maximum is perpendicular to the base line of the peak, and the distances marked by arrows are equal for the same values of mV. The adsorption surface can be determined from the hatched area.

A correction for diffusion can be obtained by assuming similar (diffusional) peak broadening for both adsorbed and non-adsorbed substances under given conditions [70]. The substances have to be chemically alike. The non-adsorbed substance is introduced into the column in such quantities that its peak height is equal to the peak height of the substance being adsorbed. The method of correcting for diffusion is shown in Fig. 1.13.

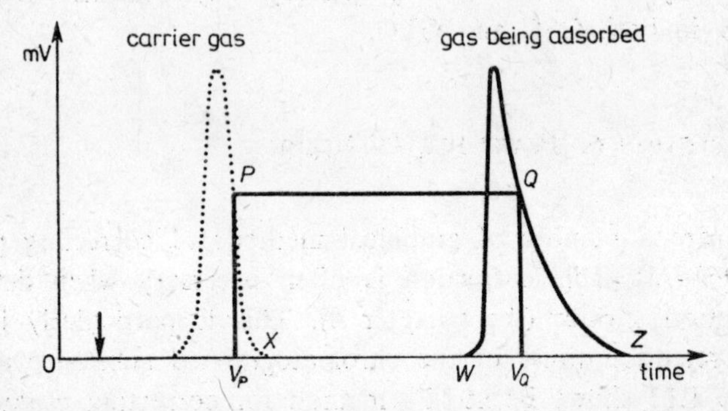

Fig. 1.13 Correction of a peak for diffusion by means of the carrier gas peak.

For a point Q located on the diffusion branch of a peak, such a correction is equal to the area PV_PX, equivalent to an appropriate quantity of adsorbate. The quantity of substance which was adsorbed at an adsorbate pressure corresponding to point Q is proportional to the area $QZXP$. Further points on the curve QZ together with their correction for diffusion are determined in a similar manner. Bechtold's graphic method of correcting peaks for diffusion has been used to determine adsorption isotherms for systems in which extremely long retention times are obtained [72]. In such cases the tail of the peak does not return to the base line, which makes it difficult to determine the area under the peak corresponding to the amount of injected substance. Figure 1.14 shows such a chromatogram. On this, the adsorption maximum is given by the area $EKJO$, but as point E is indefinable, the area AKE is unknown. This can be calculated using Bechtold's method [71]. Let area AKE_1 be equal to S_p, then $S_p = AKE - E_1KE$. Since the distances X are equal, area $E_1KE = AKP$. By using the point on the curve AK and dividing area AKP into horizontal strips, we perform the numerical integration of this area, and by adding it to S_p we obtain area AKE. Area $EKJO$ is equal to $AKE+AKJO$. In

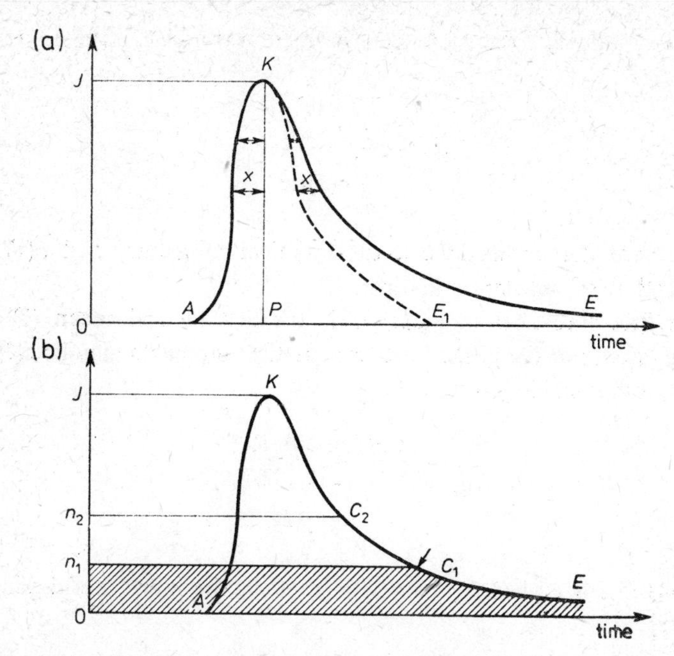

Fig. 1.14 Correction to the calculation of the adsorption surface area from a peak not returning to the base line (after D. Dollimore *et al.* [72]).

this way we can determine the adsorption surface area for an existing point on the adsorption isotherm. The remaining adsorption surface area (points of the isotherm) is obtained by the successive subtraction of trapezia *KJnC* (Fig. 1.14b) from the corrected area *EKJO*, until the base line is reached.

1.4 The Statistical Moments Method in Gas Chromatography

The processes taking place in chromatographic columns can be analysed in greater detail using the method of statistical moments [51–54, 73–86]. By making use of the coordinates of the points on the elution curve, this method facilitates the more precise calculation of various chromatographic peak parameters such as the retention time corresponding to maximum concentration, the area under the elution curve, the mean retention time for the concentration of substance in the chromatographic band, and the point of inflection of the peak. This method can also help to characterize the shape of the peaks and their asymmetry.

Mathematically, the statistical moments are given by the equation

$$\mu_n = \frac{\int_0^\infty c(\tau)\tau^n \mathrm{d}\tau}{\int_0^\infty c(\tau)\mathrm{d}\tau}, \tag{1.24}$$

where μ_n are the consecutive n-th statistical moments, and $c(\tau)$ is the concentration of substance in time.

The first statistical moment μ_1 is the arithmetical mean ($\bar{\tau}$) or the centre of gravity of the peak. Further statistical moments may be calculated from the relationship

$$\mu_n = \frac{\int_0^\infty c(\tau)[\tau-\mu_1]^n \mathrm{d}\tau}{\int_0^\infty c(\tau)\mathrm{d}\tau}. \tag{1.25}$$

Equations (1.24) and (1.25) can be written in the more useful, simplified form [85]

$$\mu_n = \frac{\sum_i x_i^n y_i}{\sum_i y_i}, \tag{1.26}$$

where x_i is the appropriate value of the retention time of the i-th point on the elution curve corresponding to the detector signal amplitude y_i, and

$$\mu_n = \frac{\sum_i [x_i-\mu_1]^n y_i}{\sum_i y_i}. \tag{1.27}$$

The zero statistical moment (μ_0) defines the area under the chromatographic peak. The first statistical moment (μ_1) usually denotes the decomposition graph of molecules. The second moment (μ_2) expresses the spread of points on the elution curve; it may be written as

$$\mu_2 = \sigma^2, \tag{1.28}$$

where σ denotes the main deviation of particular points on the chromatographic curve from the arithmetical mean.

The third statistical moment (μ_3) involves the longitudinal asymmetry of the peak. A positive value of this moment indicates that the front profile of the peak is steeper than the rear profile. The fourth statistical moment

(μ_4) characterizes the flattening of the elution curve, describing it by means of the so-called excess E, which compares the given curve with the Gaussian curve having the same standard deviation. The shape of the peak is given by the equations

$$\beta_1 = \frac{\mu_3^2}{\mu_2^3}, \tag{1.29}$$

$$\beta_2 = \frac{\mu_4}{\mu_2^2}. \tag{1.30}$$

For Gaussian decomposition $\beta_1 = 0$ and $\beta_2 = 3$. For a broadened peak whose maximum is eluted before the centre of gravity of the mass, β_1 has positive values. Conversely, if the centre of gravity of the peak is eluted before the maximum, β_1 takes on negative values. β_1 characterizes the skewness S of the elution curve with respect to the centre of gravity of the peak

$$S = \frac{\mu_3}{\mu_2^{3/2}} = \frac{\mu_3}{\sigma^3}. \tag{1.31}$$

Parameter β_2 characterizes the degree of flattening of the peak. The expression $(\beta_2 - 3)$ is determined by E

$$E = \beta_2 - 3 = \frac{\mu_4}{\mu_2^2} - 3 = \frac{\mu_4}{\sigma^4}. \tag{1.32}$$

When E is negative, the peak is flattened with respect to the Gaussian curve with the same standard deviation σ. Positive values of E indicate slender peaks. The shape of the graph showing the probable location of the concentration of the substance in the chromatographic band can be recovered if we know the various statistical modules μ_1, μ_2, μ_3 and μ_4. The first terms in the Gram–Charlier equation [82] can be used for this purpose. The number of theoretical plates N can also be determined

$$N = \frac{\mu_1^2}{\mu_2}. \tag{1.33}$$

In practice, statistical moments have been used to obtain information on adsorption and catalytic systems [87]. For example, Henry's constant over a wide range of temperature, even during the adsorption of gaseous mixtures, has been obtained (μ_1), as also the kinetic constants of adsorption and desorption (from μ_2 and μ_3) [87]. Statistical moments are widely applied in catalysis, e.g. when using pulse techniques to study the kinetics of adsorption during a reaction [87]. The application of statistical moments to the study of diffusion and catalytic processes will be discussed in detail in a subsequent section of the book.

1.5 General Comments on the Precision and Accuracy of Chromatographic Measurements

Initial doubts about the chromatographic method and a certain unwillingness to apply it to the determination of different physicochemical properties have proved unjustified. As a rule the physicochemical properties carefully determined chromatographically agree with the values obtained by other methods (see Table 5.2).

The accuracy of chromatographic results depends on whether a specific or a relative retention volume, retention time, or peak width or area is used for their estimation.

With good conventional chromatographs one may obtain reproducible results on a given column with a standard deviation of about 0.2%.

By using an automatic analogue-to-digital converter and removing different sources of errors, the standard deviation has been reduced to 0.02–0.05% [91, 92].

This exceptional precision applies more to the relative than the net retention volume. If the accuracy of determination of a retention volume under given conditions is 0.2%, then the measurements repeated by the same worker under different conditions (change in F_c, T_c and the amount of stationary phase) using the same apparatus would result in an error of 1–2%.

This 1–2% accuracy should be assumed real when determining net retention values with maximum efficiency of all the systems in a chromatograph [93]. A frequent source of differences in the data obtained in different laboratories may be the fact that retention volumes are as a rule 1–1.5% higher when using helium as a carrier gas rather than nitrogen [94]. Measurements of relative retention values are one order of magnitude more accurate (0.2%).

Table 1.1 [91] presents a comparison of accuracies in the determination of three parameters of a chromatogram.

Although the absolute values given in Table 1.1 seem to be too small, they do show the relative accuracy of their determination.

The accuracy is greatest for the retention time, lower for the peak width and lowest of all for the peak area. The peak width is a parameter for diffusive and kinetic investigations. The values determined in this way may carry a relatively bigger error, as compared with those estimated directly from retention data (e.g. thermodynamic functions of adsorption).

Table 1.1 Accuracy in determining the values of a chromatogram in high-precision apparatus [91]

Value being determined	*Accuracy* [%]
Retention time	±0.02
Peak width, HETP	±0.05
The peak area	±0.08

Using the chromatographic method at infinite dilution, good agreement of adsorption heats with calorimetric results is obtained (calorimetric data are extrapolated from higher concentrations).

The main advantages of chromatography over static methods in investigating physicochemical phenomena are:

(1) The apparatus is easy to construct and operate, allowing various investigations to be performed in one system. Standard apparatus, which can be easily adapted for physicochemical studies, is inexpensive.

(2) Gas chromatography is mainly used for examining very small samples at infinite dilution. Such concentrations can be directly applied to investigations of thermodynamic equilibrium.

(3) The accuracy of measurements of different physicochemical phenomena by chromatography is at least as high as that of other methods, and the rate of measurement is much higher.

1.6 Examples of Chromatographic Apparatus for Studying Physicochemical Phenomena

This section presents four types of chromatographic apparatus as guidelines for physicochemical investigations.

Figure 1.15 illustrates the apparatus for the precise measurement of specific retention volume [95], essential for determining various physicochemical properties.

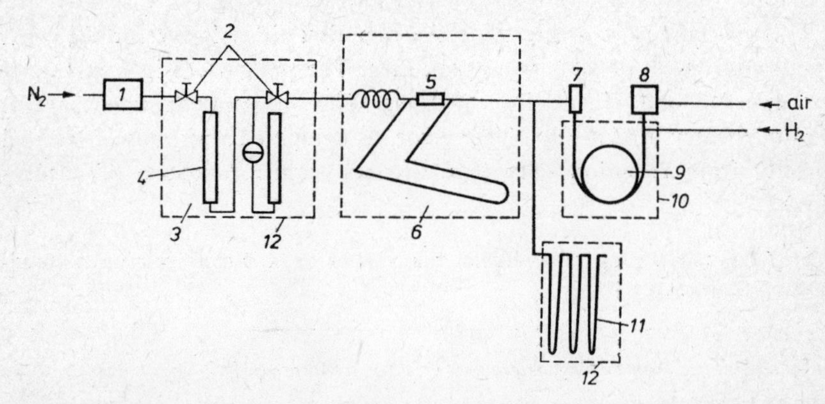

Fig. 1.15 Precision apparatus for determining specific retention volume (after O. Wicarova *et al.* [95]):

1 — tank regulator, *2* — needle valves, *3* — thermostat of manostat and valves, *4* — manostat, *5* — capillary flow-meter, *6* — water bath, *7* — injection port, *8* — flame-ionization detector, *9* — column, *10* — column thermostat glycerol bath, *11* — multiple-arm manometer, *12* — polystyrene box.

The column inlet pressure is controlled by two precision needle valves *2* and a manostat *4* which are placed in a thermostat *3*. The column outlet pressure is equal to atmospheric pressure. The flow rate at the inlet is measured by means of a capillary flow-meter *5* and the inlet pressure with a multiple V-tube manometer *11*. The column is thermostatted in a glycerol bath *10*. The samples are injected by means of a syringe *7*.

Figure 1.16 presents the apparatus for measurements at infinite

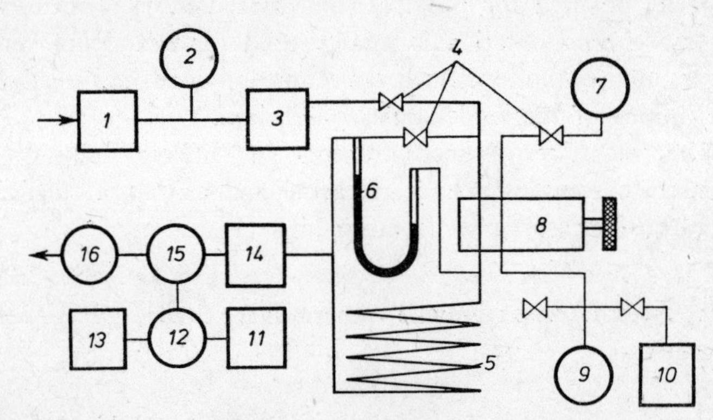

Fig. 1.16 High pressure apparatus (3 MPa) for investigating, i.a. activity and virial coefficients (after A. J. B. Cruickshank *et al.* [96]):

1 — pressure regulator, *2* — pressure gauge, *3* — sealed bubble flow-meter, *4* — valves, *5* — column, *6* — column pressure-drop manometer, *7* — solute vapour reservoir, *8* — sample injector, *9* — pressure gauge, *10* — suction pump, *11* — standard bubble flow-meter, *12* — two-way valve, *13* — detector and recorder, *14* — flow control valve, *15* — stream splitter, *16* — needle valve.

dilution at pressures raised to 3 MPa. The system is used to measure such parameters as activity and virial coefficients of gases.

The inlet pressure is regulated by means of a high-precision regulator *1* and needle valves *4*. The pressure gauge *2* is carefully calibrated. A sealed bubble flow-meter *3* is used for flow measurements at the column inlet. The outlet pressure is maintained above ambient with a thermostatted needle valve *16* and the column effluent split by a Y-junction *15*, one arm of which is connected through a narrow capillary tube to a flame detector. The pressure-drop is measured by means of a mercury manometer *6*. The column is placed in a water bath The samples are injected by means of a laboratory-constructed valve system and cylinder with a displacer piston *8*.

The elution, frontal and elution-on-a-plateau techniques (Section 1.2.3) can be applied to finite concentrations in the apparatus designed by Conder and Purnell [97], the diagram of which is presented in Fig. 1.17.

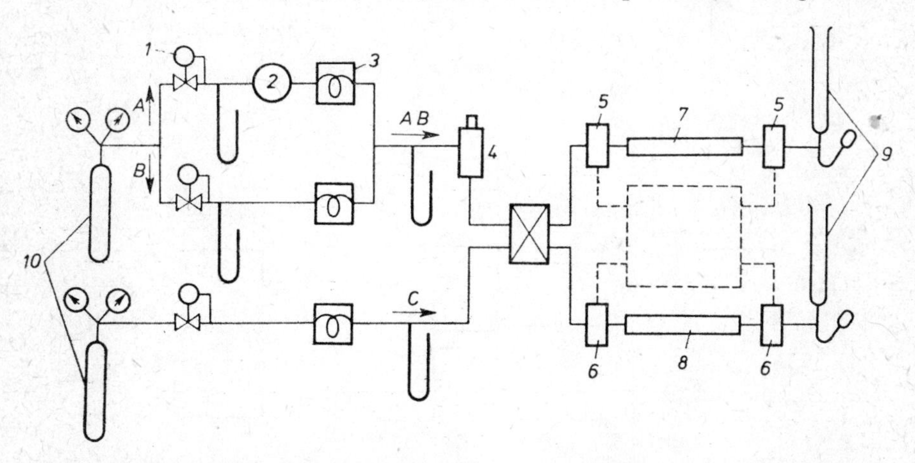

Fig. 1.17 **The scheme of a chromatograph for investigations at finite concentrations** (after J. R. Conder and J. H. Purnell [97]):

1 — needle valve, *2* — saturator, *3* — thermostatted capillaries, *4* — injection port, *5* — detector, *6* — additional detector, *7* — column, *8* — selected column, *9* — flow-meters, *10* — gas supply.

The three streams of gases *A*, *B*, *C* are carefully controlled. Stream *A* flows through a saturator, where it is saturated with the vapours of a test adsorbate, and then joins stream *B*. Stream *AB* may contain the adsorbate in the required concentration regulated by means of the flow-control valves. Manometers allow the flow rate needed for estimating the composition of stream *AB* to be determined. The samples may also be injected in pulses through an injection port. Switching of the valves results in stream *AB* or pure carrier gas *C* flowing through the column (frontal method). Both the columns employed in this system show the same flow resistance. Detectors are placed at both the inlet and the outlet of the columns. The boundary of the inlet and outlet profiles is recorded. Detectors may be used in one column only and in the other the possibility of switching to the outlet detector should be ensured.

The apparatus can be simplified by applying only the method of elution on a plateau and omitting stream *C*. When only the front method is used, the sample injector is unnecessary. The columns used for investigations for finite concentration must be packed with bigger molecules than in infinite dilution investigations.

Figure 1.18 shows a chromatographic system [98] containing a digital data acquisition device (for estimating retention time, peak height

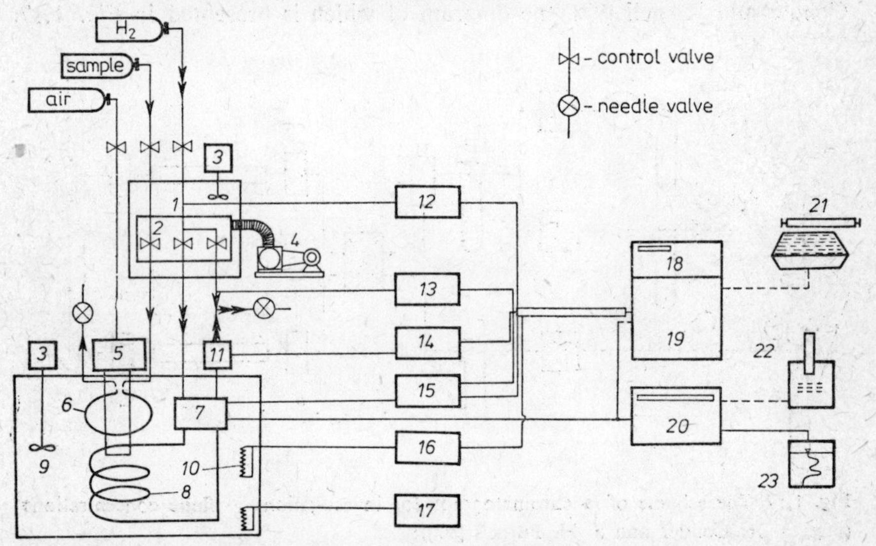

Fig. 1.18 Chromatographic apparatus with automated sample injection (after M. Goedert and G. Guiochon [98]):

1 — control valves in thermostatted liquid bath, *2* — vacuum container, *3* — heater system, 4 — vacuum pump, *5* — sampling valve, *6* — gas sample loop, *7* — katharometer, *8* — column, *9* — column thermostat, *10* — temperature sensor, *11* — flow-meter sensor, *12* — pressure gauge, *13* — precision pressure gauge, *14* — flow-meter, *15* — power supply, *16* — temperature bridge, *17* — temperature controller, *18* — digital voltmeter, *19* — data logging system, *20* — integrator, *21* — electric typewriter, *22* — printer, *23* — recorder.

and area) and automated sample injector. Two precision pressure regulators control the inlet pressure and a third regulator and needle valve maintain the column outlet pressure above ambient. Pressures are measured with a precision quartz Bourdon-tube gauge. The column is placed in an ethylene glycol (ethane 1,2-diol) bath and a katharometer is used as detector.

The samples are introduced automatically (about 100 samples during 12 hours) and the results are automatically processed to get the required chromatogram parameters.

References

[1] Littlewood A. B., *Gas Chromatography, Principles, Techniques and Applications*, 2nd ed., Academic Press, New York, London, 1970.

[2] Krugers J., (Ed.), *Instrumentation in Gas Chromatography*, Centrex Co., Eindhoven, 1968.

[3] Snyder L. B., *Principles of Adsorption Chromatography*, Marcel Dekker, New York, 1965.

[4] Sakodynskii K. I., Brazhnikov V. V., Burov A. I., Volkov S. A. and Zelvenskii V. Yu., *Pribory dlya khromatografii*, Izd. Mashinostroyenie, Moskva, 1973.

[5] Schupp O. E., *Gas Chromatography*, J. Wiley and Sons Inc., New York, 1968.

[6] Harris W. E. and Habgood H. W., *Programmed Temperature Gas Chromatography*, J. Wiley, New York, Sydney, 1966.

[7] Kulakov M. W., Shkatov E. F. and Hanberg W. A., *Gazovye khromatografy*, Izd. Energya, Moskva, 1968.

[8a] Laub R. J. and Pecsok R. L., *Physicochemical Applications of Gas Chromatography*, J. Wiley, New York, 1978.

[8b] Conder J. R. and Young C. L., *Physicochemical Measurement by Gas Chromatography*, J. Wiley, New York, 1979.

[8c] Young C. L., *Chromatogr. Reviews*, **10**, 129 (1968).

[9] Arita K., Kuge Y. and Yoshikawa Y., *Bull. Chem. Soc. Japan*, **38**, 632 (1965).

[10] Cremer E., *Anal. Chem.*, **170**, 219 (1959).

[11] Brookman D. J., Gorgrove G. L. and Sawyer D. T., *Anal. Chem.*, **39**, 1196 (1967).

[12] Czubryt J. J., Desser H. D. and Bock E., *J. Chromatogr.*, **53**, 439 (1970).

[13] Habgood H. W. and Flood E. A. (Eds.), *The Solid-Gas Interface*, E. Arnold Ltd., London, Marcel Dekker Inc., New York, 1967, Vol. 2, p. 614.

[14] Mellwrick C. R. and Phillips C. S. G., *J. Phys. E. Sci. Instr.*, **6**, 208 (1973).

[15] Paryjczak T., Jóźwiak W. K. and Góralski J., *J. Chromatogr.*, **120**, 291 (1976).

[16] Freud G., *Anal. Chem.*, **39**, 545 (1967).

[17] Litt G. J. and Adler N., *J. Gas Chromatogr.*, **3**, 250 (1965).

[18] Habgood H. W. and Hanlan J. F., *Can. J. Chem.*, **37**, 843 (1959).

[19] Pratt G. L. and Purnell J. H., *Anal. Chem.*, **32**, 1213 (1960).

[20] Jeffery P. G. and Kipping P. J., *Gas Analysis by Gas Chromatography*, Pergamon Press, Oxford, New York, Toronto, Sydney, Braunschweig, 1972.

[21] Tinti P., *J. Gas Chromatogr.*, **4**, 140 (1966).

[22] Ruchelman M. W., *J. Gas Chromatogr.*, **4**, 265 (1966).

[23] Podmore A. D., *J. Clin. Pathol.*, **19**, 619 (1966).

[24] Langdon W. M., Iranuski V. R., Putscher R. E., O'Neill J. J. and Krupnick A. C., *J. Gas Chromatogr.*, **4**, 269 (1966).

[25] Ackman R. G., *Facts Methods Sci. Res.*, **6**, (4), 6 (1965).
[26] Rijks J. A., *Characterization of Hydrocarbons by Gas Chromatography*, Eindhoven, 1973.
[27] Thorburn S. and Bevan S. C., USA Pat. 3204448 (1965).
[28] Janak J., *Chem. Listy*, **47**, 817 (1953).
[29] Vadari P. F. and Ettre K., *Anal. Chem.*, **35**, 410 (1963).
[30] Karmen A., *J. Gas Chromatogr.*, **3**, 180 (1965).
[31] Lovelock J. E., *J. Chromatogr.*, **1**, 35 (1958).
[32] Lovelock J. E., *Anal. Chem.*, **33**, 162 (1961).
[33] Parkinson R. T. and Wilson R. E., *J. Chromatogr.*, **24**, 412 (1966).
[34] Hartman C. H. and Dimick K. P., *J. Gas Chromatogr.*, **4**, 163 (1966).
[35] James A. T. and Martin A. J. P., *Biochem. J.*, **50**, 679 (1952).
[36] Kiselev A. V., Petrova R. S. and Shcherbakova K. D., *Kinet. Katal.*, **5**, 526 (1964).
[37] Belyakova L. D., Kiselev A. V. and Kovaleva N. V., *Zh. Fiz. Khim.*, **40**, 1494 (1966).
[38] Kiselev A. V., Paskonova E. A., Petrova R. S. and Shcherbakova K. D., *Zh. Fiz. Khim.*, **38**, 161 (1964).
[39] Scott R. P. W., *Gas Chromatography*, Butterworths, London, 1960.
[40] Grob R. L. (Ed.), *Modern Practice of Gas Chromatography*, J. Wiley and Sons, New York, London, Sydney, Toronto, 1977.
[41] Dal Nogare S. and Juvet R. S. Jr., *Gas-Liquid Chromatography*, Interscience Publishers, J. Wiley and Sons, New York, London, 1962.
[42] Reilley C. N., Hildebrand G. P. and Ashley J. W., *Anal. Chem.*, **34**, 1198 (1962).
[43] Zhukhovitskii A. A., Turkeltaub N. M., Gayer M., Lagashkina M. N. and Shlepuzhnikova G. M., *Zavod. Lab.*, **29**, 8 (1963).
[44] Purnell J. H., *Endeavour*, **23**, 142 (1964).
[45] Conder J. R., in: *Progress in Gas Chromatography*, Ed. Purnell J. H., J. Wiley, New York, London, Sydney, 1968.
[46] Andreev L. V. and Kuvshinnikov V. D., *Gazovaya khromatografiya*, Izd. Nieftchim, Moskva, 1967.
[47] Golberg A. K. and Vigdergauz M. S., *Kurs gazovoy khromatografii*, Izd. Khimya, Moskva, 1974.
[48] Van Deemter J. J., Zuiderweg F. J. and Klinkenberg A. P., *Chem. Eng. Sci.*, **5**, 271 (1956).
[49] Leibnitz E. and Struppe H. G., *Handbuch der Gas-Chromatographie*, Adademische Verlagsgesellschaft, Geest und Portig, Leipzig, 1966.
[50] Kubin M., *Coll. Czech. Chem. Comm.*, **30**, 1104 (1965).
[51] Kucera E., *J. Chromatogr.*, **19**, 237 (1965).
[52] Grubner O. and Kucera E., *Voträge des 5 Symposium über Gas-Chromatographie*, Akad. Verlag., Berlin, 1965.
[53] Kucera E. and Grubner O., *Coll. Czech. Chem. Comm.*, **29**, 1782 (1964).
[54] Grubner O., Ralek M. and Kucera E., *Coll. Czech. Chem. Comm.*, **31**, 1629 (1966).
[55] Grubner O., Ralek M. and Zikanova A., *Coll. Czech. Chem. Comm.*, **31**, 852 (1966).
[56] Grubner O., Zikanova A. and Ralek M., *J. Chromatogr.*, **28**, 209 (1967).
[57] Keulemans A. J. M., *Gas Chromatography*, 2nd ed., Reinhold, New York, 1959.
[58] Klinkenberg A. and Sjenitzer F., *Chem. Eng. Sci.*, **5**, 258 (1956).

[59] Giddings J. C., *J. Chromatogr.*, **3**, 443 (1960).
[60] Giddings J. C., *Anal. Chem.*, **35**, 439 (1963).
[61] Giddings J. C., *Anal. Chem.*, **36**, 1170 (1964).
[62] McNair H. M. and Bonelli E. J., *Basic Gas Chromatography*, Consolidated Printers, Oakland, California, 1967.
[63] Perrett R. H. and Purnell J. H., *Anal. Chem.*, **35**, 430 (1963).
[64] Harper J. M. and Hammond E. G., *Anal. Chem.*, **31**, 1738 (1965).
[65] Kieselbach R., *Anal. Chem.*, **35**, 1342 (1963).
[66] Knox J. H. and McLaren L., *Anal. Chem.*, **35**, 449 (1963).
[67] Knox J. H., *Sci. Progr.*, **45**, 227 (1957).
[68] Glueckauf E., in: *Gas Chromatography*, Ed. Desty D. H., Academic Press, New York, Butterworths, London, 1958.
[69] Huber J. F. K. and Gerritse R. G., *J. Chromatogr.*, **58**, 137 (1971).
[70] Kipping P. J. and Winter D. G., *Nature*, **205**, 1002 (1965).
[71] Bechtold E., in: *Gas Chromatography*, Ed. Van Swaay M., Butterworths, London, 1962, p. 62.
[72] Dollimore D., Heal G. R. and Martin D. R., *J. Chromatogr.*, **50**, 209 (1970).
[73] Giddings J. C. and Eyring H. J., *J. Phys. Chem.*, **59**, 416 (1955).
[74] Quarrie A. D., *J. Phys. Chem.*, **38**, 437 (1963).
[75] Beyon J. H., Clough S., Crocks D. A. and Lester G. R., *Trans. Faraday Soc.*, **54**, 705 (1958).
[76] Oxtoby J. C., *J. Chem. Phys.*, **31**, 3886 (1969).
[77] Weiss G. H., *Separ. Sci.*, **5**, 51 (1970).
[78] Kocirik M., *J. Chromatogr.*, **30**, 459 (1967).
[79] Patberg G. and Smith J. M., *J. Catal.*, **12**, 172 (1968).
[80] Adrian J. S. and Smith J. M., *J. Catal.*, **18**, 57 (1970).
[81] Suzuki M. and Smith J. M., *J. Catal.*, **21**, 335 (1971).
[82] Grubner O., *Anal. Chem.*, **43**, 1934 (1971).
[83] Buys T. S. and Clerk K., *J. Chromatogr.*, **63**, 193 (1971).
[84] Buys T. S. and Clerk K., *J. Chromatogr.*, **67**, 1, 13, (1972).
[85] McNair H. and Cocke W. M., *J. Chromatogr.*, **10**, 27 (1972).
[86] Goedert M. and Guiochon G., *Chromatographia*, **6**, 116 (1973).
[87] Roginskii S. Z., Yanovskii M. I. and Berman A. D., *Osnovy primenenya khromatografii v katalize*, Izd. Nauka, Moskva, 1972.
[88] Valentin P. and Guiochon G., *J. Chrom. Sci.*, **14**, 132 (1976).
[89] Guiochon G. and Jacob L., *J. Chim. phis.*, **67**, 185 (1970).
[90] Guiochon G., *J. Chromatogr.*, **14**, 378 (1964).
[91] Oberholtzer J. E. and Rogers L. B., *Anal. Chem.*, **41**, 1234 (1969).
[92] Goedert M. and Guiochon G., *Anal. Chem.*, **42**, 962 (1970); *ibid.* **45**, 1180, 1188 (1973).
[93] Pease E. C. and Thorburn S., *J. Chromatogr.*, **30**, 344 (1967).
[94] Conder J. R. and Langer S. H., *Anal. Chem.*, **39**, 1461 (1967).
[95] Wicarova O., Novak J. and Janak J., *J. Chromatogr.*, **51**, 3 (1970).
[96] Cruickshank A. J. B., Windsor M. L. and Young C. L., *Proc. Roy Soc. Ser. A*, **295**, 259, 271 (1966).
[97] Conder J. R. and Purnell J. H., *Trans. Faraday Soc.*, **65**, 839 (1969).
[98] Goedert M. and Guiochon G., *J. Chromatogr. Sci.*, **7**, 323 (1969).

Chapter 2

The Nature of Adsorption

2.1 Physical Adsorption

The nature of adsorption (physical adsorption or chemisorption) can be defined chromatographically from changes in retention volume with temperature. From this relationship we can calculate heats and other thermodynamic functions of adsorption (see Chapter 8).

Physical adsorption decreases as the temperature rises, whereas chemisorption usually reaches a maximum at a certain temperature. Furthermore, the heat of chemisorption is of the same order as the heat of a chemical reaction; thus it is much greater than the heat of physical adsorption, the value of which is approximately the same as the heat of condensation of the adsorbate.

These two fundamental criteria generally enable one to establish the type of adsorption being studied chromatographically.

For physical adsorption the relationship between log (V_g/T) and $1/T$ for a given adsorbate is linear, whereby the tangents of the angle of inclination to the x-axis is positive (thus the retention volume decreases with a rise in temperature). In such a case it is quite easy to determine the isosteric heat of adsorption (see Chapter 8).

2.2 Investigation of Irreversible and Reversible Adsorption

If the value of $\log(V_g/T)$ increases with temperature, activated sorption is taking place.

The pulse technique is particularly useful for determining the course of irreversible adsorption. If, after the adsorbate has passed through a bed of the adsorbent under test, the peak area is smaller than after it has passed through an empty column, it means that irreversible adsorption is taking place; this can be measured.

This technique can be used to study catalyst poisoning caused by the irreversible adsorption of contaminants present in the substrates of the catalytic process.

Reversible adsorption is studied by means of another technique. In this case, a sample containing a mixture of a non-adsorbing gas (such as helium or argon) and the adsorbate is injected into the carrier gas stream. If only one peak is recorded, the adsorbate has not been adsorbed; that is to say, most of the adsorbate molecules pass through the column at the same velocity as molecules not being adsorbed under the given circumstances. If there are two peaks, it means that the test substance has been adsorbed on the surface of the solid (Fig. 2.1).

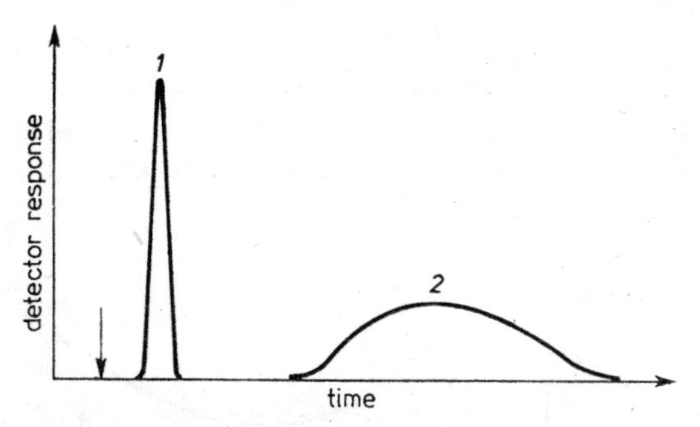

Fig. 2.1 A typical chromatogram of a sample mixture containing a non-adsorbing gas *1* and an adsorbate *2*.

A chromatogram obtained in this way (Fig. 2.1) can also tell us something about the fundamental process affecting the width of a peak.

Figure 2.1 demonstrates that for a given system it is adsorption and not diffusion that is responsible for the peak width. If diffusion played an important part in broadening the adsorbate peak, the non-adsorbing gas peak would also be much broader. In this way we can study adsorption in systems of very low adsorptive capabilities. The study of the reversible adsorption of deuterium on a nickel catalyst [1] is an illustration of this (Fig. 2.2).

Figure 2.2 shows a series of chromatograms of a deuterium–helium mixture which were obtained at temperatures from 78 K to 605 K. Hydrogen was the carrier gas. It is obvious from the figure that over the temperature range from about 161 K to 195 K deuterium is not sorbed — we get one peak only. The change of retention volume with temperature is shown in Fig. 2.3.

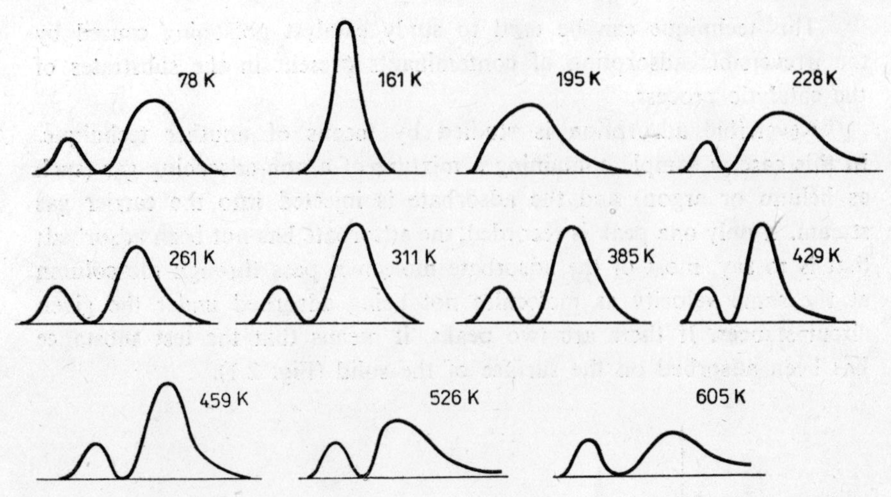

Fig. 2.2 Chromatograms of a deuterium–helium mixture on a nickel catalyst at various temperatures. The first peak is the helium peak (after A. Ozaki *et al.* [1]).

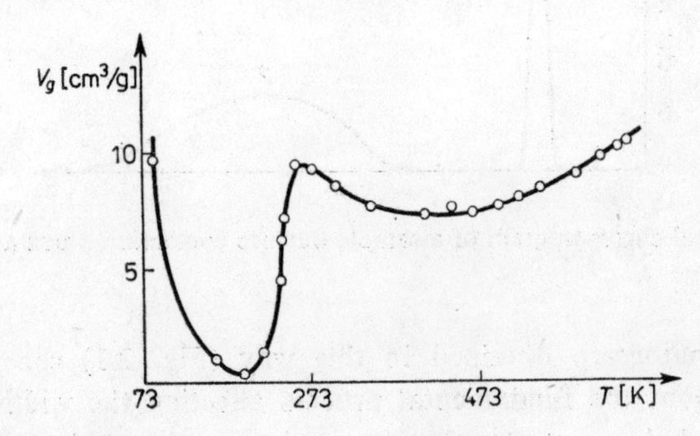

Fig. 2.3 Dependence of the retention volume of deuterium over a nickel catalyst on temperature (after A. Ozaki *et al.* [1]).

At 78 K deuterium is reversibly sorbed on the nickel catalyst in considerable quantities, but adsorption declines rapidly as the temperature increases, and at around 173 K does not take place at all. A further rise in temperature promotes adsorption which reaches a maximum at 243 K.

Two temperature areas can be distinguished on Fig. 2.3:

(1) from 78 K to 173 K, and

(2) from 243 K to 453 K,

when a rise in temperature causes a reduction in retention volume (the heat of adsorption can be determined). Over these ranges, the deuterium peaks (Fig. 2.2) are narrow, at other temperatures they are broadened.

It has also been found that over the temperature ranges (1) and (2) the complete material balance is obtained with respect to the injected deuterium.

Zhukhovitskii and Ivanova [2–4] carried out some interesting chromatographic studies on reversible and irreversible activated adsorption. To discover whether activated adsorption had taken place, it was necessary to establish how retention volumes, peak heights and areas change with temperature.

Figure 2.4 illustrates the results of studies on the adsorption of oxygen at various temperatures on industrial hopcalite (50% MnO_2, 30% CuO, 15% Co_2O_3, 5% Ag_2O) [3]. At low temperatures for various flow rates the logarithm of the specific retention volume of oxygen decreases linearly

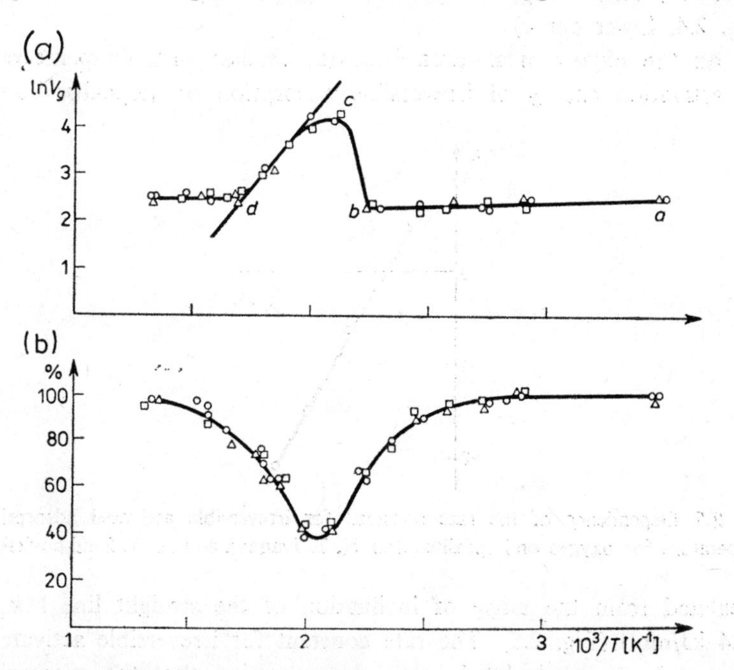

Fig. 2.4 Relationship for oxygen on hopcalite, between (a) the logarithm of retention volume $\ln V_g$ for oxygen, (b) the amount of reversibly sorbed oxygen and the reciprocal of the temperature for various carrier gas flow rates (○ — 198, □ — 294, △ — 460 cm^3/min) (after N. T. Ivanova and A. A. Zhukhovitskii [3]).

(line *ab*) with temperature rise. Over this range of temperature (line *ab*) oxygen is physically adsorbed on the hopcalite. The small angle of inclination of the straight line indicates a low heat of physical adsorption for oxygen on this catalyst (8.38 kJ/mol). As the temperature is raised to about 423 K, the retention volume increases rapidly (line *bc*) and then falls (line *cd*). The increase of retention volume with temperature rise is due to activated adsorption.

The heat of activated reversible adsorption of oxygen (41.5 kJ/mol) was calculated from the gradient of the straight line *cd*. However, the value of this heat is only approximate, since the reversible equilibrium of the process was not attained. This is because partial irreversible sorption of oxygen in this temperature range also takes place (lower part of Fig. 2.4).

A reduction in the quantity of oxygen leaving the column was observed already at 363 K; irreversible activated adsorption took place from 473 K to 498 K, only disappearing completely at temperatures above 633 K (Fig. 2.4, lower curve).

As the oxygen peak area becomes smaller with temperature rise, the activation energy of irreversible adsorption on hopcalite could be

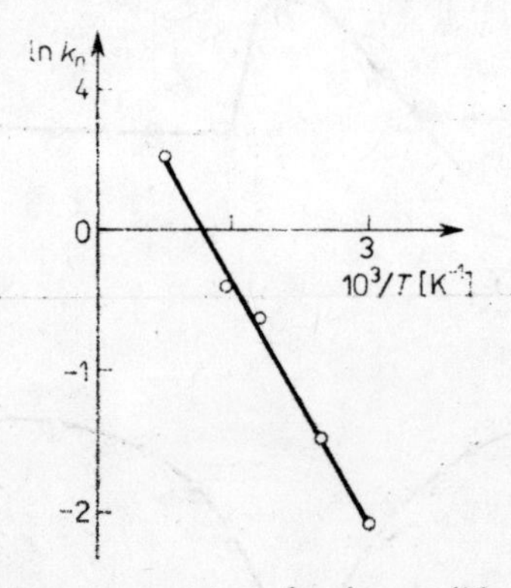

Fig. 2.5 Dependence of the rate constant for irreversible activated adsorption on temperature for oxygen on hopcalite (after N. T. Ivanova and A. A. Zhukhovitskii [3]).

calculated from the angle of inclination of the straight line $\ln k_n - 1/T$ (39.4 kJ/mol) (Fig. 2.5). The rate constant for irreversible activated adsorption k_n was calculated on the assumption that the process takes place according to a first-order equation

$$k_n = \frac{1}{t_R} \ln \frac{S^0_{peak}}{S_{peak}}, \tag{2.1}$$

where for the same sample size, S^0_{peak} is the peak area when no irreversible activated adsorption has taken place, S_{peak} is the peak area if irreversible activated adsorption has taken place, and t_R is the retention time.

The activation energy of reversible activated adsorption was determined from the changes in peak width W with temperature. As the temperature rises, the peak width passes through a maximum. In the initial stages of activated adsorption the peak width increases as the temperature rises.

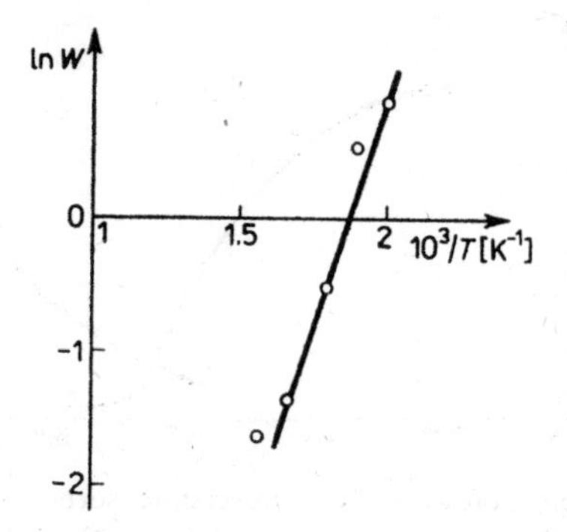

Fig. 2.6 Dependence of the logarithm of oxygen peak width on the temperature over hopcalite (after N. T. Ivanova and A. A. Zhukhovitskii [3]).

Figure 2.6 shows the reduction in peak width which takes place over the temperature range 493–593 K. The peak width is given by [5]

$$W \cong \frac{(k_a)^{1/2}}{k_d}, \tag{2.2}$$

where k_a is the adsorption rate constant, and k_d is the desorption rate constant.

The activation energy of the reversible activated adsorption of oxygen on hopcalite was calculated from Fig. 2.6 to be about 20 kJ/mol.

Chromatography has been successfully applied to the study of one of the most complex processes of activated adsorption — the adsorption of oxygen and hydrogen on activated charcoal [4]. It has been shown that at temperatures from 273 to 573 K three characteristic areas of varying interaction between oxygen and activated charcoal can be distinguished.

Up to about 353 K, only physical adsorption of oxygen is observed. The relationship of $\log V_g$ with $1/T$ decreases linearly as the temperature rises. Over this temperature range (i.e. from 273 to 353 *K*) the volume of oxygen leaving the column is equal to that entering it.

At temperatures higher than 353 *K*, apart from the continuing physical adsorption, some of the oxygen is irreversibly bound to the surface of the activated charcoal (Fig. 2.7). Carbon dioxide formation begins at around 483 K and increases in quantity as the temperature rises (Fig. 2.7, curve *2*). Oxygen is bound here in three ways: by physical adsorption, irreversible adsorption, and the reaction of the oxygen with the activated

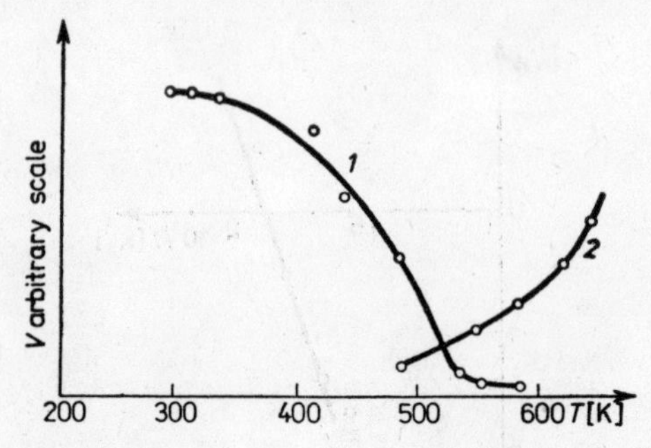

Fig. 2.7 The effect of temperature on the irreversible sorption of oxygen (plot *1*) and evolution of CO_2 (plot *2*) on activated charcoal (after N. T. Ivanova and A. A. Zhukhovitskii [4]).

charcoal to form CO_2. As CO_2 is formed at a low temperature, there is no reversible activated adsorption of oxygen in the activated charcoal–oxygen system.

Figure 2.8 shows the relationship of $\log V_g$ with $1/T$ for hydrogen on activated charcoal. As can be seen from this figure, both physical

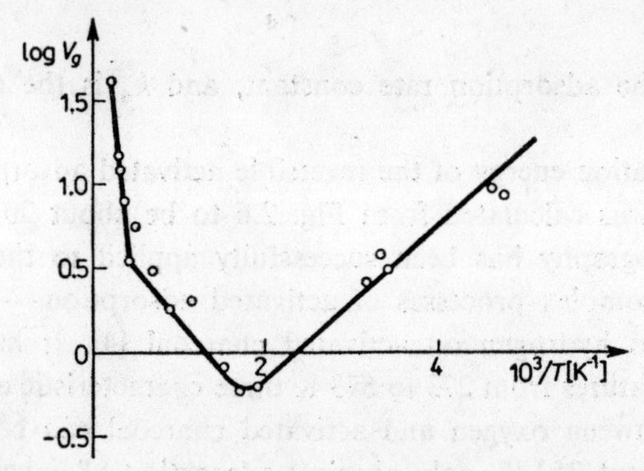

Fig. 2.8 Dependence of $\log V_g$ on $1/T$ for hydrogen on activated charcoal (after N. T. Ivanova and A. A. Zhukhovitskii [4]).

adsorption and reversible activated adsorption of hydrogen take place here (retention volume increases with temperature rise). In addition, irreversible adsorption of hydrogen has been observed at temperatures above 573 K. The rapid increase of $\log V_g$ at high temperatures indicates that adsorption processes requiring activation energy are taking place. Methane formation was observed only at temperatures above 973 K.

2.3 Investigation of the Co_3O_4–H_2 System

The nature of the interactions of hydrogen with Co_3O_4 over a wide range of temperature from 323 to 623 K was investigated chromatographically [6]. The variations in hydrogen–Co_3O_4 interactions allow the temperature range to be divided into three sections (Fig. 2.9).

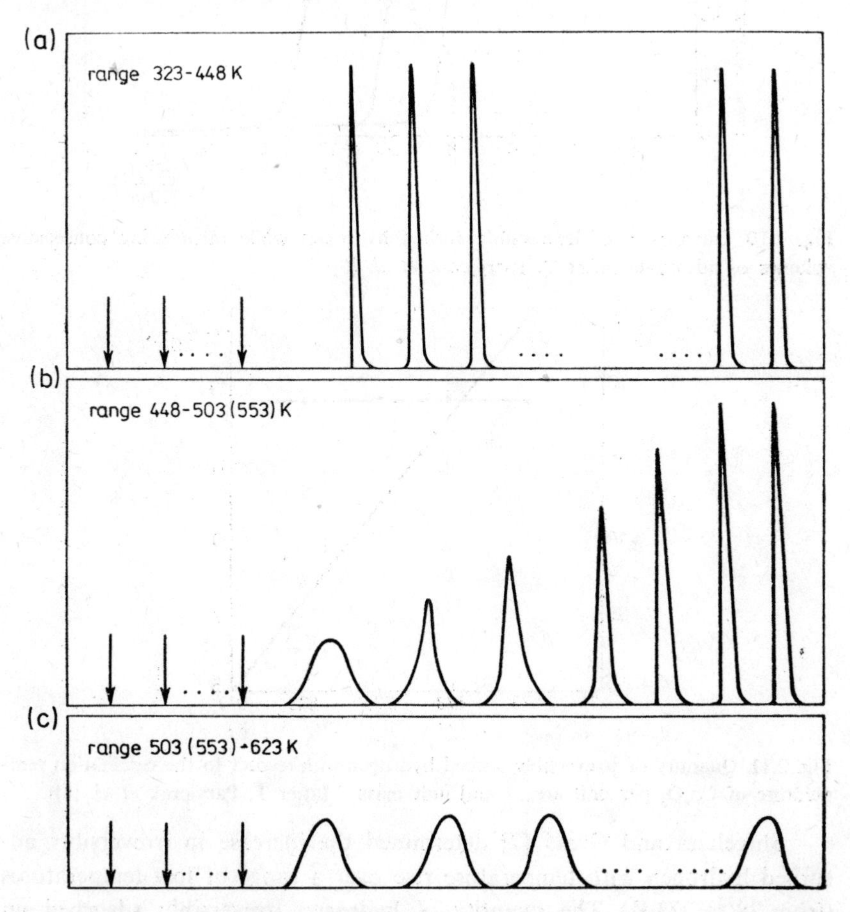

Fig. 2.9 Typical chromatogram showing hydrogen–Co_3O_4 interactions at various temperatures (after T. Paryjczak *et al.* [6]).

From 323 to 448 K the first portions of hydrogen are adsorbed irreversibly. A certain quantity having been adsorbed, the hydrogen peak now appears. The amount of irreversibly sorbed hydrogen increases with temperature; Fig 2.10 illustrates this.

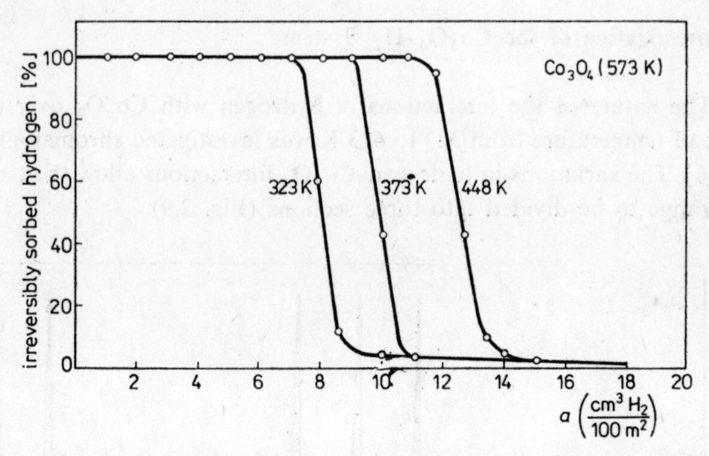

Fig. 2.10 Quantity *a* of irreversibly sorbed hydrogen while introducing consecutive volumes of adsorbate (after T. Patryjczak *et al.* [6]).

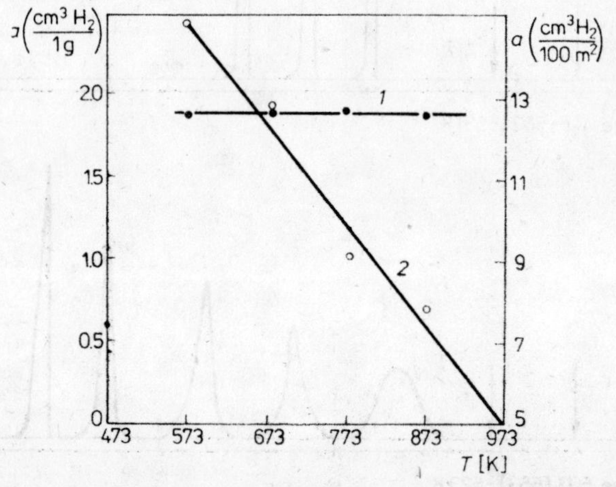

Fig. 2.11 Quantity of irreversibly sorbed hydrogen with respect to the calcination temperature of Co_3O_4 per unit area *1* and unit mass *2* (after T. Paryjczak *et al.* [6]).

Shigehara and Ozaki [7] determined the increase in irreversibly adsorbed hydrogen with temperature rise over a range of low temperatures (from 78 to 273 K). The quantity of hydrogen irreversibly adsorbed on various samples of Co_3O_4 per unit area is practically constant (Fig. 2.11).

This fact amply demonstrates the surface nature of the process. Between 448 K and 503 K the first portions of hydrogen are adsorbed irreversibly. After a certain amount of hydrogen has been adsorbed, a broad water peak appears on the chromatogram (Fig. 2.9b). Further portions of hydrogen give an increasingly symmetrical peak up to the instant when narrow hydrogen peaks of constant height appear. The reduction of the oxide commences in this temperature range. However, the unexpectedly small quantity of hydrogen required for the reduction is characteristic. It may be assumed that within this temperature range, reduction first involves surface hydroxyl groups or else the most mobile oxygen atoms from the oxide surface.

From 503 to 623 K all the hydrogen introduced is used up in the reduction of Co_3O_4 (Fig. 2.9c).

2.4. General Adsorption, Chemisorption

Using chromatography it is especially easy to determine how much of the overall adsorption process is due to chemisorption, by removing the amount of adsorbate physically adsorbed by means of the carrier gas.

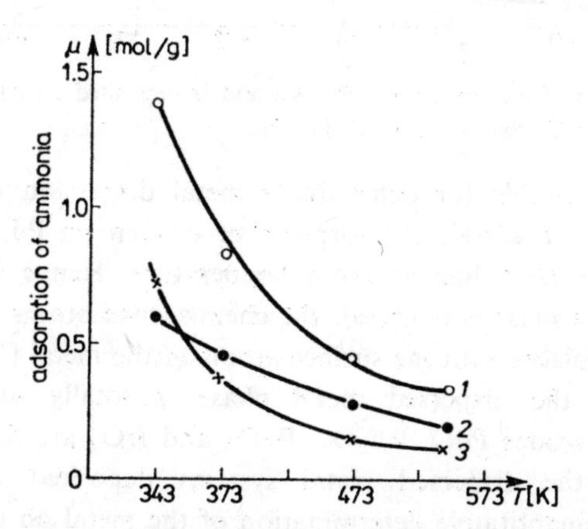

Fig. 2.12 Total adsorption *1*, chemisorption *2* and physical adsorption *3* of ammonia on an aluminosilicate catalyst with respect to temperature (after N. E. Buyanova *et al.* [8]).

Figure 2.12 shows the total adsorption, chemisorption and physical adsorption of ammonia on an aluminosilicate catalyst with respect to temperature (see Chapter 7) [8].

2.5 Study of a Metal/Support–Oxygen System

Chromatography facilitates the study of metal-oxygen interactions over a wide range of temperatures (Fig. 2.13) [9–13]. These studies were carried out within the temperature range 298–973 K.

Three temperature ranges for interactions between oxygen and Pd, Re, Rh and Ir can be distinguished on Fig 2.13. Range I — 298–473 K: surface interactions of metal atoms with oxygen mostly take place here.

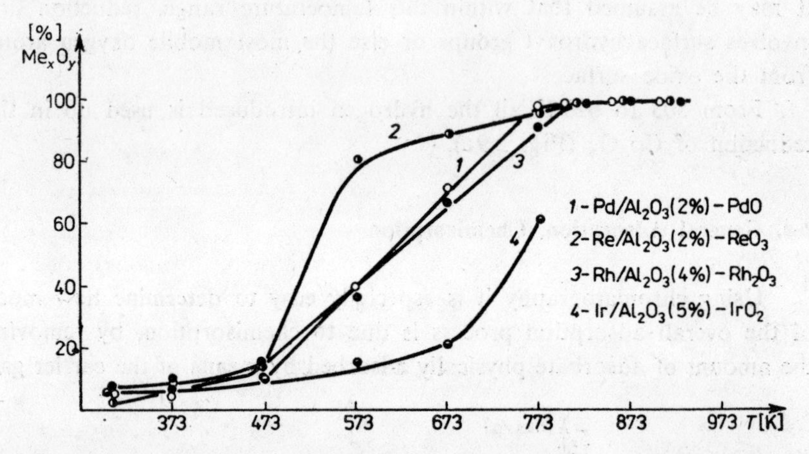

Fig. 2.13 Sorption of oxygen on Pd, Re, Rh and Ir deposited on Al_2O_3 with respect to temperature (after T. Paryjczak *et al.* [9–13]).

The range is suitable for determining metal dispersion using oxygen as the adsorbate. At 473 K, the sorption of oxygen on Pd, Re, Rh and Ir is some 30% higher than at room temperature. Range II — 473–773 K: the metal in the mass is oxidized, the chemisorbed atoms of oxygen probably changing places with the surface atoms of the metal [14]. Range III — above 773 K: the dispersed metal phase is totally oxidized and the stoichiometric oxides PdO, Rh_2O_3, ReO_3 and IrO_2 are formed. The total oxidation of the dispersed metal systems deposited on the support facilitates the quantitative determination of the metal on the support [15].

2.6 Investigation of the Properties of Different Forms of a Catalyst

The chromatographic method can be used to assess the effects of the various conditions under which catalysts and adsorbents are prepared on their sorptive properties [2–4, 16–20].

Figure 2.14 illustrates the dependence of $\log V_g$ on $1/T$ for oxygen adsorbed on MnO_2 unroasted (curve *1*) and roasted for one hour at 1223 K (curve *2*) [20]. Activated adsorption of oxygen is minimal on roasted MnO_2.

The effect of the phase structure of bismuth–molybdenum catalysts on their sorptive properties is considerable [16]. The retention volume

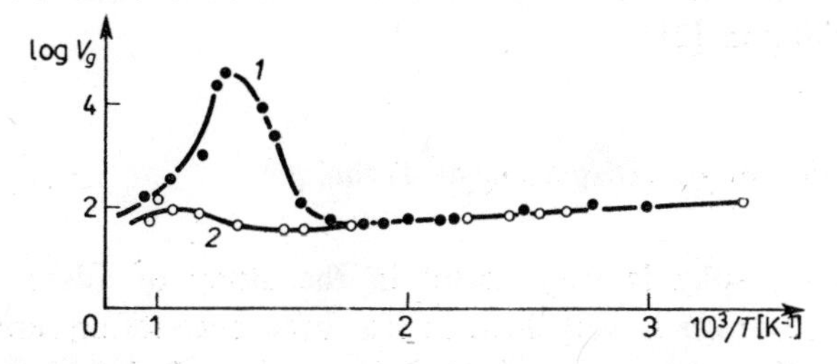

Fig. 2.14 Dependence of $\log V_g$ on $1/T$ for oxygen on MnO_2 (unroasted *1* and roasted *2*) at 1223 K (after N. T. Ivanova [20]).

of propylene on MoO_3, Bi_2O_3 and $Bi_2O_3 \cdot 2MoO_3$ (phase β) shows a slight though steady increase with temperature rise within the range 323 K to 623 K. Acrolein behaves in a similar manner. This indicates that these

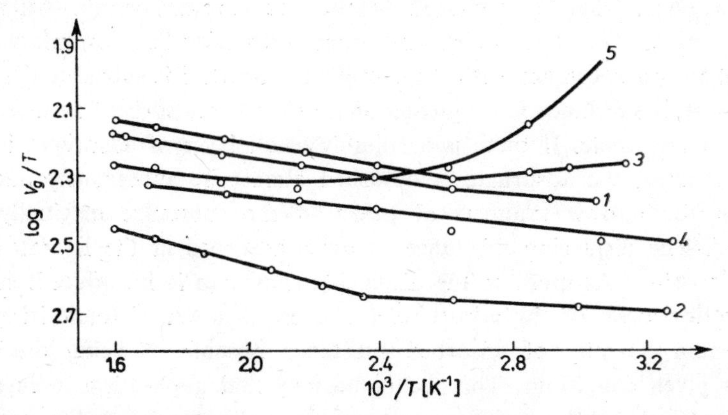

Fig. 2.15 Dependence of $\log V_g/T$ on $1/T$ for propene on (after A. Lewicki *et al.* [16]): *1* — MoO_3, *2* — Bi_2O_3, *3* — Bi-Mo-α, *4* — Bi-Mo-β, and *5* — Bi-Mo-γ.

adsorbates are actively and reversibly adsorbed on the catalysts mentioned (Fig. 2.15).

The adsorption of propene proceeds differently on $Bi_2O_3 \cdot 3MoO_3$ (phase α) and on $Bi_2O_3 \cdot MoO_3$ (phase γ) catalysts. In this case, apart from activated adsorption at higher temperatures, physical adsorption at lower temperatures also occurs and is especially great on the Bi-Mo-γ catalyst. It is true that in the case of the Bi-Mo-α catalyst, the angles of inclination of the straight lines (Fig. 2.15) are small, but on the other hand the areas under the peaks obtained do not alter with a rise in temperature, which suggests a lack of activated irreversible sorption. The different sorptive properties of Bi-Mo-β are expressed by its greater catalytic activity in propene oxidation [21].

2.7 Application of the Displacement Technique

Chromatography is very useful in the study of adsorption where the surface coverage is very low. It has been successfully applied while investigating the adsorption of normal and branched hydrocarbons on the surfaces of thin layers of water [22–24].

Much valuable information can be gathered from a study of adsorption using the displacement technique [25, 26]. The principle of this is based on the pulse-wise introduction of adsorbate (or adsorbate mixture) into the carrier gas stream and the saturation of the adsorbent in the microreactor. This is connected to the gas chromatograph. After the adsorbent surface has become saturated with adsorbate or mixture of adsorbates, a substance with displacement properties is introduced pulse-wise — this substance has a greater affinity for the adsorbent surface than the test adsorbate. If there is a suitably small layer of adsorbent in the microreactor, the adsorbate is desorbed almost instantaneously and we obtain the narrow symmetrical peaks of the substance originally adsorbed. The displacing substance becomes adsorbed at the liberated adsorption sites. As more of the displacing substance is introduced, so the desorption peak of the adsorbate increases to a size characterizing the maximum quantity of adsorbed substance capable of being displaced under given conditions. This technique may find application in research into catalyst–reaction mixture systems, in order to define the sorptive properties of the particular components of reactants and products on the surface of a catalyst, and in studies of catalyst poisoning.

Furthermore, adsorption isotherms can be determined from these peaks using one of the methods given in Chapter 4. For example, Fig. 2.16 shows a typical pulse-pulse chromatogram of a mixture of isopropanol, propanol and 3-methylbutan-1-ol adsorbed on Al_2O_3

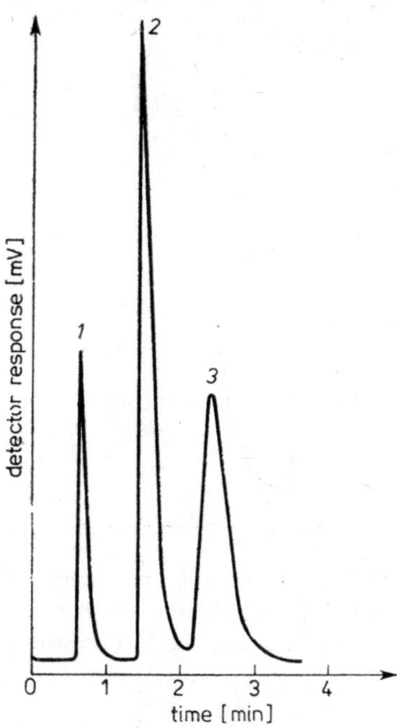

Fig. 2.16 Pulse-pulse chromatogram of a mixture of alcohols adsorbed on Al_2O_3 at 373 K (after L. V. Andreev *et al.* [26]):

1 — isopropanol, *2* — propanol, *3* — 3-methylbutan-1-ol (displacing substance — water; flame-ionization detector).

at 373 K. Water was the displacing substance which was not recorded by the flame-ionization detector. Measurements can also be made by maintaining a constant concentration of adsorbate in the carrier gas and introducing pulse-wise the displacement substance only [25].

2.8. Investigation of Slow Sorption Processes on Fe/SiO_2 Catalysts

The slow sorption of oxygen on Fe/SiO_2 catalysts at temperatures from 193 to 723 K has been successfully studied by means of chromatography [27]. Having reduced the catalyst at 723 K, the sample is eluted for 15 minutes in the carrier gas and then cooled to the temperature of measurement. The results of oxygen sorption are presented on Figs. 2.17 and 2.18 (continuous curves). Analogous results are obtained by adding the consecutive increments of oxygen sorption at 197, 298, 433 and 723 K. This demonstrates that the sorption of oxygen within this range of temperature is additive and that it is not desorbed into the carrier gas stream.

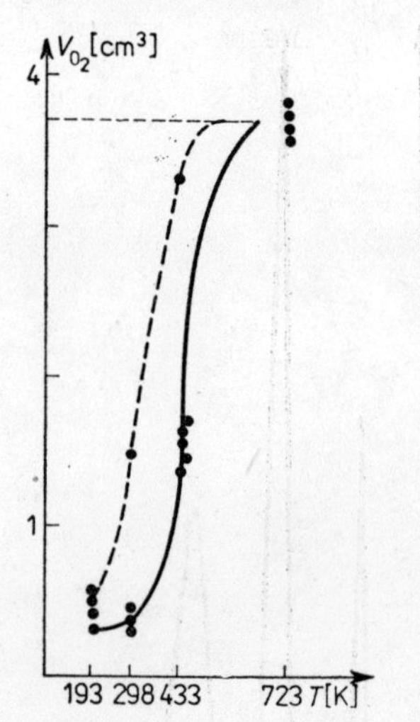

Fig. 2.17 Oxygen sorption on a reduced 1% iron catalyst (Fe/SiO_2) as a function of temperature — continuous curve. Oxygen sorption after prolonged contact with oxygen at various temperatures — dashed curve (after T. Paryjczak and P. Zieliński [27]).

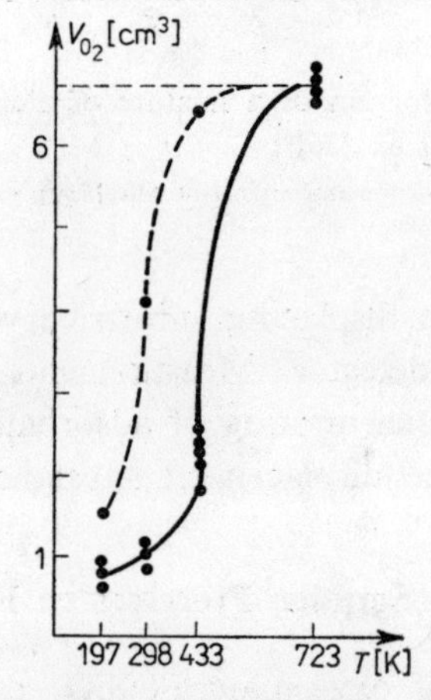

Fig. 2.18 Oxygen sorption on a 3% catalyst (Fe/SiO_2) — continuous curve — and after 48 h oxidation in a stream of oxygen obtained by indirect method — dashed curve (after T. Paryjczak and P. Zieliński [27]).

The points on the dashed curve were obtained by measuring the additional sorption of oxygen, which was sorbed at 723 K after prolonged contact with oxygen at a given temperature, and marking the values obtained, starting from the horizontal dashed line (oxygen sorption at 723 K) and going towards the temperature axis [27].

The continuous curves from Figs. 2.17 and 2.18 show the course of rapid oxygen sorption (the pulse method), whereas the dashed curves show the course of total oxygen sorption as a function of temperature. They were obtained by measuring the quantity of additional oxygen sorption at 723 K after prolonged flow of oxygen over the catalyst at the measurement temperature. The magnitude of oxygen sorption obtained in this way was treated as that amount required to complete oxidation, starting on Figs. 2.17 and 2.18 from the maximum value of sorption at 723 K towards the temperature axis. The difference between the curves of total and rapid sorption is thus a measure of the slow sorption of free oxygen on an iron catalyst. Chromatography can be used in this way to study slow processes. The slow sorption of oxygen rises together with the temperature. Slow sorption at low temperatures is relatively small [27]. Figure 2.19 illustrates the oxygen sorption at 723 K on a 3% iron catalyst

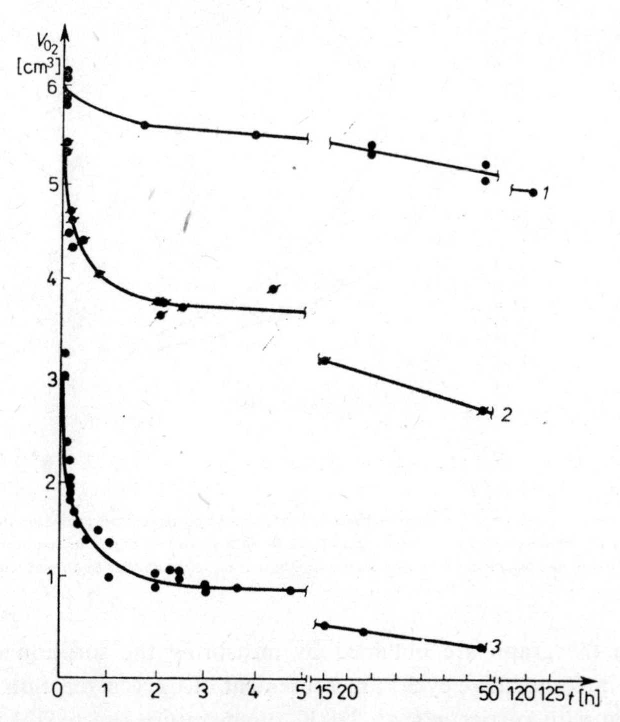

Fig. 2.19 Oxygen sorption at 723 K on a 3% iron catalyst with respect to the previous contact period of the sample with a stream of oxygen at a low temperatures (after T. Paryjczak and P. Zieliński [27]).

curve *1* — 193 K, curve *2* — 298 K, curve *3* — 433 K.

with respect to the earlier period of the catalyst's contact with oxygen at low temperatures (*1* — 193 K, *2* — 298 K, *3* — 433 K). At the same time, the results are characteristic of the changes in the slow sorption of oxygen.

A greater degree of oxidation for a given temperature of catalyst contact with oxygen can be achieved not only by increasing the period of contact. The activating effect of temperature can also be used: this is illustrated in Fig. 2.20 for catalysts containing 1% and 3% iron. The

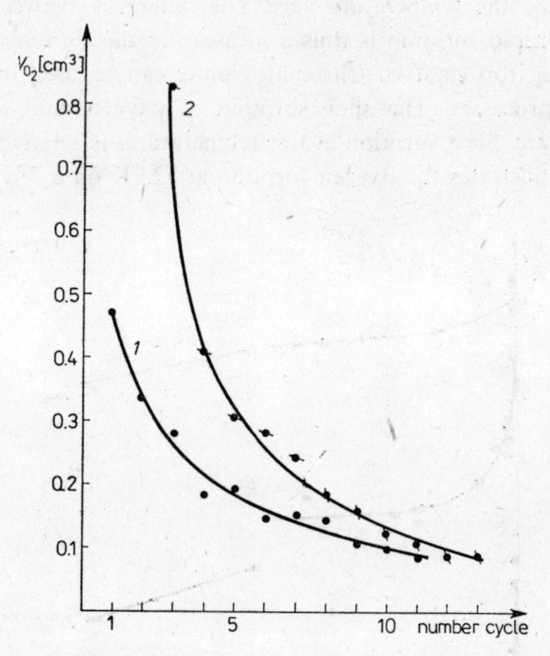

Fig. 2.20 Oxygen sorption at 298 K on an iron catalyst (*1* — 1%, *2* — 3%) (after T. Paryjczak and P. Zieliński [28]):

The points were obtained in the following cycles: measurement of oxygen sorption, temperature rise to 723 K (after a 15-minute elution with carrier gas at 298 K) in a stream of argon, temperature reduction to 298 K, then further measurement of oxygen sorption. Curve *2* has been shifted by three cycles to make the diagram clearer.

points on the graph are obtained by measuring the sorption of oxygen at 298 K in consecutive cycles: measurement of oxygen sorption, a 15-minute elution with carrier gas at 298 K, temperature rise to 723 K (always in a stream of argon), cooling of the sample to 298 K, then further measurement of oxygen sorption.

The period spent by the sample at 723 K was of no great importance.

It is interesting that after 13 such cycles, when the sorption values approached the measurement error, a "supplementary" oxygen sorption carried out at 723 K amounted to 2.8 cm^3/sample on a 3% catalyst, which was equivalent to the catalyst having been in contact with oxygen for about 2 days at 298 K (Fig. 2.19). The consequence of this would be that "pumping" oxygen into the sample with the aid of temperature would be restricted to only the number of equivalent slow sorptions at 298 K, in all, about half the oxygen required for complete oxidation. After pulsewise oxidation at 298 K, such behaviour is probably the consequence of having brought the system to thermodynamic equilibrium by raising the temperature, and this would be observed for other metals [11]. During this process, part of the metal surface undergoes reactivation, possibly as a result of the exchange of places mechanism, thus facilitating the further observed rapid sorption of oxygen at 298 K.

The proportion of slow sorption in the total sorption was found for iron some years ago [29], though for low temperatures it was relatively small. The considerable increase in slow sorption with temperature (Figs. 2.17 and 2.18) points to the high-temperature nature of this process, although if at low temperatures the thickness of the surface layer of catalyst oxidized during slow sorption presented an almost insuperable diffusion barrier, at 473 K it proceeds during a proportionally longer time as the catalyst has been completely oxidized. This is reflected in the process of thermoprogrammed oxidation, in which a maximum is obtained on the graph at about 473 K [28].

References

[1] Ozaki A., Nozaki F. and Maruya K., *J. Catal.*, **4**, 234 (1967).

[2] Ivanova N. T., Zhukhovitskii A. A. and Savcillo S. V., *Zavod. Lab.*, **32**, 136 (1966).

[3] Ivanova N. T. and Zhukhovitskii A. A., *Zhur. Fiz. Khim.*, **41**, 1823 (1967).

[4] Ivanova N. T. and Zhukhovitskii A. A., *Zhur. Fiz. Khim.*, **43**, 2339 (1969).

[5] Zhutkhovitskii A. A. and Turkeltaub N. M., *Gazovaya khromatografiya*, Izd. Gostontekhizdat, Moskva, 1962.

[6] Paryjczak T., Rynkowski J. and Król A., *J. Chromatogr.*, **139**, 349 (1977).

[7] Shigehara Y. and Ozaki A., *J. Catal.*, **21**, 78 (1971).

[8] Buyanova N. E., Gudkova G. B. and Karnaukhov A. P., *Metody Issled. Katal. React., Otd. Sibir. Otd. Akad. SSSR*, Novosibirsk, **2**, 55 (1965).

[9] Paryjczak T., Jóźwiak W. K. and Góralski J., *J. Chromatogr.*, **155**, 9 (1978).

[10] Paryjczak T., Gebauer D. and Kozakiewicz A., *J. Colloid Interface Sci.*, **70**, 320 (1979).

[11] Paryjczak T., Jóźwiak W. K. and Góralski J., *J. Chromatogr.*, **166**, 65 (1978).
[12] Paryjczak T., Zieliński P. and Jóźwiak W. K., *J. Chromatogr.*, **160**, 247 (1978).
[13] Paryjczak T., Jóźwiak W. K. and Góralski J., *J. Chromatogr.*, **166**, 75 (1978).
[14] Anderson J. R., *Chemisorption and Reactions on Metallic Film*, Academic Press, London, New York, 1971.
[15] Paryjczak T., Jóźwiak W. K. and Góralski J., *J. Chromatogr.*, **120**, 291 (1976).
[16] Lewicki A., Paryjczak T. and Bereś J., *Roczniki Chem.*, **44**, 981 (1973).
[17] Eberly E. P. jr., *J. Phys. Chem.*, **65**, 68 (1961).
[18] Paryjczak T., Grzywna R. and Lewicki A., *Zeszyty Naukowe P. Ł. Chemia*, **27**, 109 (1973).
[19] Grzywna R., Kaźmierczak A. and Paryjczak T., *Roczniki Chem.*, **46**, 1586 (1972).
[20] Ivanova N. T., Ph. D. Thesis, Moscow, 1968.
[21] Bartist Ph. A., Lippens B. C. and Schuit G. G. A., *J. Catal.*, **5**, 55 (1966).
[22] Karger B. L., Sewell P. A., Castells R. C. and Hartkopf A., *J. Colloid Interface Sci.*, **35**, 328 (1971).
[23] Karger B. L., Castells R. C., Sewell P. A. and Hartkopf A., *J. Phys. Chem.*, **75**, 3870 (1971).
[24] King J. W., Chatterjec A. and Karger B. L., *J. Phys. Chem.*, **76**, 2769 (1972).
[25] Andreev L. V., Baiburskii V. L. and Kuvshinnikov V. D., *Zhur. Fiz. Khim.*, **46**, 80 (1972).
[26] Andreev L. V., Baiburskii V. L., Laptieva R. I. and Kuvshinnikov V. D., *Zhur. Fiz. Khim.*, **44**, 2350 (1970).
[27] Paryjczak T. and Zieliński P., *J. Chromatogr.*, **205**, 425 (1981).
[28] Paryjczak T. and Zieliński P., *Pol. J. Chem.*, **57**, 1303 (1983).
[29] Wyn Roberts M., *Trans. Faraday Soc.*, **57**, 99 (1961).

Chapter 3

The Heterogeneous Surfaces of Adsorbents and Catalysts

3.1 Introduction

The first basic work on the heterogeneity of adsorbent and catalyst surfaces was published during the forties and fifties, mainly by Roginskii [1–3]. The last 25 years have seen the very rapid growth of research into the effects of surface heterogeneity [4–55]. The energetic heterogeneity of a surface may be due to differences in the properties of atoms and ions located on the corners, edges and the various planes of crystals. It may also be the consequence of defects in the crystal lattice, voids, dislocations, admixtures of foreign ions dissolved in crystals or adsorbed on the surface. Catalysts usually consist of more than one phase; this can lead to further sources of heterogeneity such as interphase planes, additional solid solutions, transition phases, etc.

Since both adsorption and catalysis occur in the surface of a solid, the energetic heterogeneity of the surface fundamentally affects these processes. The most convenient way of describing differences in the properties of surface sectors is to use two magnitudes: the heat of adsorption for adsorptive properties and the activation energy for catalytic properties. Areas with different heats of adsorption (activation energies) are randomly distributed, but during the process itself they appear as groups having uniform (or approximately uniform) heats of adsorption (activation energies).

GC offers a very convenient and useful method of studying the effects of the energetic heterogeneity of surfaces. Particularly valuable are those papers from which the energy distribution function can be calculated directly from chromatographic data [16–35].

From this point of view there are two possible ways of determining the energy distribution function. We can investigate: either (1) the temperature relationships of retention data, or (2) the pressure relationships of retention data.

The first is based on a virial description of physical adsorption. The consecutive gas-solid virial coefficients, characterizing the interaction of an adsorbate molecule with the surface of an adsorbent or catalyst, can be determined from retention data [16]. A number of workers have suggested the possibility of applying the virial description to quantitative studies of the energetic heterogeneity of a surface [7, 17–19]. Using the temperature relationships of chromatographic data has the advantage that only very small samples of adsorbate are needed, which, from the theoretical stand-point, means that the description of the chromatographic process can be much simplified. However, in experimental practice, this technique is quite troublesome. If we use this method, we must ensure that there are no temperature gradients along the column. The column temperature must be kept very constant, which of course is difficult to achieve with the various types of standard apparatus. With this practical aspect in mind, attention was turned to the pressure relationships of retention data [20–35]. The starting point of this method is the work of Conder and Purnell [36–38] and Harris [39–40]. A large number of papers deal with the possibilities of using the pressure relationships of adsorption data to calculate the function $\chi(\varepsilon)$, but only a few of them offer useful ways of determining it [39, 43, 44, 48, 49, 57, 58]. As far as GC is concerned, the method described by Hobson [44] appears to serve this purpose best, as retention data can be applied directly.

The idea of using the pressure relationships of retention volumes for determining the differential distribution of the adsorption energy $\chi(\varepsilon)$, initiated by Waksmundzki, Rudziński and co-workers [20, 21, 27, 41], is currently being further developed [46, 50]. Adamson's method is also used [23, 48, 49], as are methods based on the Stieltjes and Laplace transformations [42].

3.2 A Method to Determine the Adsorption Energy Distribution from the Pressure Relationships of Retention Data

If we treat the surface of an adsorbent or catalyst as an area comprising diverse sectors with identical adsorption properties (or nearly so within one sector), the total adsorption isotherm in units of total coverage $\theta_t(p, T)$ can be expressed by the Sips equation [42,43]

$$\theta_t(p, T) = \int_{\Omega} \chi(\varepsilon)\theta_1(\varepsilon, p, T)\mathrm{d}\varepsilon\,, \tag{3.1}$$

where $\chi(\varepsilon)$ is the differential distribution of the adsorption energy defined as $\partial N_\infty/\partial\varepsilon$ (N_∞ is the volume of a monolayer), $\theta_l(\varepsilon, p, T)$ is the local adsorption isotherm on a sector of adsorption energy ε and Ω is the interval (set of intervals) in which the energies ε are contained.

Hobson's method [44] is used to determine the distribution function of the adsorption energy on the basis of the above equation. Hobson assumes that adsorption in a uniform sector initially takes place according to Henry's isotherm, and that this is followed by discrete condensation of the adsorbate when the surface of the sector has become full. The local isotherm $\theta_l(\varepsilon, p, T)$ for each sector of energy ε can be written thus

$$\theta_l(\varepsilon, p, T) = \frac{p}{K}\exp\left(\frac{\varepsilon}{RT}\right) \quad \text{for } p<p', \tag{3.2}$$

$$\theta_l(\varepsilon, p, T) = 1 \quad \text{for } p\geqslant p', \tag{3.3}$$

where p is the pressure of adsorbate vapours, T is the temperature of adsorption, R is the gas constant, p' is the pressure at which the value of the local isotherm reaches unity and K is Henry's constant.

The condensation of the adsorbate releases forces acting on its molecules. Hobson [44] accounts for this effect in the following equation:

$$p' = K\exp\left[-\frac{(\varepsilon+\varepsilon_0)}{RT}\right], \tag{3.4}$$

where ε_0 is the energy of mutual interaction between adsorbate molecules. According to Kiselev and Yashin [45], the constant K for simple adsorbate molecules can be expressed by the equation

$$K_T = 1.76\times 10^4(MT)^{1/2}, \tag{3.5}$$

where M is the molecular mass of the adsorbate, and T is the temperature of adsorption. The constant K can also be calculated directly from chromatographic data [34]. Equations (3.2) and (3.3) can be written in an equivalent form

$$\theta_l(\varepsilon, p, T) = \frac{p}{K}\exp\left(\frac{\varepsilon}{RT}\right) \quad \text{for } \varepsilon<\varepsilon', \tag{3.6}$$

$$\theta_l(\varepsilon, p, T) = 1 \quad \text{for } \varepsilon\geqslant\varepsilon', \tag{3.7}$$

where

$$\varepsilon' = -RT\ln\left(\frac{p}{K}\right)-\varepsilon^0. \tag{3.8}$$

Hobson [44] showed that ε^0 has little effect on the shape of the function $\chi(\varepsilon)$ obtained. The magnitude of ε^0 is of the nature of a standard error dependent on the temperature and is equal to 1.18 RT [21]. The effect of this is to shift the graph of $\chi(\varepsilon)$ to the left on the energy scale. After introducing equations (3.6) and (3.7) into equation (3.1), and assuming that $\varepsilon^0 = 0$, we obtain

$$\chi(\varepsilon) = -\left(\frac{\partial\theta_t}{\partial\varepsilon}\right)_T - RT\left(\frac{\partial^2\theta_t}{\partial\varepsilon^2}\right)_T. \tag{3.9}$$

If we carry out the chromatographic measurements at a sufficiently high temperature and at small concentrations of adsorbate vapour, we approach the ideal conditions assumed in equation (3.9). Therefore equation (3.9) is often used in chromatographic calculations. However, if $\varepsilon^0 \neq 0$, the equation for $\chi(\varepsilon)$ becomes very complicated, and is thus not very useful in practice. Equation (3.9) can be rewritten in the form [20]

$$\chi(\varepsilon) = -\left(\frac{\partial\theta_t}{\partial p}\right)_T\left(\frac{-p}{RT}\right) - RT\left\{\frac{\partial}{\partial p}\left[\left(\frac{-p}{RT}\right)\left(\frac{\partial\theta_T}{\partial p}\right)_T\right]\right\}\left(\frac{-p}{RT}\right). \tag{3.10}$$

After reduction

$$\chi(\varepsilon) = \frac{-p^2}{RT}\left(\frac{\partial^2\theta_t}{\partial p^2}\right)_T. \tag{3.11}$$

The right-hand side of equation (3.11) contains the second differential of the adsorption isotherm.

The equation for the retention volume V'_R, reasonable for low and moderate relative pressures of adsorbate, takes the form [36]

$$V'_R = j\left(\frac{\partial N_t}{\partial d}\right)_T, \tag{3.12}$$

where N_t is the quantity of adsorbate in the surface layer, d is the density of adsorbate in the volume phase, and j is the pressure gradient correction factor.

If we assume the ideality of the gas phase ($p = dRT$), we can then write equation (3.12) in this form

$$V'_R = jRT\frac{\partial N_t}{\partial p}. \tag{3.13}$$

Furthermore

$$N_{t(p)} = N_\infty \theta_{t(p)}, \tag{3.14}$$

where N_∞ is the volume of the monolayer.

Equation (3.13) can therefore be written

$$V'_{R(p)} = N_\infty jRT\left(\frac{\partial\theta_t}{\partial p}\right)_T . \quad (3.15)$$

From equations (3.11) and (3.15) we see that

$$\chi(\varepsilon) = \left(-\frac{1}{jN_\infty}\right)\left(\frac{p}{RT}\right)^2\left(\frac{\partial V'_R}{\partial p}\right)_T . \quad (3.16)$$

So, in order to determine the function $\chi(\varepsilon)$, the right-hand side of equation (3.16) has to be expressed as a function of the energy ε.

This method is based on certain simplifications which result mainly from the assumption that there is no mutual interaction among the adsorbate molecules within the small areas of adsorbent surface covered. The method has allowed for a considerable simplification of Hobson's method [44] both theoretically and experimentally. Rudziński [19, 46] has significantly modified this method.

An exponential expression giving the retention volume on heterogeneous adsorbents has recently been proposed [24, 25, 34]

$$V'_R = \exp\left(\sum_{n=0}^{m} B_n p^n\right), \quad (3.17)$$

where p is the adsorbate pressure and B_n is the appropriate coefficient, counted by approximation with a polynomial.

For linear chromatography, equation (3.17) can be reduced to

$$V'_R = \exp(B_0). \quad (3.18)$$

The value of $\exp(B_0)$ can be determined from the following equation [47]:

$$\exp(B_0) \approx \frac{jRTN_\infty}{K}\exp\left(\frac{\bar{\varepsilon}}{RT}\right), \quad (3.19)$$

where $\bar{\varepsilon}$ is the mean energy of adsorption.

For a homogeneous surface, equation (3.19) can be reduced by $\exp(\varepsilon/RT)$ since $\varepsilon = \bar{\varepsilon}$.

Equation (3.17) was found extremely useful for determining the energy distribution function directly from chromatographic data. The following expression for $\chi(\varepsilon)$ corresponds to it [24]:

$$\chi(\varepsilon)_{(p)} = -\frac{1}{j\ln 2}\left(\frac{p}{RT}\right)^2\left(\sum_{n=1}^{m} nB_n p^{n-1}\right)\exp\left(\sum_{n=0}^{m} B_n p^n\right), \quad (3.20)$$

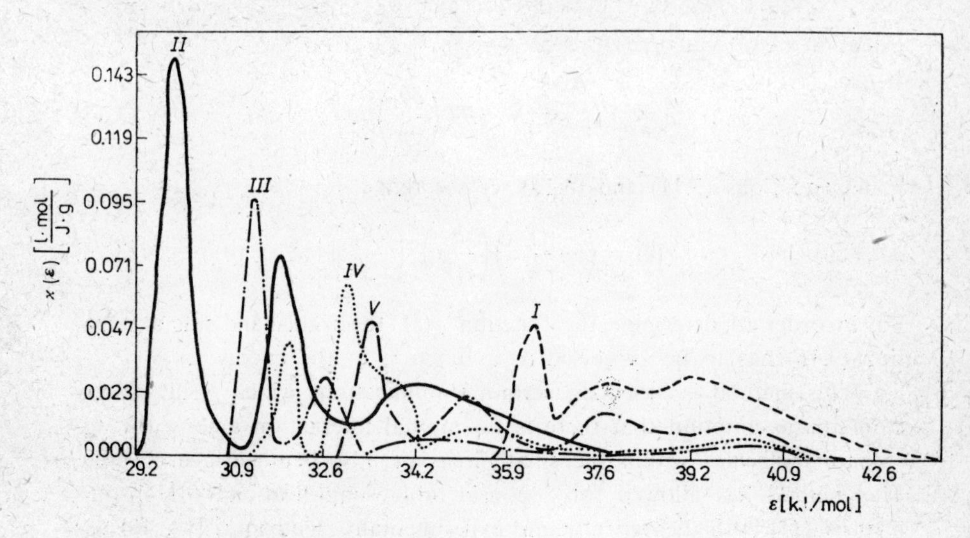

Fig. 3.1 Differential energy distribution functions for chloroform adsorbed on (after R. Leboda *et al.* [31]):

I — Co_3O_4; *II* — SiO_2; *III* — 63% SiO_2 + 37% Co_3O_4; *IV* — 50.1% SiO_2 + 49.9% Co_3O_4; *V* — 30.3% SiO_2 + 69.7% Co_3O_4.

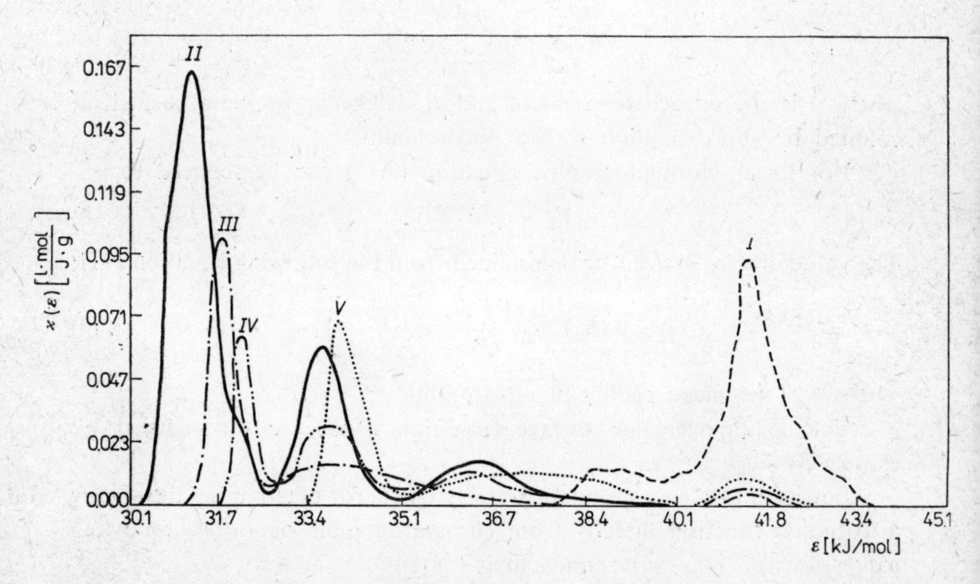

Fig. 3.2 Energy distribution functions for carbon tetrachloride adsorbed on (after R. Leboda *et al.* [31]):

I — Co_3O_4; *II* — SiO_2; *III* — 63% SiO_2 + 37% Co_3O_4; *IV* — 50.11% SiO_2 + 49.89% Co_3O_4; *V* — 30.28% SiO_2 + 69.72% Co_3O_4.

where

$$p = \frac{1}{K} \exp\left(-\frac{\varepsilon}{RT}\right). \tag{3.21}$$

In equations (3.20) and (3.21) Henry's constant (K) is calculated from chromatographic data [34].

Figure 3.1 and 3.2 illustrate the differential adsorption energy distribution functions, calculated from equation (3.20), for chloroform and carbon tetrachloride on SiO_2, Co_3O_4 and mechanical mixtures of these oxides [31].

On the Co_3O_4 curves, there are three distinct maxima for $CHCl_3$ and four for CCl_4. On the surface of Co_3O_4 the adsorption sites are represented mainly by Co^{2+} and Co^{3+} ions. The third peak for $CHCl_3$ can be attributed to molecular interaction between the adsorbate and O^{2-} ions. Three maxima each can be distinguished on the $\chi(\varepsilon)$ curves for both test substances adsorbed on SiO_2. For $CHCl_3$ and CCl_4 the adsorption sites on this adsorbent are free and partially-bound surface hydroxyl groups and Si^{4+} ions.

Comparison of the functions of $\chi(\varepsilon)$ for the mechanical mixtures of Co_3O_4 and SiO_2 shows that there is a strict correlation between the shape of the energy distribution function and the composition of the mixture. The shapes of the function $\chi(\varepsilon)$ for the mixtures is the resultant of their compositions. In the case of the oxide mixtures a greater peak shift with respect to the ε axis is observed for peaks representing energy centres of lower energy. As regards the strongest adsorption sites, the peak maxima practically overlap. The mean adsorption energy on the surface of a heterogeneous adsorbent is given by

$$\bar{\varepsilon} = \sum S_n \varepsilon_n, \tag{3.22}$$

where S_n denotes that fraction of the adsorbent surface having n-type adsorption sites of mean adsorption energy ε_n.

The correlation between the curves of $\chi(\varepsilon)$ for pure components and those for complex systems indicates that the investigation of adsorption energy distribution functions can, in the case of compound catalysts, be a useful method of determining their surface heterogeneity and the nature of the adsorption sites on their surfaces.

3.3 Adamson's Method for Analysing the Pressure Relationships of Retention Volumes

Adamson's method [48, 49] uses the integral form of the adsorption energy distribution $\chi(\varepsilon)$ and is defined as follows:

$$\chi(\varepsilon) = \frac{\partial \chi}{\partial \varepsilon}. \tag{3.23}$$

The substituted integral equation (3.1) can therefore be reduced to the form

$$\theta_t(p, T) = \int_0^1 \theta_l(\varepsilon, p, T)\,d\chi. \tag{3.24}$$

The total isotherm θ_t enables a first approximation of the function $\chi(\varepsilon)$ to be made; this will henceforth be denoted by $\chi^{(1)}(\varepsilon)$.

For each value of the adsorbate pressure, the assumed local adsorption isotherm θ_l may be expressed only as a function of the adsorption energy. Then, from the graph of χ as a function of ε and from the graph of θ_l as a function of ε we compile a plot of θ_l as a function of χ, for a certain adsorbate pressure. A similar procedure is adopted with respect to every experimentally tested value of the adsorbate pressure.

The second approximation of the function $\chi^{(2)}(\varepsilon)$ is found from the following relationship [48]:

$$\chi^{(2)}(\varepsilon) = \chi^{(1)}(\varepsilon)\frac{\theta_{t(p,T)}}{\theta^1_{t(p,T)}}. \tag{3.25}$$

The procedure described above is now repeated step by step, taking curve $\chi^{(2)}(\varepsilon)$ instead of $\chi^{(1)}(\varepsilon)$. The method of obtaining successive, higher approximations for the function $\chi(\varepsilon)$ is similar. At first, Adamson and his co-workers [48] used the Langmuir and Fowler–Guggenheim isotherms as the local isotherm, but later [49] they generalized the method in such a way that the BET equation could be used in it as a local isotherm.

In the final version, the dependence of θ_t on $\log(p_s/p)$ was used as the first approximation for $\chi(\varepsilon)$.

Adamson's method was the first advanced numerical method for determining the differential adsorption energy distribution. It was successfully adapted by Waksmundzki *et al.* [23] for the analysis of experimental data obtained chromatographically. The condensation function $\chi_c(\varepsilon)$ is taken to be the first approximation $\chi^{(1)}(\varepsilon)$ of the function $\chi(\varepsilon)$

$$\chi_c(\varepsilon) = \frac{V'_R[pc(\varepsilon)]p_s}{jN_\infty(RT)^2} \exp \frac{\varepsilon_l - \varepsilon}{RT}, \tag{3.26}$$

where ε_l is the heat of condensation of the adsorbate at the isotherm temperature. The second approximation of this function is obtained in two further stages. First, a theoretical calculation is made of the retention volumes $V_R^{(1)}(p)$ for all the experimentally tested values of the adsorbate pressure

$$V_R'^{(1)}(p) = jN_\infty RT \int_0^\infty \frac{\partial\theta_l(p, \varepsilon)}{\partial p} \chi^{(1)}(\varepsilon)\, d\varepsilon . \tag{3.27}$$

The second approximation of the function $\chi^{(2)}(\varepsilon)$ is obtained from the equation

$$\chi^{(2)}(\varepsilon) = \chi^{(1)}(\varepsilon)\left[\frac{V'_R(p)}{V_R'^{(1)}(p)}\right]_p = pc(\varepsilon) . \tag{3.28}$$

In order to find the third approximation of the function $\chi^{(3)}(\varepsilon)$, $\chi^{(2)}(\varepsilon)$ is substituted for $\chi^{(1)}(\varepsilon)$ in the integral of equation (3.27) and the procedure is repeated. When the distribution functions obtained from two consecutive approximations are about the same, we can take this result to be the final approximation.

3.4 The Laplace and Stieltjes Transformation Methods in Chromatographic Data Analysis [27, 46, 54, 55]

The equation for Jovanovic's adsorption isotherm [53, 55] can be presented in the following form:

$$\theta_l(p, \varepsilon) = 1 - \exp\left\{-\frac{p}{K}\exp\left(\frac{\varepsilon}{RT}\right)\right\}. \tag{3.29}$$

For the global retention volume $V'_{Rt}(p)$ we get this equation [27]

$$V'_{Rt}(p) = j\frac{RT}{K}\int_{\varepsilon_m}^{\infty} \exp\left(\frac{\varepsilon}{RT}\right)\exp\left[-\frac{p}{K}\exp\left(\frac{\varepsilon}{RT}\right)\right]\chi(\varepsilon)\, d(\varepsilon) . \tag{3.30}$$

By substituting $x = p/p_s$ and

$$t = \frac{p_s}{K}\left[\exp\left(\frac{\varepsilon}{RT}\right) - \exp\left(\frac{\varepsilon_a}{RT}\right)\right] \tag{3.31}$$

we get

$$G(x) = \int_0^\infty F(t)[\exp(-tx)]\,dt\,, \tag{3.32}$$

where

$$G(x) = \frac{V'_{Rt}(x)p_s}{j(RT)^2}\exp\left[\frac{xp_s}{K}\exp\left(\frac{\varepsilon_a}{RT}\right)\right] \tag{3.33}$$

and

$$F(t) = \chi[\varepsilon(t)]\,. \tag{3.34}$$

Finding the function $\chi(\varepsilon)$ leads to the solution of the Laplace transformation (3.32). The problem can be solved using Papoulis's method [56] and presenting the function $F(t)$ as a series of Laguerre functions $\varphi_K(t)$

$$F(t) = \sum_{K=0}^{\infty} C_K \varphi_K(t)\,, \tag{3.35}$$

where

$$\varphi_K(t) = \frac{d^K}{dt^K}\left[\frac{t^K}{K!}\exp(-t)\right]. \tag{3.36}$$

The function $G(x)$, obtained from experimental data, is approximated by the following polynomial:

$$G(x) = \sum_{K=0}^{S} a_K x^K\,. \tag{3.37}$$

The following link exists between the coefficients C_K in equation (3.35), and also between the coefficients a_K in equation (3.37):

$$C_K = \sum_{j=0}^{K}\binom{K}{j}a_{K-j}\,. \tag{3.38}$$

If the infinite series in the numerical calculations are replaced by certain of their partial sums we get

$$\chi[t(\varepsilon)] = \sum_{K=0}^{S} C_K \frac{d^K}{dt(\varepsilon)^K}\left[\frac{t(\varepsilon)^K}{K!}\exp(-t(\varepsilon))\right]. \tag{3.39}$$

Taking the local Langmuir isotherm into account,

$$\theta_l(p, \varepsilon) = \left[\frac{K}{p} \exp\left(-\frac{\varepsilon}{RT}\right)+1\right]^{-1} . \tag{3.40}$$

The equation for the global retention volume $V'_{\mathrm{Rt}}(p)$ can be written as

$$V'_{\mathrm{Rt}}(p) = j\frac{RT}{K}\int_{\varepsilon_a}^{\infty} \frac{\exp(\varepsilon/RT)}{[1+\exp(\varepsilon/RT)(p/K)]^2}\chi(\varepsilon)\,\mathrm{d}\varepsilon . \tag{3.41}$$

By substituting

$$\exp\left(\frac{\varepsilon}{RT}\right) = u+\exp\left(\frac{\varepsilon_a}{RT}\right) \tag{3.42}$$

and

$$\frac{K}{p} = y-\exp\left(\frac{\varepsilon_a}{RT}\right) \tag{3.43}$$

we reduce equation (3.41) to a generalized form of the Stieltjes transformation

$$g(y) = \int_0^{\infty} \frac{f(u)}{[u+y]^2}\,\mathrm{d}u , \tag{3.44}$$

in which the functions $f(u)$ and $g(y)$ take the following form:

$$f(u) = \chi[\varepsilon(u)] , \tag{3.45}$$

$$g(y) = \frac{K}{jRT}p^2(y)\,V'_{\mathrm{Rt}}[p(y)] . \tag{3.46}$$

In order to solve this transformation with respect to function $f(u)$, we write function $g(y)$ as follows:

$$g(y) = \sum_{i=1}^{n} A_i y^{(2-1/(i+k))}, \quad k \geqslant 1 . \tag{3.47}$$

Function $\chi(\varepsilon)$ then takes the form

$$\chi(\varepsilon) = \sum_{i=1}^{n} \frac{1}{\Gamma[1/(1+k)]\Gamma[(i+k+1)/(i+k+2)]}\times$$

$$\times\left[\exp\left(\frac{\varepsilon}{RT}\right)-\exp\left(\frac{\varepsilon_a}{RT}\right)\right]^{-1/(i+k)}, \tag{3.48}$$

where Γ is the so-called gamma function.

In the case of the Laplace transformation, the function $G(x)$, determined from experimental data, is approximated by the polynomial by means of the least squares method. The coefficients a_K are numerically chosen by the best fit of the polynomial to the experimental data. A knowledge of the coefficients a_K makes it possible to determine coefficients C_K which can then be used to calculate the adsorption energy

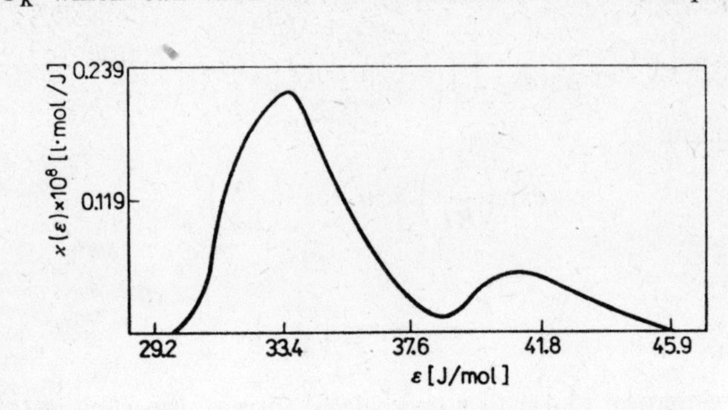

Fig. 3.3 Function $\chi(\varepsilon)$ for hexane on Polsorb C (after A. Waksmundzki *et al.* [27]).

distribution function $\chi(\varepsilon)$. A similar procedure is adopted with the generalized Stieltjes transformation, where the coefficients A_i are chosen from the best fit of function $g(y)$ to the experimental data.

By applying the generalized Stieltjes transformation, Waksmundzki and co-workers [27] determined the function $\chi(\varepsilon)$ for hexane on Polsorb C (Fig. 3.3). It can be seen from this figure that there are two types of adsorption sites on the surface of Polsorb C.

3.5 Determination of the Differential Energy Distribution Function $\chi(\varepsilon)$ — An Example

The differential energy distribution function $\chi(\varepsilon)$ for $CHCl_3$ and CCl_4 was determined on Co_3O_4, on SiO_2 and on mechanical mixtures of Co_3O_4 and SiO_2 [31]. The specific surface area of Co_3O_4 was 8 m^2/g; that of SiO_2 was 99 m^2/g. The carrier gas was purified argon and flowed at a volumetric rate of 20 cm^3/min. The chromatographic measurements were performed on a Giede 18.3 chromatograph equipped with a thermal conductivity detector. The column, made from acid-resistant steel, was 0.5 m long with an internal diameter of 0.2 mm. Adsorbates were injected by means of Hamilton and Zimmerman syringes in quantities from 0.1

to 1 μl and 20 μl. The retention volume can be calculated from equation (3.17). The expression (3.20) for $\chi(\varepsilon)$ corresponds to this equation. The constant K in equation (3.21) was determined from the temperature dependences of the retention volume, extrapolated to zero $V'_R(0)$, on the density of the adsorbate in the gaseous phase. The temperatures at which the measurements were made and the values of $V'_R(0)$ obtained are set out in Table 3.1.

Table 3.1 ADSORPTION PROPERTIES OF SiO_2 AND Co_3O_4 SYSTEMS AND MIXED CATALYSTS AT DIFFERENT TEMPERATURES. ADSORBATE — CHLOROFORM AND CARBON TETRACHLORIDE

	Carbon tetrachloride			*Chloroform*		
Composition	T [K]	$\ln V_{N,t}(0)$	$q^0_{st} \approx \bar{\varepsilon}$ [kJ/mol]	T [K]	$\ln V_{N,t}(0)$	$q^0_{st} \approx \bar{\varepsilon}$ [kJ/mol]
100% SiO_2	353.7	−4.276	30.17	353.7	−4.42	29.33
	360.8	−4.54		360.8	−4.68	
	369.3	−4.69		369.3	−4.82	
	380.1	−4.95		380.1	−5.10	
100% Co_3O_4	352.9	−5.28	43.99	353.0	−5.55	41.06
	364.4	−5.73		361.6	−5.85	
	374.8	−6.15		369.2	−6.12	
	393.1	−6.79		381.1	−6.54	
63% SiO_2 + 37% Co_3O_4	353.0	−4.48	36.45	353.0	−4.58	32.68
	362.6	−4.77		362.6	−4.89	
	373.6	−5.11		373.6	−5.17	
	381.6	−5.36		381.6	−5.42	
50.11% SiO_2 + 49.89% Co_3O_4	352.3	−4.61	39.38	353.0	−4.87	35.19
	361.6	−4.93		361.6	−5.16	
	372.3	−5.27		372.3	−5.47	
	382.3	−5.58		382.3	−5.79	
30.28% SiO_2 + 69.72% Co_3O_4	352.9	−4.90	41.27	352.9	−4.93	36.68
	362.1	−5.23		362.1	−5.28	
	369.2	−5.49		369.2	−5.54	
	381.5	−5.81		381.5	−5.92	

Measurements for calculating the energy distribution function were made at 353 K. The calculations were done on the basis of equation (3.20) and the results are presented in Figs 3.1 and 3.2.

References

[1] Roginskii S. Z., *Adsorption und Katalyse an Inhomogenen Oberflächen*, Akademie Verlag, Berlin, 1958.

[2] Roginskii S. Z., *Zhur. Fiz. Khim.*, **31**, 2381 (1957).

[3] Roginskii S. Z., *Problemy Kinet. i Katal.*, **9**, 5 (1957).

[4] Pierotti R. A. and Thomas H. E., *Physical Adsorption: The Interaction of Gases with Solids*, J. Wiley, New York, 1964.

[5] Halsey C. D. and Taylor H. S., *J. Chem. Phys.*, **15**, 624 (1974).

[6] Barker J. A. and Everett D. H., *Trans. Faraday Soc.*, **58**, 1080 (1962).

[7] Steele W. A., *J. Phys. Chem.*, **67**, 2016 (1963).

[8] Freeman M. P. and Kolb K., *J. Phys. Chem.*, **67**, 2117 (1963).

[9] Thomas J. M. and Thomas W. J., *Introduction to the Principles of Heterogeneous Catalysis*, Academic Press, London, 1967.

[10] Halsey C D., *J. Phys. Chem.*, **67**, 2038 (1963).

[11] Waksmundzki A., Rudziński W. and Suprynowicz Z., *J. Gas Chromatogr.*, **2**, 93 (1966).

[12] Waksmundzki A., Rudziński W., Suprynowicz Z. and Rayss J., *J. Chromatogr.*, **74**, 3 (1972).

[13] Waksmundzki A., Rayss J., Rudziński W. and Suprynowicz Z., *Chem. Anal.*, **18**, 695 (1973).

[14] Suprynowicz Z., Waksmundzki A. and Rudziński W., *J. Chromatogr.*, **67**, 21 (1972).

[15] Suprynowicz Z., Waksmundzki A. and Rudziński W., *J. Chromatogr.*, **72**, 5 (1972).

[16] Rudziński W., Suprynowicz Z. and Rayss J., *J. Chromatogr.*, **66**, 1 (1972).

[17] Rudziński W., *Chem. Phys. Lett.*, **10**, 183 (1971).

[18] Rudziński W., *Phys. Lett.*, **42**, 7 (1973).

[19] Rudziński W., *Physical Adsorption on Heterogeneous Surfaces of Solids*, Zeszyty UMCS Lublin, 1973.

[20] Rudziński W., Waksmundzki A., Leboda R., Suprynowicz Z. and Lasoń M., *J. Chromatogr.*, **92**, 25 (1974).

[21] Rudziński W., Waksmundzki A., Leboda R. and Jaroniec M., *Chromatographia*, **7**, 663 (1974).

[22] Waksmundzki A., Jaroniec M. and Suprynowicz Z., *J. Chromatogr.*, **110**, 381 (1975).

[23] Waksmundzki A., Sokołowski S., Jaroniec M. and Rayss J., *Vuoto*, **8**, 113 (1975).

[24] Suprynowicz Z., Jaroniec M. and Gawdzik J., *Chromatographia*, **9**, 161 (1976).

[25] Suprynowicz Z. and Jaroniec M., *J. Chromatogr.*, **117**, 11 (1976).

[26] Sokołowski S., Jaroniec M. and Cerofolini G. F., *Surface Sci.*, **47**, 428 (1975).

[27] Waksmundzki A., Sokołowski S., Rayss J., Suprynowicz Z. and Jaroniec M., *Separ. Sci.*, **11**, 29 (1976).

[28] Jaroniec M., Leboda R., Sokołowski S. and Waksmundzki A., *Separ. Sci.*, **11**, 409 (1976).

[29] Leboda R. and Sokołowski S., *J. Colloid Interface Sci.*, **61**, 365 (1977).

[30] Leboda R., Sokołowski S. and Rynkowski J., *Chem. Anal.*, **22**, 29 (1978).

[31] Leboda R., Sokołowski S., Rynkowski J. and Paryjczak T., *J. Chromatogr.*, **138**, 309 (1977).

[32] Leboda R., Waksmundzki A. and Sokołowski S., *Ann. Soc. Chim.*, **50**, 1717 (1976).
[33] Sokołowski S., Leboda R. and Waksmundzki A., *Ann. Soc. Chim.*, **51**, 385 (1977).
[34] Gawdzik J., Suprynowicz Z. and Jaroniec M., *J. Chromatogr.*, **121**, 185 (1976).
[35] Suprynowicz Z. and Jaroniec M., *J. Chromatogr.*, **117**, 11 (1976).
[36] Conder J. R. and Purnell J. H., *Trans. Faraday Soc.*, **64**, 3100 (1968).
[37] Conder J. R., *J. Chromatogr.*, **39**, 273 (1969).
[38] Conder J. R., Locke D. C. and Purnell J. H., *J. Phys. Chem.*, **73**, 700 (1969).
[39] Harris L. B., *Surface Sci.*, **10**, 129 (1968).
[40] Harris L. B., *Surface Sci.*, **13**, 377 (1969).
[41] Waksmundzki A., Rudziński W., Suprynowicz Z. and Leboda R., *J. Chromatogr.*, **92**, 9 (1974).
[42] Sips J. R., *J. Phys. Chem.*, **16**, 490 (1948).
[43] Sips J. R., *J. Phys. Chem.*, **18**, 1024 (1950).
[44] Hobson J. P., *Can. J. Phys.*, **43**, 1934 (1965).
[45] Kiselev A. V. and Yashin Ya., *Kolloid. Zh.*, **21**, 581 (1955).
[46] Suprynowicz Z. (Ed.), *Modern Tendencies in Chromatographic Theory and Practice*, Ossolineum PAN, 1976, p. 253 (in Polish).
[47] Suprynowicz Z., Gawdzik J. and Jaroniec M., *J. Chromatogr.*, **133**, 349 (1977).
[48] Adamson A. W. and Ling I., *Advan. Chem.*, **33**, 51 (1961).
[49] Dormant L. M. and Adamson A. W., *J. Coll. Interface Sci.*, **38**, 285 (1972).
[50] Hsu C. C., Rudziński W. and Wojciechowski B. W., *Chromatographia*, **8**, 633 (1975).
[51] Cerofolini G. F., *Surface Sci.*, **24**, 391 (1971).
[52] Cerofolini G. F., *Temp. Phys.*, **6**, 473 (1972).
[53] Jovanovič D. S., *Koll. Zeit. und Z. Polymere*, **235**, 1203 (1969).
[54] Rudziński W. and Jaroniec M., *Surface Sci.*, **42**, 552 (1974).
[55] Jaroniec M., *Surface Sci.*, **50**, 553 (1975).
[56] Papoulis A., *Q. Appl. Math.*, **14**, 405 (1957).
[57] Takizawa A., *Kolloid. Z.*, **222**, 141 (1966).
[58] Rudziński W., Toth J. and Jaroniec M., *Phys. Lett.*, **41A**, 449 (1972).

Chapter **4**

Determination of the Adsorption Isotherm

4.1 Introduction

The adsorption isotherm is the foundation upon which the surface characteristics of adsorbents and catalysts are defined. From it we can determine the magnitude of the specific surface area, capillary distribution (from the desorption curve), porosity and other properties of a solid; using adsorbates with diverse physical and chemical characteristics, we can define the type of adsorbate–adsorbent interactions involved and the nature of adsorption in the system being tested.

We can use either static [1–4] or dynamic methods [5–7] to determine the adsorption isotherm. Up till now, static volumetric and gravimetric (McBain balance) methods have most often been applied. Measurements made using some kind of static method take a long time and require fairly complicated vacuum apparatus. While static vacuum apparatus is suitable for work with clean solid surfaces, it is of no use when studying adsorption under conditions approaching those of most technological sorption processes, especially at high temperatures and pressures. For small specific surface areas of a solid (1–5 m^2/g) the readings contain a considerable error. These faults can generally be avoided by using dynamic methods, among which first place should be given to GSC.

Adsorption can be studied by means of GSC at both low and high temperatures and pressures (about 10 MPa) [8–10].

The retention time is the sum of the time an adsorbate molecule spends in the gaseous phase and the time during which it is adsorbed on the surface of an adsorbent or catalyst. The time spent by an adsorbate molecule on the surface of a solid under equilibrium conditions obviously involves the adsorption isotherm.

Analysis of the chromatogram will, apart from delineating the adsorption isotherm, provide data on the kinetics of adsorption and desorption. Chromatography is frequently the only method available for determining the adsorption isotherm; it is also extremely sensitive and capable of detecting minimal changes in concentration. This is particularly important when determining the irreversible adsorption which does take place to a slight degree under certain conditions (see Chapter 2).

It was Wilson [12] in 1940, and later Weis and De Voult [13, 14], who first showed that it was possible to determine the adsorption isotherm from chromatographic data in the case of ideal linear chromatography applied to a liquid-solid system.

Glueckauf [15–19] worked out a method of calculating the adsorption isotherm from a liquid-frontal chromatogram. Wicke [20], Cremer [21, 22], James and Phillips [23] used the Glueckauf equation to determine the adsorption isotherm from GC measurements. Gregg and Stock [24, 25] checked that it was possible to determine adsorption isotherms from chromatographic data for all five types of Brunauer's isotherm.

Even though higher adsorbate concentrations were applied, the sorption effect and pressure gradient were neglected in experimental work published before 1968. An exception are the papers by Schay and co-workers [26, 27, 97, 98]. Many authors realized the influence of these effects but no corrections have been made.

It was only the series of papers by Conder and Purnell [5, 128–130] published in 1968–69 concerning the theoretical and practical bases of chromatography at finite concentrations, which allowed physicochemical investigations for to be carried out these concentrations.

Section 4.2.1 presents the basis for determining adsorption isotherms for ideal GC (infinite dilution). Section 4.2.3 deals with the above problems for non-linear and non-ideal chromatography (finite concentration), taking the sorption effect and pressure gradient into account.

Various chromatographic methods for determining adsorption isotherms have been described in the literature [8–80]; they include the isotherms of gaseous mixtures [97–107].

4.2 Theoretical Principles

4.2.1 Ideal Chromatography. Elution at Infinite Dilution

While a real chromatographic column is in operation, the conditions of ideal GC are not entirely fulfilled because complete thermodynamic equilibrium is never established there. However, it is possible to produce conditions in a real column which approach the requirements of ideal GC. To do this, the optimum carrier gas flow rate should be used (minimum on the van Deemter curve), the size and shape of the adsorbent or catalyst particles should be as uniform as possible, the whole column should be packed evenly, and a sufficiently high temperature should be used. By adhering to these conditions, diffusional and kinetic broadening of the

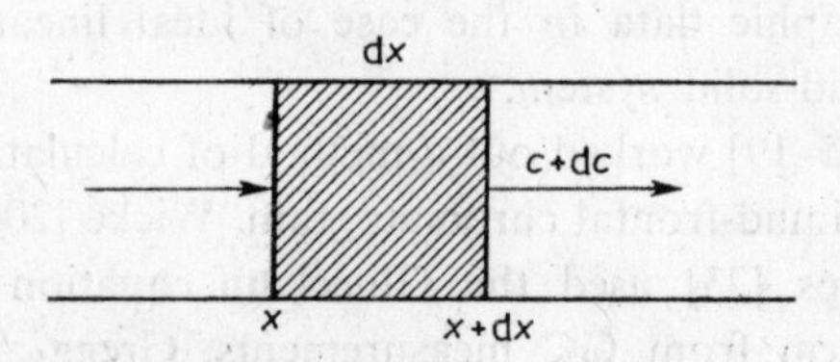

Fig. 4.1 The change in adsorbate concentration across an increment of the chromatographic column of length dx.

chromatograms can be reduced. Any distortion of the chromatogram is then mainly due to the deviation of the adsorption isotherm from Henry's isotherm.

Assuming that in each part of the column adsorption equilibrium is eventually established, let us consider the material balance equation for an elementary section of such a column of length dx (Fig. 4.1).

The adsorbate concentration c in the mobile phase is a complex function of the time t and the distance x of the layer under investigation from the column inlet

$$c = f(t, x) \,. \tag{4.1}$$

For a volumetric flow rate F_c across the column increment dx, the following quantity of adsorbate is accumulated

$$-F_c\left(\frac{\partial c}{\partial x}\right)_t \mathrm{d}x \,. \tag{4.2}$$

This quantity of adsorbate in the column increment dx is distributed between the mobile phase and the stationary phase. If V denotes the volume of the mobile phase, and V'_s the volume of the adsorption layer per unit length of the column, the quantity of adsorbate per unit length of column is $Vc+V'_s c_s$, where c_s is the concentration of adsorbate in the adsorption layer.

The rate of change of the quantity of adsorbate in the layer dx is

$$\left[\frac{\partial}{\partial t}(Vc+V'_s c_s)\right]_x dx\,. \tag{4.3}$$

At equilibrium

$$-F_c\left(\frac{\partial c}{\partial x}\right)_t dx = \left[\frac{\partial}{\partial t}(Vc+V'_s c_s)\right]_x dx \tag{4.4}$$

or

$$-F_c\left(\frac{\partial c}{\partial x}\right)_t = V\left(\frac{\partial c}{\partial t}\right)_x + V'_s\left(\frac{\partial c_s}{\partial t}\right)_x\,. \tag{4.5}$$

By accounting for the method of packing the column we can write [30, 63]

$$-F_c\left(\frac{\partial c}{\partial x}\right)_t = \varepsilon q\left(\frac{\partial c}{\partial t}\right)_x + q(1-\varepsilon)\left(\frac{\partial c_s}{\partial t}\right)_x\,, \tag{4.6}$$

where ε is that part of the column cross-section not occupied by the stationary phase, q is the cross-sectional area of the column, $(1-\varepsilon)$ is that part of the column cross-section occupied by the stationary phase.

By combining the change in adsorbate concentration in the stationary phase $(\partial c_s/\partial t)_x$ with the change in its concentration in the mobile phase $(\partial c/\partial t)_x$ we can write

$$\left(\frac{\partial c_s}{\partial t}\right)_x = \left(\frac{\partial c_s}{\partial c}\right)_x\left(\frac{\partial c}{\partial t}\right)_x\,. \tag{4.7}$$

The derivative $(\partial c_s/\partial t)_x$ represents the dependence of the adsorbate concentration in the stationary phase c_s on its concentration in the mobile phase c at a given temperature; it thus represents the adsorption isotherm.

Equation (4.7) can be rewritten

$$\left(\frac{\partial c_s}{\partial t}\right)_x = \frac{dc_s}{dc}\left(\frac{\partial c}{\partial t}\right)_x\,. \tag{4.8}$$

Substituting equation (4.8) in equation (4.5) we obtain

$$-F_c\left(\frac{\partial c}{\partial x}\right)_t = \left(V+V'_s\frac{dc_s}{dc}\right)\left(\frac{\partial c}{\partial t}\right)_x\,. \tag{4.9}$$

As the adsorbate concentration c in the mobile phase is a function of x and t

$$\mathrm{d}c = \left(\frac{\partial c}{\partial x}\right)_t \mathrm{d}x + \left(\frac{\partial c}{\partial t}\right)_x \mathrm{d}t\,. \tag{4.10}$$

By dividing equation (4.10) by $\mathrm{d}t$ at constant adsorbate concentration in the mobile phase, $c(\mathrm{d}c = 0)$, we obtain an equation combining the partial derivatives

$$\left(\frac{\partial c}{\partial t}\right)_x = -\left(\frac{\partial c}{\partial x}\right)_t \left(\frac{\partial x}{\partial t}\right)_c, \tag{4.11}$$

where

$$\left(\frac{\partial x}{\partial t}\right)_c = u_c\,. \tag{4.12}$$

In equation (4.12), u_c is the linear migration velocity at which the adsorbate at concentration c moves along the column. By substituting equations (4.11) and (4.12) in equation (4.9) we get

$$F_c = \left(V + V_s' \frac{\mathrm{d}c_s}{\mathrm{d}c}\right) u_c\,. \tag{4.13}$$

Rearranging this expression, we obtain the fundamental equation for ideal GC

$$u_c = \frac{F_c}{V + V_s' \dfrac{\mathrm{d}c_s}{\mathrm{d}c}}\,. \tag{4.14}$$

If we take into consideration the method of packing the column, we can write the formula for the linear velocity of adsorbate along the column in the form [29]

$$u_c = \frac{F_c}{1 + \left(\dfrac{1-\varepsilon}{\varepsilon}\right) \dfrac{\mathrm{d}c_s}{\mathrm{d}c}}\,. \tag{4.15}$$

The linear migration velocity of an adsorbate of concentration c along the column for a given volumetric carrier gas flow rate F_c and column packing $((1-\varepsilon)/\varepsilon)$ depends on the derivative $\mathrm{d}c_s/\mathrm{d}c$ which represents the isotherm of adsorption (or solution in GLC) of the adsorbate on a solid in the column. If the isotherm is linear, Henry's equation is satisfied

$$\frac{\mathrm{d}c_s}{\mathrm{d}c} = K, \tag{4.16}$$

where K is Henry's constant, and equation (4.15) now becomes

$$u_c = \frac{F_c}{1 + \left(\frac{1-\varepsilon}{\varepsilon}\right) K}. \tag{4.17}$$

In linear GC, the linear velocity of adsorbate u_c is dependent on Henry's constant. If F_c is constant, the linear velocity u_c is also constant (for a small pressure drop along the column). The linear velocity is the greater, the smaller the value of K, i.e. the more weakly a given adsorbate is adsorbed; conversely, the smaller the linear velocity of the adsorbate, the better it is adsorbed. Under experimental conditions, the carrier gas should remain practically unadsorbed. The linear velocity of the carrier gas, u_c, thus determines the volumetric flow rate F_c. If the adsorption isotherm is not linear (ideal non-linear chromatography), which is often the case, the derivative $\mathrm{d}c_s/\mathrm{d}c$ is not constant, but alters with changes in the concentration c. The linear migration velocity of the adsorbate along the column is therefore not constant either, and we get a chromatogram with an extended front or rear profile (Fig. 1.9 b, c). We obtain an extended rear profile on the chromatogram (Fig. 1.9b) when the derivative $\mathrm{d}c_s/\mathrm{d}c$ decreases as the adsorbate concentration c increases, i.e. for small adsorbate concentrations, the value of $\mathrm{d}c_s/\mathrm{d}c$ is greater than for large concentrations.

We can see from equation (4.15) that the linear migration velocity of an adsorbate in small concentrations is lower than the migration velocity of an adsorbate at higher concentrations. This results in an asymmetrical peak. The beginning of the peak is steep, but the end is much broadened (Fig. 1.9b). The reverse is the case on a chromatogram for which the derivative $\mathrm{d}c_s/\mathrm{d}c$ increases as the adsorbate concentration c rises (Fig. 1.9c). Equation (4.15) shows that small concentrations of adsorbate move along the column faster than high concentrations. As a consequence, the beginning of the peak is broadened, but the end is steep (Fig. 1.9c). The shape of the chromatogram helps us to define the general course of the adsorption isotherm (Fig. 1.9) — and conversely, the course of the isotherm can tell us what the shape of the chromatogram is likely to be.

Normally, the concentrations of adsorbate in the carrier gas are in the range of application of ideal chromatography, so small that adsorption or desorption of adsorbate does not affect the volumetric flow rate F_c.

For higher concentrations of adsorbate in the carrier gas (Section 4.2.3), its linear velocity for a linear isotherm can be determined from the equation given by Huber and Gerritse [29], viz.

$$u_{c_x} = \frac{F_{c_x}}{(k^*+1)\left(1-\frac{k^*}{1+k^*}c_x\right)^2}, \tag{4.18}$$

where $k^* = K(1-\varepsilon)/\varepsilon$, K is Henry's constant, c_x is the mole fraction of adsorbate in the carrier gas, F_{c_x} is the average velocity of the mobile phase in the presence of component c_x.

The linear velocity u_c of adsorbate along the column can also be expressed in terms of the retention time t_R and the column length L as

$$u_c = \frac{L}{t_R}. \tag{4.19}$$

From equations (4.14) and (4.19) we get, for a constant volumetric flow rate,

$$L\left(V+V_s'\frac{dc_s}{dc}\right) = F_c t_R. \tag{4.20}$$

If we introduce the amount of substance adsorbed by 1 g of solid, a, instead of the surface concentration c_s ($a = V_s'c_s/m$, where m is the mass of adsorbent or catalyst in the column) we obtain

$$V_M + m\frac{da}{dc} = V_R, \tag{4.21}$$

where $V_M = LV$ is the gas holdup and $V_R = F_c t_R$ is the retention volume.

Rearranging this equation we get

$$\frac{da}{dc} = \frac{V_R - V_M}{m} = \frac{V_R'}{m} = V_{g(c)}, \tag{4.22}$$

where V_R' is the adjusted retention volume and $V_{g(c)}$ is the specific retention volume for concentration c.

From equation (4.22) it is easy to determine the magnitude of adsorption, a, for an equilibrium concentration of adsorbate, c, in the mobile phase; thus the adsorption isotherm

$$a = \frac{1}{m}\int_0^c V'_R \mathrm{d}c \qquad (4.23)$$

therefore

$$a = \int_0^c V_{g(c)} \mathrm{d}c \,. \qquad (4.24)$$

4.2.2 Determination of Adsorption and Equilibrium Pressure from the Chromatogram for Ideal Gas Chromatography

Regardless of which chromatographic technique is used to determine the adsorption isotherm, the problem is to find the amount of adsorbed substance, a, and its corresponding equilibrium pressure in the mobile phase, p, for each point on the isotherm.

By introducing into equation (4.23) the magnitudes obtained from the chromatogram and giving the detector deflections h in units of concentration c, we obtain an equation from which we can calculate the value of the adsorption a (mmol/g) [32, 47, 67]

$$f(c) = a = \frac{kF_c}{mw}\int_0^h (l_h - l_0)\mathrm{d}h = \frac{kF_c}{mw} S_{ads} \,, \qquad (4.25)$$

where l is the distance on the recorder tape, $S_{ads} = \int_0^h (l_h - l_0)\mathrm{d}h$ is the area on the recorder tape bounded by the height h between the outflow of the non-adsorbing gas, l_0, and the extended profile of the chromatogram (Figs. 4.2, 4.3), w is the tape speed (cm/min), m is the mass of adsorbent or catalyst in the column (g), k is the detector constant (mmol/cm^{3}cm), and

$$k = \frac{c}{h}. \qquad (4.26)$$

The detector constant k is best determined using the frontal method by measuring the recorder pen deflections h for various concentrations of adsorbate, c, in the carrier gas. The value of k can also be determined from elution curves, injecting into the column a precisely measured quantity of adsorbate, n_a, [69] and measuring the peak area corresponding to this

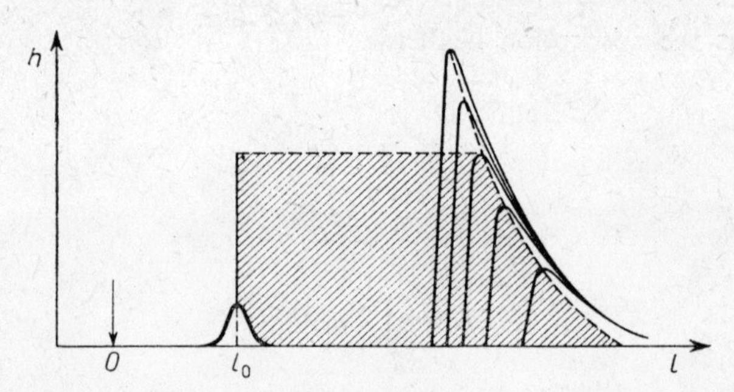

Fig. 4.2 A typical chromatogram for determining the adsorption isotherm using the peak maxima method; the hatched area represents the adsorption surface area.

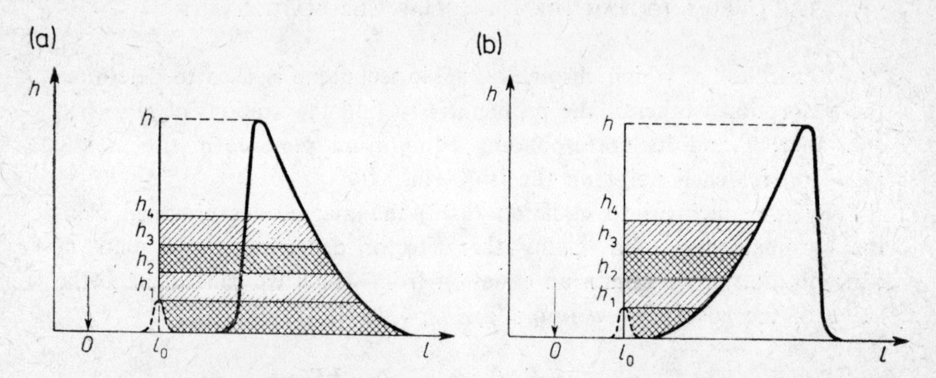

Fig. 4.3 Graphic integration of chromatograms and calculation of adsorption isotherms from them using the peak profile method: (a) peak with steep front profile and extended tailing line; (b) peak with extended front profile and steep rear profile.

quantity of adsorbate (for a given detector sensitivity, carrier gas flow rate and recorder tape speed). Since

$$n_a = \frac{kF_c}{w} \int_0^\infty h \, dl = \frac{kF_c}{w} S_{peak}, \tag{4.27}$$

where S_{peak} is the peak area (Table 4.1), it follows that the detector-con stant is equal to:

$$k = \frac{n_a w}{F_c S_{peak}}. \tag{4.28}$$

The various methods of determining peak areas have been described by Schupp [71].

Table 4.1 METHODS OF CALCULATING THE PEAK AREA

Graphic methods	1. based on geometric methods of measuring the area of a triangle or trapezium; 2. based on the analysis and transformation of a Gaussian curve equation.
Instrumental methods	1. using a planimeter; 2. weighing the cut-out peaks.
Automatic measurement	1. mechanical integrators; 2. electromechanical integrators; 3. electronic integrators.

By substituting equation (4.28) in equation (4.25) we obtain

$$a = \frac{n_a S_{ads}}{m S_{peak}}. \tag{4.29}$$

This simple formula is most frequently used to determine the value of adsorption from an elution chromatogram.

The equilibrium concentration of adsorbate in the mobile phase can be derived from equation (4.28), bearing in mind that $k = c/h$ [67, 76], viz.

$$c = \frac{n_a wh}{F_c S_{peak}}. \tag{4.30}$$

The equilibrium pressure is determined from the equation $p = cRT$. After substituting this relationship in equation (4.30), we get a formula from which we can calculate the equilibrium pressure from an elution chromatogram

$$p = \frac{n_a whRT}{F_c S_{peak}}. \tag{4.31}$$

4.2.3 NON-LINEAR, NON-IDEAL GAS CHROMATOGRAPHY

Finite concentrations. In 1968 Conder and Purnell [5, 128–130] worked out the bases of modern GC theory in the range of finite concentrations.

It is of fundamental importance in GC physicochemical investigations, including the determination of adsorption isotherms.

The retention volume at concentration c is a basic value for the determination of adsorption isotherms.

When deriving the retention equation there are several factors to be considered [5, 131]:

(a) curvature in the distribution isotherm;
(b) sorption effect;
(c) gas compressibility;
(d) dependence of the isotherm on total pressure;
(e) gas imperfection;
(f) thermal effect;
(g) concentration dependence of gas viscosity;
(h) sorption of carrier gas;
(i) non-ideality.

These factors are not independent and should properly be treated together. In thermodynamic measurements the first two factors (a) and (b) are the most important. As a rule, the adsorption isotherm for higher concentrations takes a non-linear course. This follows from the change in adsorbate partial pressure accompanied by a change in adsorption coefficient. The retention volume alters with the changes in adsorbate concentration. The sorption effect (b) results in a shortening of the retention time. The phenomenon is evoked as a result of adsorption or desorption processes by a local increase in the velocity of the mobile phase while introducing considerable amounts of adsorbate vapours. When the effects occur, both the retention time and the retention volume measured lose their physical sense. They should be taken into account in retention equations.

A thermal effect (f) accompanies "temperature waves" formed while the adsorbate migrates along the column. They result from the fact that adsorption is an exothermic process and desorption an endothermic one. Thermal effects depend on many factors, including the thermal conductivity of the column material. They are, as a rule, less important than the sorption effect and non-linearity of isotherms.

The effect of factors (e), (g) and (i) can be reduced by the application of coarse-mesh packing, a long column and setting the gas velocity for minimum plate height. Simultaneous consideration of all the factors greatly complicates the derivation of retention equations, although the result is relatively simple.

Conder and Purnell [5] have derived retention equations taking into account factors (a) and (d). In paper [131] factors (a), (b) and (c) have been considered. Taking into consideration mass balance in the column increment dx (Fig. 4.1) and the above-discussed factors, Conder and Purnell [5] derived the retention equation in a way analogous to that for ideal GC (Section 4.2.1, equation (4.21)). The equation is of fundamental importance and may be applied in the range of both finite concentrations and infinite dilution. The equation for GSC takes the following form:

$$V_R^0 = jV_R = V_m^0 + m(1 - a'jy_0)\left(\frac{\partial a}{\partial c}\right)_{p=p_m}, \tag{4.21a}$$

where

$$a' = \frac{b_2^1}{b_3^2}\left[1 + \frac{2y_0 p_0 B_{11}}{RT}(1 - y_0 J_2^1)\right], \tag{4.21b}$$

$$b_n^m = 1 + k(1 - J_n^m y_0). \tag{4.21c}$$

In these expressions a, c are the adsorbate concentrations in equilibrium (on the solid surface a and in the gaseous phase c); y_0 is the mole fraction of adsorbate in the carrier gas at the column outlet; m (in equation (4.21a)) is the adsorbent mass in the column; K is the "capacity factor", i.e. the ratio of the amount of adsorbate on the solid surface to that in the gas phase at equilibrium $(am)cV_M^0$; V_R^0 is the corrected retention volume ($V_R^0 = jV_R$); $V_M^0 = jV_M$; V_M is the gas holdup; p_m is the mean pressure in the column, $p_m = p_0 J_3^4$;

$$j = J_3^2\left[1 + \frac{y_0^2 p_0 B_{11}}{RT}(J_3^2 - 1)\right]; \tag{4.21d}$$

$$J_n^m = \frac{n}{m}\left[\frac{(p_i/p_o)^m - 1}{(p_i/p_o)^n - 1}\right]; \tag{4.21e}$$

B_{11} is the second virial coefficient of the pure adsorbate; p_i is the column inlet pressure, and p_0 is the outlet pressure.

For infinite dilution $a'jy_0 \to 0$ and equation (4.21a) reduces to equation (4.21). Equation (4.21a) is true for pressures higher than those normally used in GC. This equation can, in practice, be simplified and then a small error due to gas imperfection arises. When $j = J_3^2$ and $a = 1$ equation (4.21a) takes the following form:

$$V_R^0 = jV_R = V_M^0 + m(1 - J_3^2 y_0)\left(\frac{\partial a}{\partial c}\right)_{p=p_0 J_3^4}. \tag{4.21f}$$

While estimating V_R^0 a correction (sorption effect) for the outlet gas rate should be introduced

$$V_R^0 = jF(jy_0)t_R\,, \tag{4.21g}$$

where t_R is the retention time for the characteristic point of concentration c.

The volumetric flow rate $F(jy_0)$ can be estimated from the equation

$$\frac{F(jy_0)}{F(0)} = \frac{1+k}{1+k(1-jy_0)}, \tag{4.21h}$$

where $F(0)$ is the volumetric flow rate at zero concentration of the adsorbate.

Determination of adsorption value from the chromatogram for finite concentrations (Section 4.2.2, equation (4.25)). Starting from equation (4.21a), Conder and Purnell [5] presented an accurate equation enabling the amount of adsorbed substance a to be determined

$$a = \frac{p_0}{mRT}\left\{\frac{(\alpha+\beta)(1+k)F(0)}{y_0}\ln\left[1+\frac{jy_0}{1+k(1-jy_0)}\right]\right.$$

$$\left.+V_M\ln(1-jy_0)-\beta F(0.8y_0)\right\}, \tag{4.25a}$$

where α and β are areas on the chromatogram: $\alpha = KLRQ$ (Fig. 4.7c, d) and $\beta = QRS$ ($+\beta$ — Fig. 4.7c; $-\beta$ — Fig. 4.7d).

Equation (4.25a) can be approximated to give a simplified form

$$a = \frac{p_0}{mRT}\left[\frac{(\alpha+\beta)jF(0)}{1-jy_0} - jV_My_0 - \beta F(0.8y_0)\right]. \tag{4.25b}$$

Equation (4.21h) may be simplified (since usually $K \gg 1$ and $y < 0.5$)

$$\frac{F(0)}{1-jy_0} = F(jy_0)\,. \tag{4.25c}$$

V_M can be calculated from the equation

$$V_M = t_M F(jy_0)\,. \tag{4.25d}$$

When either $\beta \ll \alpha$ or $y \ll 1$ and $j \approx 1$, equation (4.25b) may be approximated to

$$a = \frac{jp_0 F(jy_0)}{mRT}\,. \tag{4.25e}$$

Equation (4.25e) is a simple and convenient form used for estimating the adsorption a both from elution and frontal chromatograms. It is in fact less accurate than equation (4.25a) or (4.25b) but is much more so than equation (4.25). It takes into account both the pressure gradient and the sorption effect.

The accuracy of the equation diminishes with increasing β/α or y. The equilibrium concentration of adsorbate c in the gas phase is calculated from the corresponding mole fraction y_0 at the column outlet (equation (4.25h)) from the dependence

$$C = \frac{y_0 p_0}{RT + Bp_0}\,, \tag{4.25f}$$

where

$$B = y_0^2 B_{11} + 2y_0(1-y_0)B_{12} + (1-y_0)^2 B_{22}\,. \tag{4.25g}$$

B_{11} and B_{22} are the second virial coefficients of the pure adsorbate and pure carrier gas respectively, B_{12} is the mixed second virial coefficient.

The apparatus for investigations at finite concentrations is presented in Fig. 1.17.

A simplified method may be used for determining of the amount of adsorbed substance (for $p/p_s = 1$) based on equation (4.32) (Fig. 4.8) [59].

4.3 Methods of Determining the Adsorption Isotherm

4.3.1 The Peak Maxima Method [48, 58, 69]

The determination of the adsorption isotherm using this method is simply a question of injecting a series of adsorbate samples of varying size into the column. One sample of a given size gives one point on the isotherm; a and p are calculated from equations (4.29) and (4.31). Figure 4.2 illustrates a typical chromatogram. The diagram shows the extended profiles of the chromatogram (diffusion effects) corrected along the peak maxima of the various sample sizes [48, 69]. The adsorption surface area is determined up to the corrected tailing line of the chromatogram.

4.3.2 ELUTION BY CHARACTERISTIC POINT (ECP) METHOD [24, 31, 32, 38 39, 43–45, 47, 48, 56, 58, 60–62, 67, 73–77, 91]

This method of determining adsorption isotherms is frequently used because of its rapidity, and because it can be used directly on propriety chromatographs without further adaptation. This method is similar to the peak maxima method but the course of the isotherm (over a certain

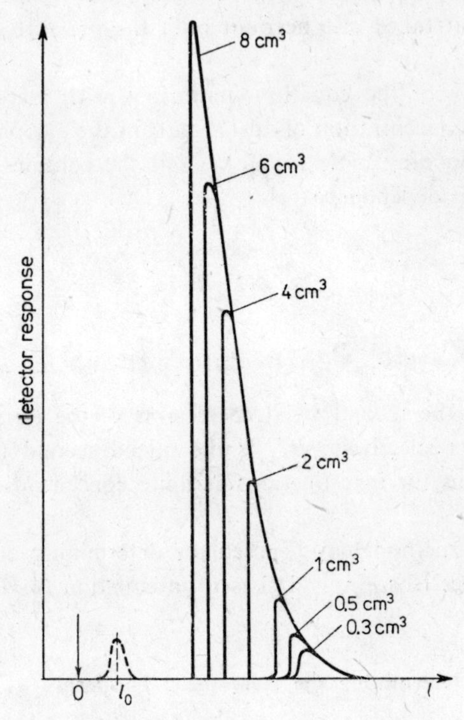

Fig. 4.4 Chromatograms of propane on SiO_2 for various sample sizes (after A. V. Kiselev and Y. I. Yashin [81]).

range) is determined from a single chromatogram. The adsorption surface area is determined from the outflow of the non-adsorbing gas, l_0, to the extended profile ascending to or descending from the peak (Fig. 4.3). It is divided into n segments parallel to the base line and n points on the isotherm are calculated according to equations (4.29) and (4.31).

The method gives good results if the front or rear profiles of the peaks for various sample sizes overlap (Fig. 4.4). Often one has to select a suitably higher temperature so that the extended chromatogram curves for various sample sizes overlap [81], or else appropriate corrections to the peaks have to be made (see Section 1.3.4).

The elution by characteristic point (ECP) method has been applied to the determination of adsorption isotherms with one or two points of

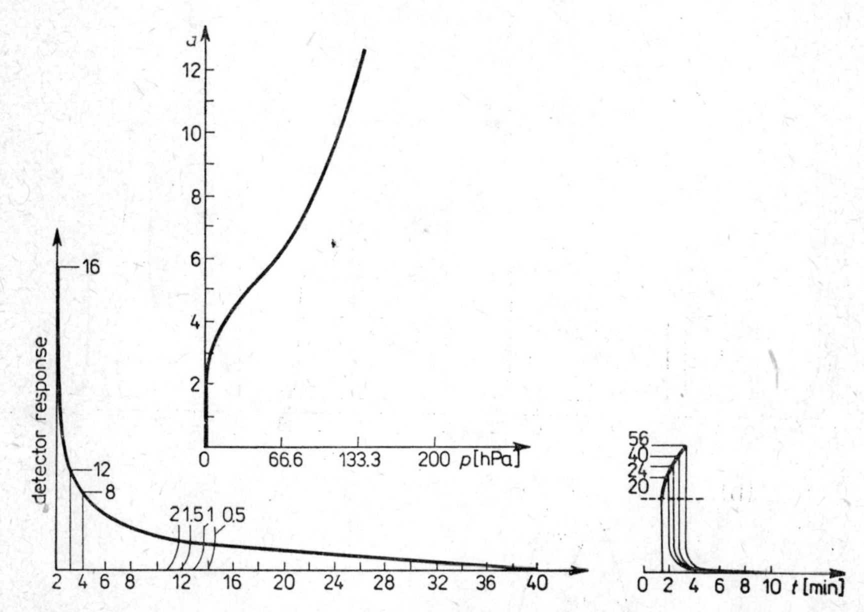

Fig. 4.5 Chromatograms of benzene on graphitized carbon black for various sample sizes (in μl) at 303 K; integrated up to the magnitudes defined by the thick line; above — the adsorption isotherm calculated from the chromatogram (after L. D. Belyakova *et al.* [61]).

inflection [61, 64, 84]. Figure 4.5 shows the chromatogram of benzene on homogeneous graphitized carbon black. The adsorption isotherm of this system has one point of inflection.

For small samples of adsorbate we get an extended tailing line. The appropriate section of the isotherm is conveyed towards the axis of adsorption. As we increase the sample size within a certain middle range, we obtain vertical front and rear profiles. This corresponds to the central part of the adsorption isotherm — the straight section near the point of inflection. For large samples of benzene (20 μl and more) we get a chromatogram with an extended front profile. This corresponds to that part of the isotherm which after the point inflection is convex towards the vapour pressure axis.

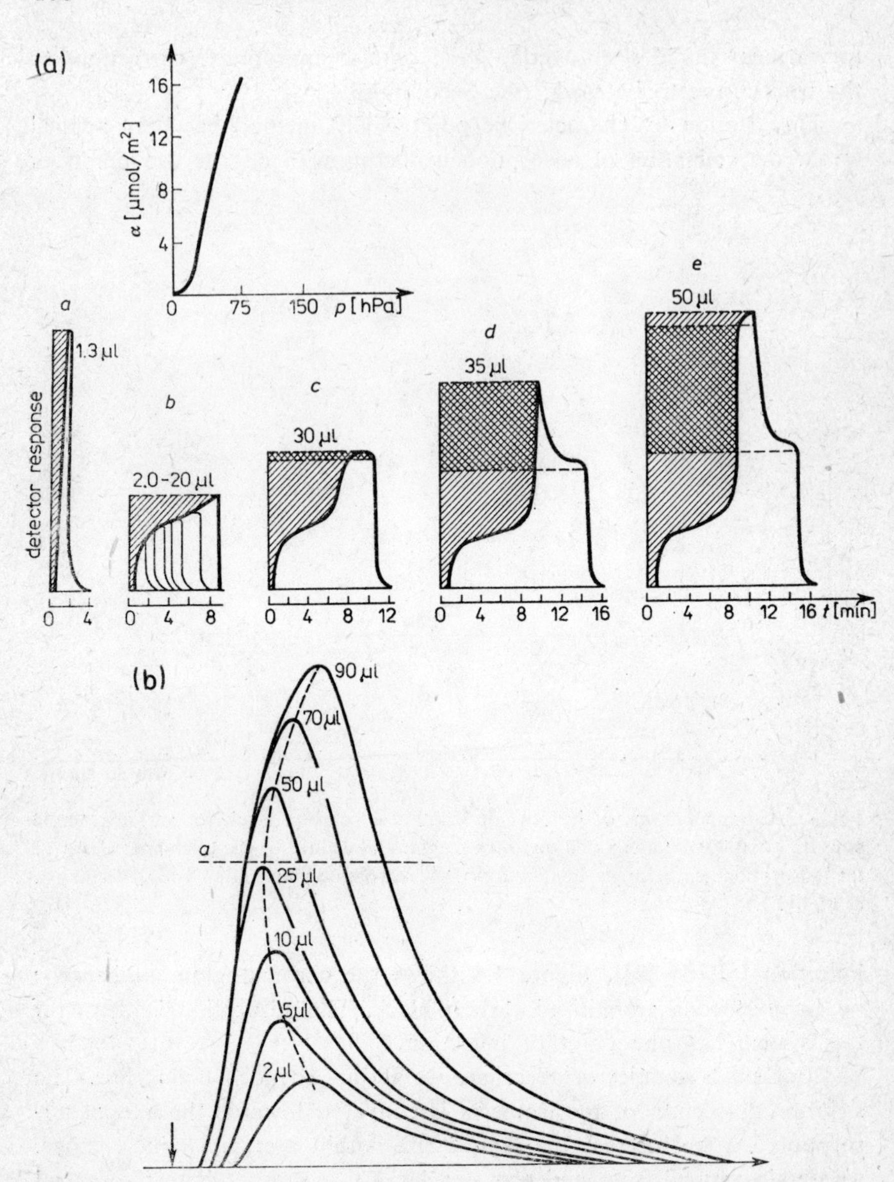

Fig. 4.6 (a) Chromatograms of methanol on graphitized carbon black for various sample sizes at 303 K; above — the adsorption isotherm calculated from the chromatograms (the katharometer sensitivity decreases from *a* to *e*) (after A. V. Kiselev [84]); (b) example of peaks which cannot be used for ECP measurements since the diffusive boundaries do not coincide (samples of water on polyamide-66 at 313 K) (after G. Edel and B. Chabert [132]).

Figure 4.6a illustrates chromatograms of methanol on graphitized carbon black for various sample sizes. For small samples we get an extended front profile (the isotherm is conveyed towards the pressure axis). As the sample size increases, the front profile is first extended, then in the area of the isotherm's discontinuity we get a section corresponding to a number of values of a for the same value of p. When the adsorbate samples are large, the tailing line d becomes extended, and if the samples are larger still, we again have an extended front profile e after the second point of inflection.

Figure 4.6b presents an example of chromatograms which cannot be used to determine the adsorption isotherm as the diffusive rear boundaries are not coincident for the samples of varying sizes. Simultaneously, it may be observed that the curvature of the isotherm changes at a concentration corresponding to a sample size of about 25 μl. From the figure it follows that the retention time initially decreases with increasing sample sizes to reach a minimum (line a), and then increases.

4.3.3 Frontal Analysis by Characteristic Point (FACP) Method [5, 15–19, 24, 31, 32, 35, 37, 40, 47, 49, 50, 52–56, 59, 75–80 128–131]

This method is often known as Glueckauf's method. It is one of the commonest methods of determining adsorption isotherms. They may be calculated from frontal chromatograms in two ways:

(1) The adsorption isotherm is calculated from the shape of the broadened front boundary or rear boundary (Figs. 4.7, 4.8). This is the so-called frontal analysis by characteristic point method (FACP).

(2) Frontal analysis (FA). A separate chromatogram is needed for each concentration point but self-sharpening boundaries can be used as well as diffuse boundaries.

The adsorbate at constant concentration in the carrier gas is injected into the column until saturation (plateau) is reached. Then the adsorbed substance is eluted by the carrier gas, and this gives us the rear profile of the chromatogram. The amount of substance adsorbed is proportional to the area between the front of the adsorbate and the non-adsorbing gas [26] (hatched area on Fig. 4.7 a, b, c, d).

If sorption effect and pressure gradient are neglected, adsorption a may be calculated from equation (4.25) and the equilibrium pressure from the

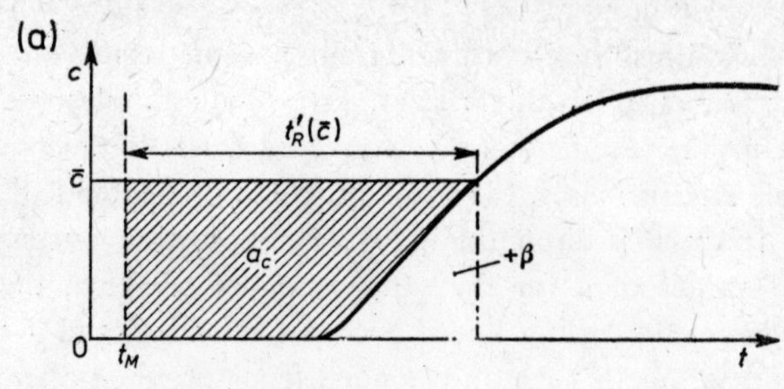
(a)
c
$t'_R(\bar{c})$
$\bar{c}$
a_c
+β
0
t_M
t

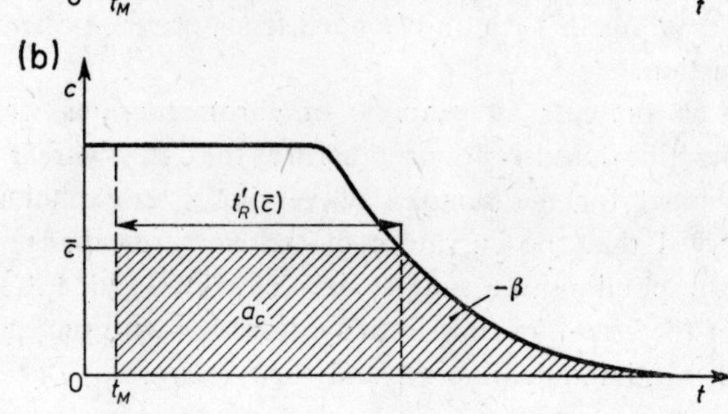
(b)
c
$t'_R(\bar{c})$
$\bar{c}$
a_c
−β
0
t_M
t

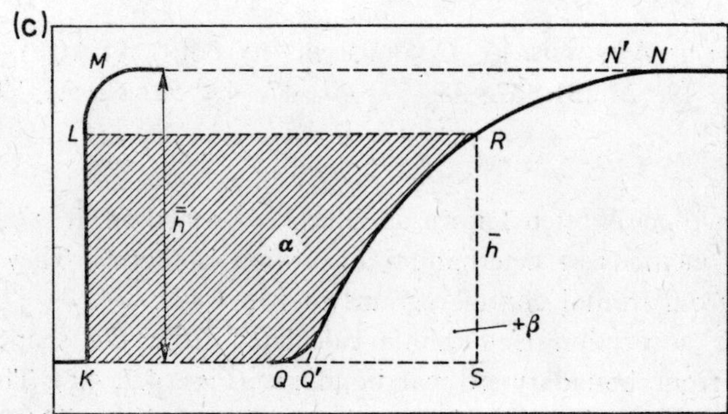
(c)
M
N'
N
L
R
$\bar{\bar{h}}$
α
$\bar{h}$
+β
K
Q
Q'
S

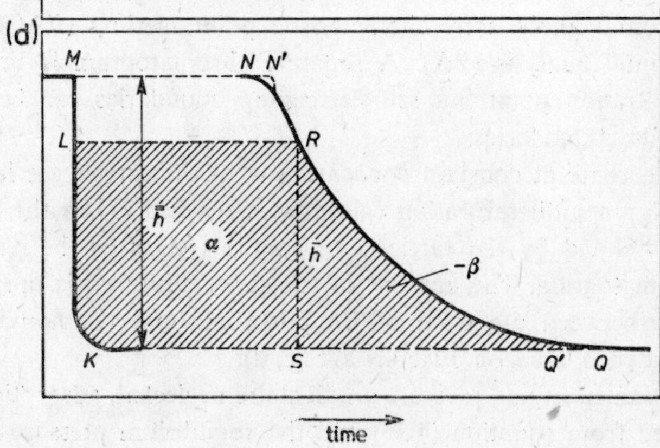
(d)
M
N
N'
L
R
$\bar{\bar{h}}$
α
$\bar{h}$
−β
K
S
Q'
Q
time

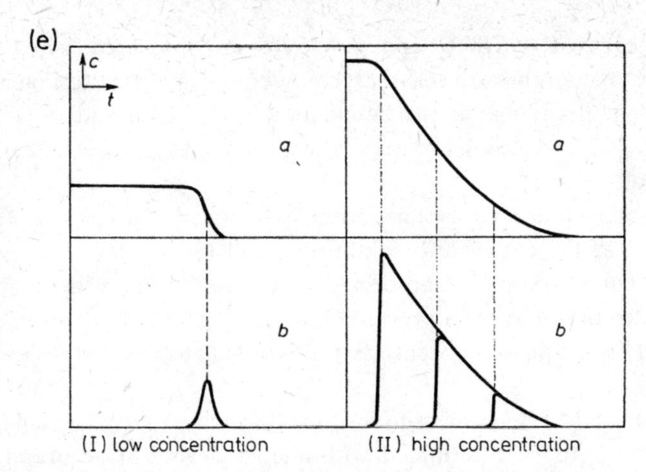

Fig. 4.7 Graphic integration of a frontal chromatogram to calculate the adsorption isotherm: (a) diffuse front boundary; (b) diffuse rear boundary. Construction of frontal chromatograms allowing determination of adsorption isotherm by FACP method: (c) a diffuse front boundary; (d) a diffuse rear boundary through the column. Lines *KL* and *NQ* — indications of detectors at inlet and outlet. Hatched area $\alpha = KLRQ$, the area β is equal to $\pm$ area *QRS* and is positive for (c) and negative for (d) (after J. R. Conder and J. H. Purnell [5]). (e) Comparison of the runs of elution and front chromatograms in low and high concentration ranges (after J. R. Conder and C. L. Young [32]).

dependence (2.31). Point *a* for concentration *c* on the isotherm can be obtained easily by measuring the hatched area a_c on the chromatogram (Fig. 4.7a, b). The isotherm can be determined from several characteristic points *c* of different height on the chromatogram [4].

Refined FACP technique. The measurement apparatus is presented in Fig. 1.17. Chromatograms from Fig. 4.7c, d were obtained by using two detectors; at the inlet (line *KLM*) and outlet (line *NQ*). Height *h* is measured from the baseline and is proportional to the gas phase mole fraction y_0. For each point required on the isotherm, a straight line is drawn parallel to the time axis (e.g. line *LR*). The height *h* of the line *LR* corresponds to the mole fraction y_0 calculated from the known plateau mole fraction y_0 via the equation

$$\bar{y}_0 = \bar{\bar{y}}_0 \frac{\bar{h}}{\bar{\bar{h}}}, \tag{4.25h}$$

where $\bar{\bar{h}}$ is the plateau height shown in Fig. 4.7c, d.

The areas $\alpha = KLRQ$ and $\beta = QRS$ are measured by planimeter for a chromatogram with self-sharpening boundaries $\beta = 0$. Figure 4.7c, d shows slight roundings of the boundary Q (Fig. 4.7c) and N (Fig. 4.7d). They can be corrected by extrapolation to points Q' (Fig. 4.7c) and N' (Fig. 4.7d).

The area added by extrapolation is compensated for cutting off an equal area at the complete breakthrough end (N' or Q').

The concentration of adsorbate $\bar{a}$ in equilibrium with a gas phase of concentration $\bar{c}$ at total pressure $p_m = p_0 J_3^4$ is calculated from equation (4.25a). The gas-phase concentration $\bar{c}$ is calculated according to formula (4.25f).

Equation (4.25a) allows the sorption effect and pressure gradient for an imperfect gas to be determined with a high degree of accuracy. If these effects are neglected, equation (4.25a) reduces to a simple equation (4.25).

In Figure 4.7e the runs of elution and front chromatograms for low and high concentrations have been compared. In the low concentration range linear GC may be applied, neglecting a sorption and thermal effects and gas viscosity. For higher concentrations non-linear chromatography is used.

The quantity of adsorbed substance (for $p/p_s = 1$) can also be determined from the following equation (Fig. 4.8) [59]:

$$a = \frac{c(F_c t - V_M)}{m}, \tag{4.32}$$

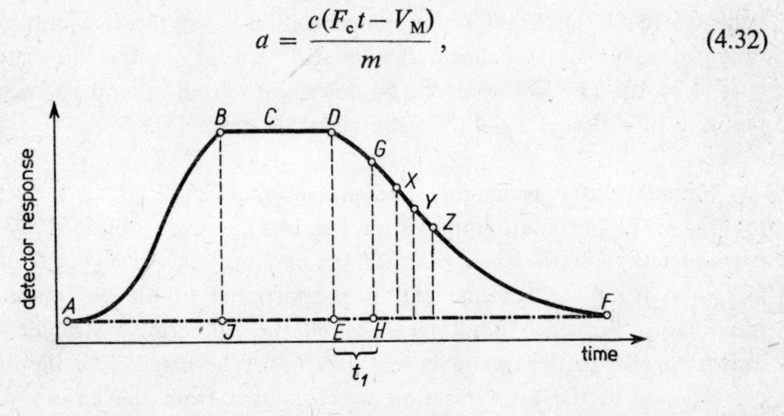

Fig. 4.8 Frontal chromatogram showing the adsorption and desorption curve from which the adsorption isotherm can be calculated (after A. Waksmundzki *et al.* [59]).

where t is the time (min), c is the concentration of adsorbate in the carrier gas (mmol/cm^3), V_M is the gas holdup from the instant the adsorbate is introduced into the detector (cm^3).

Area *DEFD* (Fig. 4.8) corresponds to the total quantity of substance adsorbed in the column. Any randomly chosen area, for example, *DEGH* represents the amount of adsorbate eluted by pure carrier gas during time t_1. The difference between the total area *DEFD* and area *DEGH* gives the quantity of adsorbate still to be eluted. Since the quantity of adsorbate corresponding to area *DEGH* can be determined from equation (4.32), it is easy to calculate the amount adsorbed for the elution times corresponding to points *X*, *Y*, *Z*.

Assuming that the detector readings are proportional to the concentration of adsorbate in the gaseous phase, the height *ED* corresponds to the value of p_s. The heights measured from points *G*, *X*, *Y*, *Z* correspond to the vapour pressures of the adsorbate in adsorption equilibrium at any given instant.

The other way of obtaining the adsorption isotherm from a frontal chromatogram can be used when the adsorbate front is relatively steep. It is based on the measurement of the retention time of the front; the corresponding point on the isotherm is then calculated. Measurements of the retention time of the front or of breakthrough curves require a separate measurement for each point on the isotherm and are usually done when the concentrations of adsorbate in the carrier gas are large.

Determination of the adsorption isotherm using the step profile method requires that we know the area of the desorption surface under the rear profile of the chromatogram (Figs 4.7 and 4.8). If we use small concentrations of polar adsorbates on the active surfaces of solids, we cannot apply this method because the rear profile approaches the base line asymptotically and it is difficult to calculate the desorption surface area.

Parcher and Urone [54] solved this problem using Glueckauf's method (Fig. 4.9).

From the frontal retention volume of the sample we can determine one point on the isotherm at the maximum concentration c_1. The material balance requires the area $c_1 V_1$ to be equal to the total area under the desorption line of the chromatogram (Fig. 4.9). Determination of the area $c_1 V_1$ removes the need to measure the whole area under the desorption line. Only the area marked Δu has to be measured. By altering the area Δu up to the concentration at which the desorption line reaches the base line, we can determine the adsorption isotherm. The total quantity of adsorbed substance, a_c, is $a_c = c_1 V_1$. The quantity of substance, a, adsorbed in a definite equilibrium state is given by $a = a_c - \Delta a$, where $a = V_2(c_1 - \bar{c}) + \Delta u$.

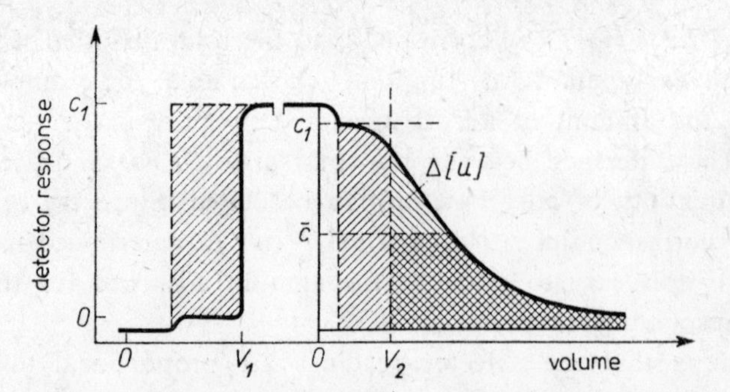

Fig. 4.9 A typical adsorption-desorption chromatogram enabling the adsorption isotherm to be determined without having to calculate the total adsorption surface area (after J. F. Parcher and P. Urone [54]).

Taking the above relationships into consideration, we can determine the points of the isotherm from the equation

$$a = c_1 V_1 - [V_2(c_1 - \bar{c}) + \Delta u] \,. \tag{4.33}$$

The symbols are explained in Fig. 4.9.

This method of calculating the isotherm has all the advantages of Glueckauf's method, but without requiring the total area of the desorption surface to be measured. The isotherm obtained in this way shows good agreement with that obtained using the classical frontal method.

4.3.4 Elution-on-a-Plateau (EP) Method

This method has found application when determining adsorption isotherms at considerable adsorbate partial pressures in the carrier gas.

The apparatus for these investigations is depicted in Fig. 1.17. The process is initially carried out by the FA technique.

After the plateau for a given adsorbate concentration in the carrier gas has been established, very small samples of adsorbate in carrier gas are introduced to the gas stream and, as a result of elution, positive (adsorbate) and negative (carrier gas) peaks are obtained at a given concentration of adsorbate, c, in the stationary phase (Fig. 4.10).

In this method it is essential to maintain a constant concentration c all through the column. This may be achieved by using a very small pressure — drop along the column and stabilizing its temperature accurately. The adsorbent should be coarse-meshed (particles smaller than 20–30 mesh).

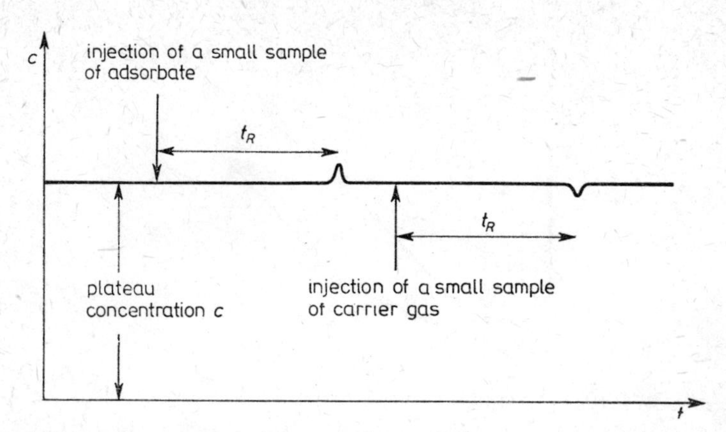

Fig. 4.10 Chromatogram of elution on a plateau (EP):
t_R — retention time, which should be identical for fairly small samples of adsorbate (positive peak) and carrier gas (negative peak).

The retention times of positive and negative peaks are identical if small samples are used (Fig. 4.10). As the plateau concentration increases, so does the height equivalent to one theoretical plate (HETP). As a result, both positive and negative peaks retention measurements are less accurate and that limits the concentrations used in the EP technique. If the concentration, c, of a plateau is increased, base line noises tend to grow.

In order to determine the adsorption isotherm, retention volumes are measured for a series of plateau concentrations. The EP technique is therefore similar to FA with a self-sharpening chromatogram.

The retention volume may be determined from dependence (4.21a), the value of c from (4.25f) and the value of a from equation (4.25e).

4.3.5 Schay's Method [26, 27, 40, 85–87]

The modified frontal technique for determining the adsorption isotherm as proposed by Schay and his co-workers takes into account diffusion and the change in the gas stream velocity as a result of adsorption processes. This method is especially convenient in the case of large adsorbate concentrations in the carrier gas.

Figure 4.11 shows the relationship of the change in volume of the gas entering the column (OB) and the gas leaving the column (curve OA) with time for frontal chromatography in the case where one component is sorbed. Curve OA consists of three straight sections: α, β and γ. Section α corresponds to the progress of the mixture from the column inlet to the

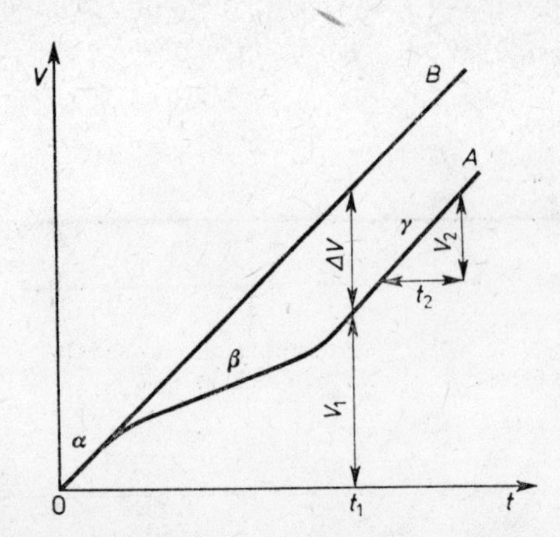

Fig. 4.11 Curves showing the change in gas volume at the column inlet *OB* and at its outlet *OA* with time for frontal chromatography in the case where one component is sorbed (after G. Schay *et al.* [87]).

start of the adsorbent layer. As there is no adsorption here, this section is common to both lines (*OB* and *OA*). After the gas stream has entered the sorbent layer in the column, adsorption starts — this is reflected in the reduced velocity of the gas at the column outlet. Section β corresponds to the adsorption process in the column. Adsorption equilibrium having been established throughout the column, the outlet velocity of the gaseous phase once again becomes equal to the rate of flow at the inlet (section γ). Obviously ΔV in a given time is equal to the volume of gas adsorbed from the stream. The value of a can be calculated from the equation

$$a = \frac{\Delta V}{m_l L}, \tag{4.34}$$

where m_l is the mass per unit length of adsorbent layer and L is the column length.

The value of ΔV can be easily calculated from the following relationship (Fig. 4.10):

$$\frac{V_1 + \Delta V}{t_1} = \frac{V_2}{t_2} \tag{4.35}$$

or

$$\Delta V = \frac{V_2 t_1 - V_1 t_2}{t_2}. \tag{4.36}$$

By varying the adsorbate concentration c in the gaseous phase, this method can be used to determine the points on the adsorption isotherm.

4.3.6 Determination of the Adsorption Isotherm of Gaseous Mixtures

Not much attention has been devoted to the adsorption of the components of gaseous mixtures, although this problem is of considerable practical significance. The serious experimental difficulties and the theoretical complexities involved in working up the results are the reasons why so few papers have been published on this topic. Jaroniec [121–126] and others have recently done much to remedy this situation: considerable progress has been made in the theoretical treatment of the adsorption of multicomponent gas mixtures on the surfaces of solids. Static volumetric and gravimetric methods are used to determine the adsorption isotherms of the components of gaseous mixtures [94–96, 115]; in addition, GC has recently been applied with good results [97–106, 118, 119]. Frontal [97–99] and pulse chromatography [102–107] are used. Particularly good results have been achieved using the pulse method with labelled atoms, elaborated by Peterson and Helfferich [83, 102, 106], where adsorption is studied much in the same way as in the elution-frontal method (see Section 1.2.3). The carrier gas containing the adsorbate (or mixture of adsorbates) at constant concentration is allowed to flow through the sample until adsorption equilibrium is attained, i.e. until the concentration of adsorbates is the same before and after the column. Adsorption equilibrium having been reached, the labelled adsorbate is injected pulse-wise into the gas stream. Isotope exchange takes place within the column and the "labelled pulse" is identified with a suitable detector. It is assumed that both labelled and unlabelled adsorbate molecules affect the elementary column processes to an equal extent. Measurements are made when the surface has an appropriate covering of adsorbate. By gradually varying the adsorbate concentration in the carrier gas, the adsorption isotherm can be determined over its whole range, and by introducing successive "labelled impulses" of the different adsorbates, the adsorption isotherms of all the components in a gaseous mixture can be drawn. In this way one can also measure the rate of sorption and the sorption equilibrium for different surface coverages.

Peterson and Helfferich's method gives very good results, but it does require special instrumentation for detecting the radioactive isotopes. If the isotopes are stable, a mass spectrometer can be used as detector. The adsorption isotherms of the various components can also be determined with typical GC apparatus. Yanovskii, Roginskii and co-workers [99] proposed a method of measuring the adsorption of the components of a gaseous mixture in which the passage through the adsorbent layer of the carrier gas containing n test components each at an initial concentration of $c_A^0, c_B^0, ..., c_n^0$ is permitted until adsorption equilibrium is established. This done, pure carrier gas only is now allowed to flow through the column. Each adsorbate forms a separate band which migrates along the adsorbent layer [107, 108]. Then streams of the adsorption mixture and the pure carrier gas are once again allowed through. The adsorption isotherms of the components of the mixture can be determined from the chromatograms obtained, in the same way as for the single adsorbates discussed earlier. If the substance is weakly adsorbed (slight broadening of the input curve on the chromatogram) the following equations are used:

$$f_A(c_A, c_B^0) = \frac{1}{m} \int_0^{c_A^0} V \mathrm{d}c_A \,, \qquad (4.37)$$

$$f_B(c_A^0, c_B) = \frac{1}{m} \int_0^{c_B^0} V \mathrm{d}c_B \,, \qquad (4.38)$$

where V is the volume of mixture allowed through (cm^3), and m is the mass of adsorbent.

For stronger adsorption (leading to considerable broadening of the output curve on the chromatogram), the following equations are used:

$$f_A(c_A, c_B^0) = f_A(c_A^0, c_B^0) - \int_{c_A^0}^{c_A} V \mathrm{d}c_A \,, \qquad (4.39)$$

$$f_B(c_A^0, c_B) = f_B(c_A^0, c_B^0) - \int_{c_B^0}^{c_B} V \mathrm{d}c_B \,, \qquad (4.40)$$

where $f_A(c_A^0, c_B^0)$ is the quantity of substance A adsorbed at concentrations c_A^0 and c_B^0. This value is determined from the frontal chromatogram in the usual way (see Section 4.3.3). $f_B(c_A^0, c_B^0)$ is the analogous value for adsorbate B.

Recently, Van der Vlist and Van der Mejden [101] worked out a simple way of determining the adsorption isotherms of the components of gaseous mixtures from an equation which combines the change in retention volume with the change in concentration of a bicomponental mixture. The equation is

$$V_R = V_M + \frac{m}{c_{A+B}}\left(c_B \frac{da_A}{dc_A} + c_A \frac{da_B}{dc_B}\right), \tag{4.41}$$

where V_R is the retention volume (cm^3), V_M is the gas hold-up (cm^3), m is the mass of adsorbent in the column (g), $c_{A+B} = c_A + c_B$; c_A, c_B are the concentrations of components A and B in the gaseous phase (mmol/cm^3), a_A, a_B are the quantities of components A and B adsorbed (mol/g), da_A/dc_A, da_B/dc_B are the gradients of the isotherms of components A and B.

Rearranging equation (4.41) and substituting partial and total pressures for concentrations, we get

$$\frac{(V_R - V_M)}{mRT} p = \frac{V'_R}{mRT} p = (p - p_A)\frac{da_A}{dp_A} + p_A \frac{da_B}{dp_B} = G(p_A), \tag{4.42}$$

where p is the total pressure, p_A, p_B are the partial pressures of components A and B, V'_R is the adjusted retention volume.

$G(p_A)$ is a function of the k-degree polynomial dependent on p_A

$$G(p_A) = G_0 + G_1 p_A + G_2 p_A^2 + \dots + G_k p_A^k, \tag{4.43}$$

$$a_A = a_1 p_A + a_2 p_A^2 + a_3 p_A^3 + \dots + a_k p_A^k, \tag{4.44}$$

$$a_B = b_1 p_B + b_2 p_B^2 + b_3 p_B^3 + \dots + b_k p_B^k. \tag{4.45}$$

For a bicomponental N_2–O_2 mixture good results have been obtained using a third degree polynomial. Experimentally, the end points of adsorption $(a_A)_{pA} = p$ and $(a_B)_{pB} = p$ are easily determined from the isotherm of the single components using helium as carrier gas. For O_2–He and N_2–He mixtures $a_B = 0$ (helium is not adsorbed under experimental conditions), and the coefficients a can be calculated directly from $G(p_A)$.

The coefficients of the polynomial for a pressure of 0.1 MPa can be calculated from the following equations:

$$a_1 = G_0,$$
$$b_1 = G_0 + G_1 + G_2 + G_3,$$
$$a_2 = [G_1 - 2(a_B)_{p2=1} + a_1 + b_1] : 2,$$
$$a_3 = (a_A)_{pA=1} - a_2 - a_1,$$
$$b_3 = G_3 + 3a_3,$$
$$b_2 = (a_B)_{pB=1} - b_3 - b_1.$$

A diagram of the apparatus used to determine the adsorption of gaseous mixtures is shown in Fig. 4.12 [66]. The carrier gas for the ad-

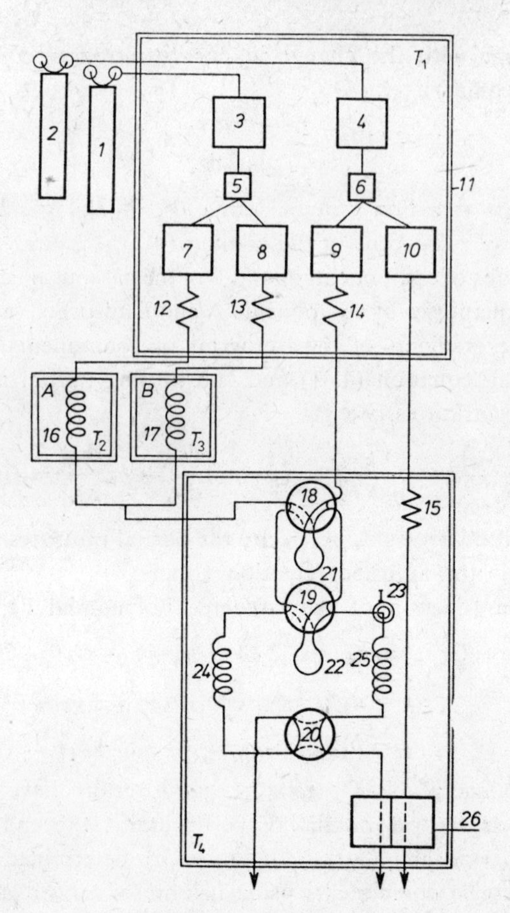

Fig. 4.12 Block diagram of the chromatographic apparatus for determining the adsorption of gaseous mixtures (after R. G. Gerritse and J. F. K. Huber [66]):

1 — cylinder containing 99% He and 1% N_2, *2* — cylinder containing pure helium, *3, 4* — manometers *5, 6* — purification filters, *7, 8, 9* — flow-meters, *10* — needle valve, *11* — air thermostat, *12, 13, 14, 15* — capillaries, *16, 17* — column saturators, *18, 19, 20* — rotating plate valves, *21* — adsorber, *22* — tube of known volume, *23* — injector, *24* — inert column, *25* — chromatographic column, *26* — conductometric detector.

sorbates is a mixture of 99% helium and 1% nitrogen. After purification on filter *5*, this mixture (cylinder *1*) is separated into two streams. The velocity of each stream is measured by flow-meters *7, 8* and regulated in capillaries *12* and *13*. The carrier gas then flows through columns *16* and *17* in which it becomes saturated with the vapours of the test adsorbates A and B. Columns *16* and *17* are 500 × 4 mm copper tubes packed with a solid support (Chromosorb), which is covered from 40% to 50% by weight with component A or B. The vapour pressure of the adsorbates is controlled by the temperature of a fluid bath (T_2 and T_3). Pure helium as carrier gas (cylinder *2*) is used in the chromatographic separation in column *25* and for the removal of adsorbed components A and B in adsorber *21*. The helium is purified *6* and divided into two streams. After passing through flow-meter *9* and capillary *14*, one of the streams is led to the feeder tap *18*. The other stream functions as a reference for the control cell of the katharometer *26*. The control instruments *3–14* are located in an air thermostat.

By opening the feeder valve *18*, the gas mixture ($He + 1\% N_2$) containing the vapours of compounds A and B or pure helium is allowed to flow through the adsorber *21* filled with the test adsorbent. In the first case the adsorbates A and B are adsorbed, in the second, they are desorbed. The second valve *19* is so connected with valve *18* that, depending on its position, it links tube *22* with pure helium or the helium–nitrogen–adsorbate mixture. Tube *22* does not contain any adsorbent, and its volume, taken together with that of valve *19*, is known. Valve *20* forwards the helium–nitrogen mixture and the test adsorbates A and B into the chromatographic column *25* or the inert column *24*. The adsorption data of components A and B on the adsorbent in tube *21* are determined from chromatographic data, whereby either the composition of the mixture (helium + nitrogen + adsorbates A and B) or that of the mixture in equilibrium with the adsorbent is determined (Fig. 4.13).

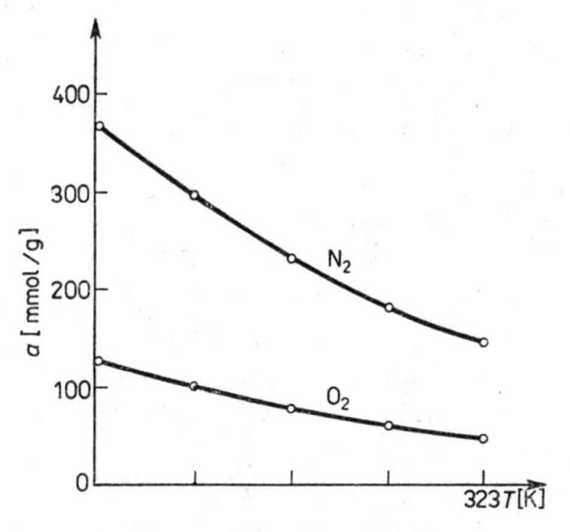

Fig. 4.13 Isobars of oxygen and nitrogen (pressure 0.1 MPa) on Linde 5 A molecular sieves (after E. Van der Vlist and J. Van der Mejden [101]).

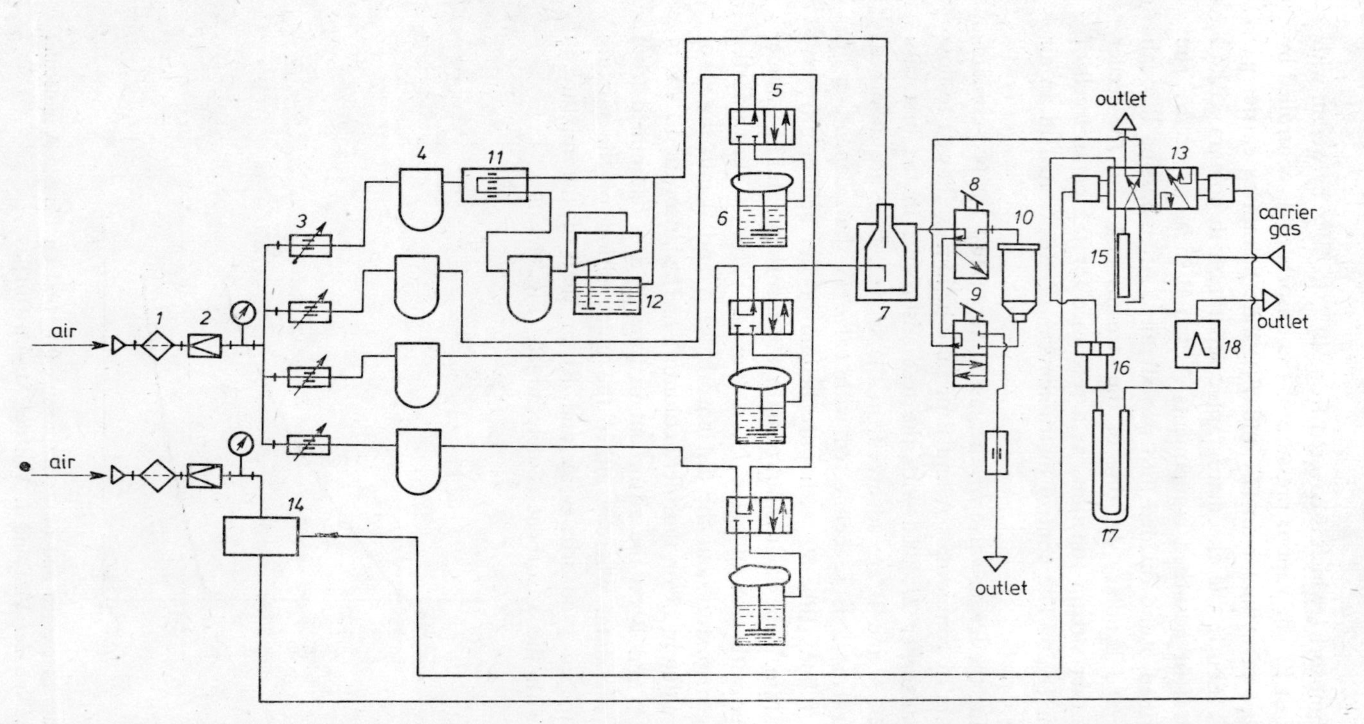

Fig. 4.14 Chromatographic apparatus for studying the adsorption dynamics of multicomponental mixtures of gases (after M. M. Dubinin *et al.* [118]):

1 — purification filter, *2* — pressure regulator, *3* — needle valve, *4* — rheometer, *5*, *8*, *9* — rotating plate valves, *6* — evaporator (saturator), *7* — mixer, *10* — adsorber, *11* — stream divider, *12* — humidifier, *13* — feeder valve, *14* — automatic injection of samples into the chromatographic column, *15* — tube of known volume, *16* — injection chamber, *17* — chromatographic column, *18* — detector.

Figure 4.13 illustrates the isobars of O_2 and N_2 at 0.1 MPa pressure on Linde 5A molecular sieves.

Figure 4.14 shows a different diagram of chromatographic apparatus for studying the adsorption dynamics of multicomponental gaseous mixtures [118]. This apparatus can be used for a wide range of physico-chemical investigations into adsorption processes using both frontal and elution chromatography, and also for modelling technological processes which have been optimized by means of sorption techniques.

After purification on filter *1*, air from a compressor or cylinder flows through the pressure regulator *2*, needle valves *3*, rheometers *4*, rotatory plate valves *5* into the saturators *6*. Bubbling through the layer of test adsorbates, the air becomes saturated with their vapours and enters the mixer *7* where a mixture of a given composition is prepared. The mixture passes on through rotatory plate valves *8* and *9* to the adsorption tube *10* in which there is an adsorbent bed of known height.

The rotatory plate valves *8* and *9* can alter the normal "analysis" — gas flow — "calibration" operational procedure of the apparatus. The stream divider *11* and humidifier *12* enable a gas stream of given humidity to be obtained. As the mixture leaves the adsorber *10*, it is analysed by elution chromatography using an automatic injector *14* and injection tube *15*. The samples are fed into the chromatographic column *17* where separation of the various adsorbates takes place; these are then recorded by the detector system *18*. If the adsorbates are organic substances, a flame-ionization detector is normally used, quantitatively calibrated with respect to the test adsorbates.

Besides liquid chromatography, GC is also an excellent technique for determining the adsorption isotherms of multicomponental solutions [107–110].

4.4 Determination of the Porosity of Solids

The type of pores, and especially their volume and distribution according to radius, plays an important part in adsorptive and catalytic processes taking place on the surface of porous solids. The structure of such solids is determined by the porosimetric method or the capillary condensation method.

Chromatographically, it is also possible to determine the distribution of pores using the capillary condensation method on the basis of adsorption or desorption isotherms obtained over a whole range of relative pressures [88–90, 111–114].

The change in the relative pressure of an adsorbate in a gaseous mixture (usually nitrogen in helium as carrier gas) can be obtained in various ways.

Fedorov and Izmailov [88–90] and Winter [112] altered the relative pressure of nitrogen by changing the percentage composition of the adsorption mixture, while at the same time maintaining an overall pressure

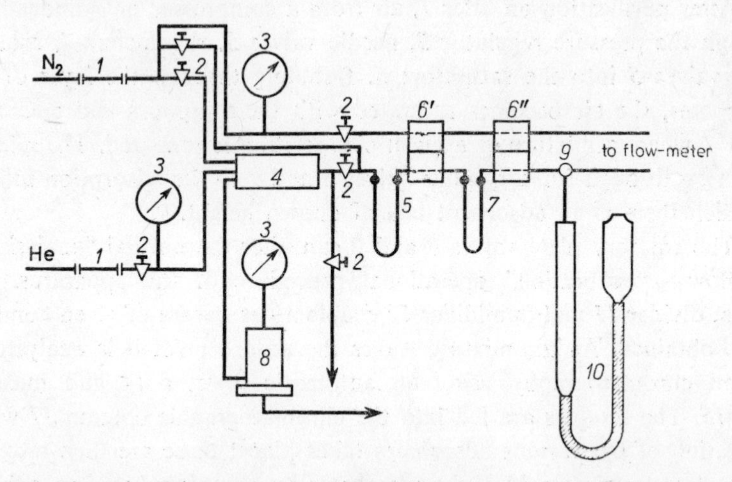

Fig. 4.15 Diagram of apparatus for determining the desorption isotherm of gases (after G. I. Fedorov and R. I. Izmailov [90]):

1 — capillaries, *2* — needle valve, *3* — manometer, *4* — mixing chamber, *5* — moisture freezer, *6'* and *6"* — katharometers, *7* — tube containing catalyst or adsorbent, *8* — pressure regulator, *9* — three-way valve, *10* — measuring burette.

of about 0.1 MPa. On the other hand, Hally [113], and Cahen *et al.* [114] altered the total pressure of the gaseous mixture while keeping the composition constant in order to obtain a given relative pressure of adsorbate.

Figure 4.15 illustrates the apparatus used by Fedorov and Izmailov [88] to determine the desorption isotherm of nitrogen. The adsorbent or catalyst in the U-tube *7* is saturated with pure nitrogen at the temperature of liquid nitrogen. After establishing the base line on both katharometers *6'* and *6"*, pure helium is introduced into the mixing chamber *4*; at the same time, the nitrogen supply is shut off. The volumetric flow rate of the gas mixture is kept constant (at about 6 cm^3/min) throughout the experiment by means of the pressure regulator *8*. The composition of the mixture can gradually be varied from pure nitrogen to pure helium. The concentration of nitrogen in the gas mixture is reduced at such a rate that the mixture leaving the adsorber is in equilibrium with the adsorbate remaining on the adsorbent. Having attained a relative pressure of nitrogen of around 0.06–0.07, the gas stream is diverted through the three-way valve *9* into the measuring burette *10*, and at the same time, the vessel containing liquid nitrogen is removed from under the U-tube *7*. Katharometer *6''* records the desorption peak of nitrogen, and tap *9* is restored to its original position. The time between one change of position of tap *9* and the next is recorded. During this period, a volume V_1 of mixture is collected in the gas burette. The volume V_1 consists of:

(a) the volume of desorbed nitrogen at pressure p/p_s;

(b) the volume of gas passing through the sample in the given time;

(c) the volume of gas additionally collected in U-tube *7* as a result of the low temperature.

In order to determine the proportions of volumes (b) and (c), an adsorption and desorption cycle with pure helium is carried out. If the volume of gas in the burette during a similar time is V_2, the volume of desorbed nitrogen is $V_1 - V_2$ at a given relative pressure p/p_s.

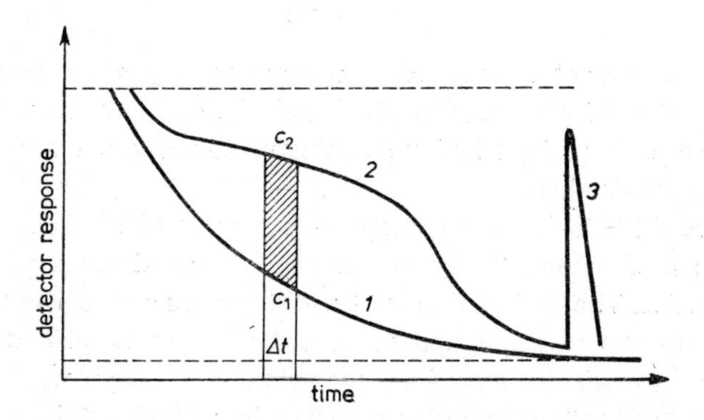

Fig. 4.16 Curves showing the changes in concentration of a nitrogen-helium mixture, obtained from a desorption cycle at the temperature of liquid nitrogen (after G. I. Fedorov and R. I. Izmailov [90]):

1 — change in concentration of the mixture entering the adsorber, *2* — change in concentration of the mixture leaving the adsorber, *3* — desorption peak obtained while heating the adsorbent.

Since the thermal conductivity of a He–N_2 mixture is not an additive magnitude, the relationship between the deviation on the recorder and the concentration of nitrogen has to be established experimentally. Figure 4.16 shows the traces of both detectors. The lower curve *1* shows the controlled gradual reduction in the concentration of nitrogen in the mixture entering the adsorber, whereas the upper curve *2* depicts the changes in the concentration of nitrogen in the outflowing mixture. The distance between the curves provides the quantity of nitrogen desorbed into the gas mixture. The final desorption of nitrogen (peak *3*) is obtained after heating the adsorber (removal of liquid nitrogen). When determining the entire desorption curve, we have to take the thermally desorbed amount of nitrogen into consideration. During any given period of time Δt, $F_{c_1} c_1 \Delta t$ cm^3 of nitrogen flow into the adsorbent (detector *6′*), where F_{c_1} is the volumetric flow rate of the stream entering the adsorber (cm^3/min), and c_1 is the mean volume fraction of nitrogen in the mixture during the time interval Δt. Having passed through the adsorbent into detector *6″*, $F_{c_2} c_2 \Delta t$ cm^3 of nitrogen flow in as a result of desorption.

Since $F_{c_2} = F_{c_1} + \Delta V'$, where $\Delta V'$ is the volume of pure nitrogen desorbed from the adsorbent in unit time (cm^3/min), we have

$$(F_{c_1} + \Delta V') c_2 \Delta t - F_{c_1} c_1 \Delta t = \Delta V' \Delta t \,, \tag{4.46}$$

$$\Delta V' = \frac{F_{c_1}(c_2 - c_1)}{1 - c_2} \,. \tag{4.47}$$

The quantity of nitrogen desorbed during any given time interval can be calculated from equation (4.47) and Fig. 4.16. By gradually raising the relative pressure from its lowest value up to unity, one can determine the desorption isotherm.

Figure 4.17 depicts the desorption isotherms of nitrogen calculated using this method and the graphs of capillary distribution with respect to their radius. The dashed lines on the distribution curves give the results obtained in a static vacuum apparatus. It should be stressed that for pores whose radius is smaller than 4 nm the values of the capillary distribution obtained with the static and chromatographic methods are in good agreement. For adsorbents with larger pores, the maximum on the $\Delta a / \Delta r$ curve is obtained within a range of smaller capillary radii than in the static method. This difference increases as the pore size grows. Good agreement of the $\Delta a / \Delta r$ curve with the static method was obtained when using benzene as adsorbate [88].

Hally [113] obtained a change in the relative pressure of nitrogen by varying the overall pressure of the mixture while keeping its concentration constant. When the mixture contains 10% nitrogen, a relative pressure of $p/p_s = 1$ is obtained with a mixture pressure of 1 MPa; when

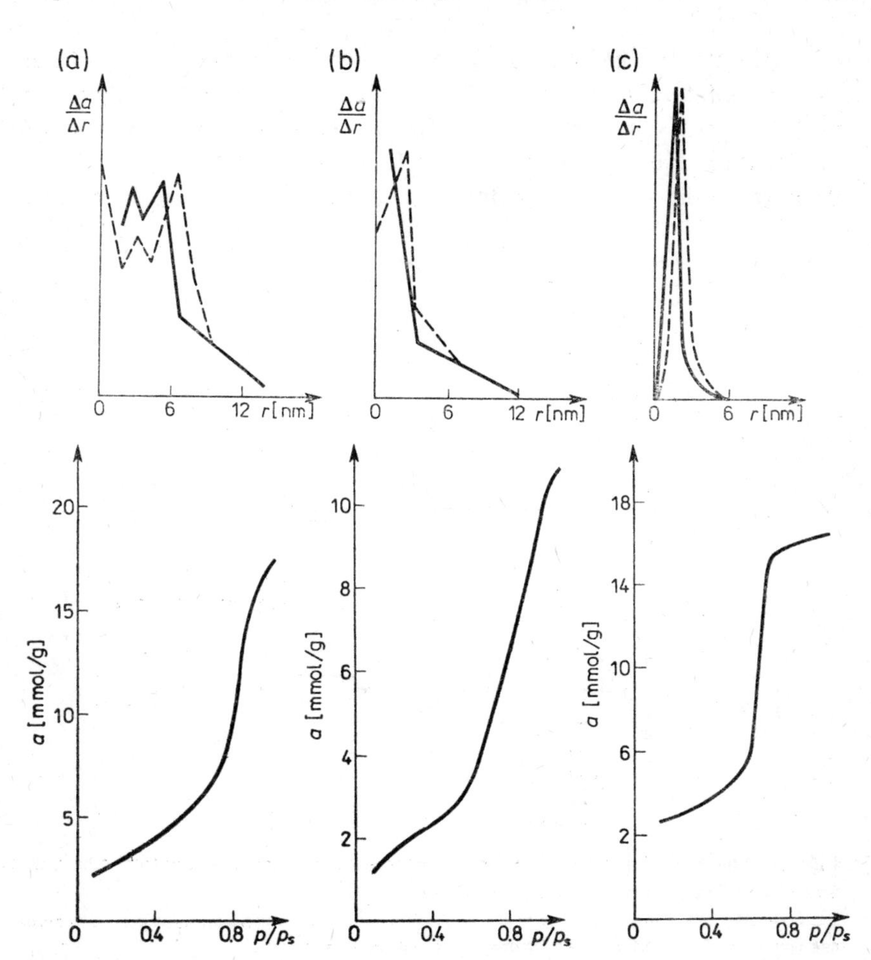

Fig. 4.17 Desorption isotherms for nitrogen. Upper — curves show the distribution of capillaries with respect to their radius for (a) Al_2O_3, (b) WS_2–NiS–Al_2O_3 and (c) aluminosilicate catalyst (dashed lines — results obtained in vacuum apparatus). Lower curves are the corresponding desorption isotherms of nitrogen (after G. I. Fedorov and R. I. Izmailov [90]).

the nitrogen content is 20%, it is 0.5 MPa, and so on. Figure 4.18 shows a diagram of the apparatus used here.

A nitrogen–helium mixture of given composition is divided into two streams — experimental and control. They pass through the purifier and dessicator *5*, then their pressures are reduced by means of the regulators *4*, *6* and *10*. Manometer *7* measures the pressure in adsorber *8*, while the pressure before the katharometer cells is checked with the aid of manometers *3*. The four-way valve *12* serves to introduce pure helium when calibrating the detector. The outflow rates of both streams are measured with rotameters *1*. Adsorption and desorption isotherms can be determined using this apparatus. In the adsorption cycle, the total pressure of the mixture is reduced to atmospheric pressure in order to

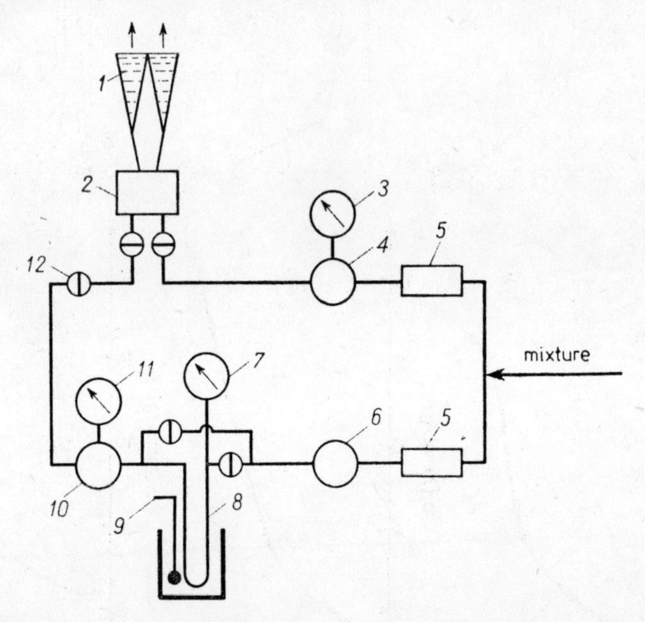

Fig. 4.18 Diagram of the chromatographic apparatus for determining the total adsorption and desorption isotherm (after A. L. Hally [113]):

1 — rotameters, *2* — katharometers, *3*, *7*, *11* — manometers, *4*, *6*, *10* — pressure regulators, *5* — purifier and dessicator, *8* — adsorber, *9* — thermometer, *12* — four-way valve.

obtain the first point on the isotherm. The adsorption is carried out at the temperature of liquid nitrogen and is determined by the quantity of nitrogen adsorbed as recorded on the adsorption chromatogram. If the nitrogen content in the mixture is 10%, we get adsorption $p/p_s = 0.1$ at a total pressure of 0.1 MPa. Further points on the adsorption isotherm are determined by gradually increasing the pressure in the adsorber by means of the pressure regulators *6* and *10*, until $p/p_s = 1$ is attained.

While the isotherm is being determined, desorption proceeds reversibly. The pressure in the adsorber is gradually reduced by simultaneously increasing the flow of the gas mixture into it (regulator *6*) and increasing the outflow (regulator *10*).

Every time the mixture pressure is raised or lowered, adsorption or desorption takes place, which is recorded in the form of adsorption or desorption peaks. Figure 4.19 shows a typical series of desorption peaks.

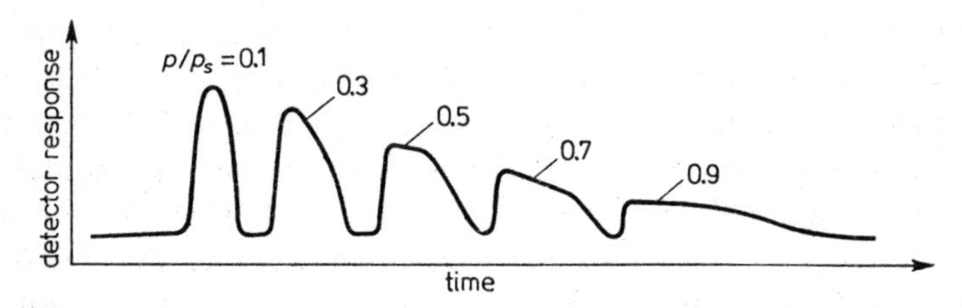

Fig. 4.19 Desorption peaks of nitrogen obtained for various values of p/p_s (after A. L. Hally [113]).

As p/p_s increases, the peaks become lower and broader as the rates of adsorption and desorption decrease at higher relative pressures.

Cahen *et al.* [114] have modernised their apparatus in such a way that the mixture pressure can be changed continuously (increase of pressure

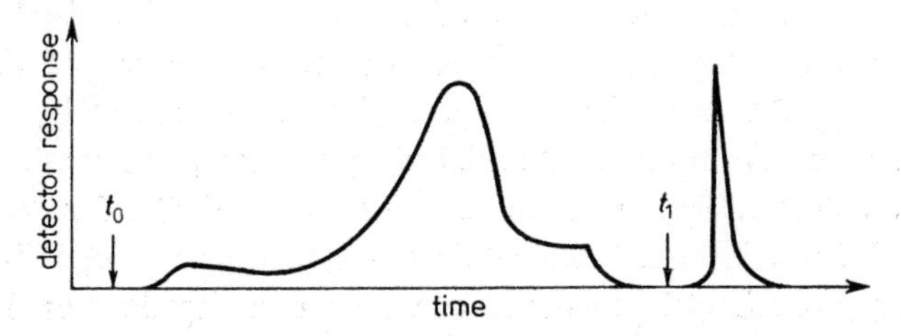

Fig. 4.20 Desorption chromatogram of nitrogen (after A. L. Hally [113]): t_0 — instant at which the pressure in the system begins to fall, t_1 — heating of sample started.

during adsorption and decrease during desorption); automatic recording of the adsorption and desorption is also possible. The desorption chromatogram obtained by Cahen is shown in Fig. 4.20.

The broad peak corresponds to the nitrogen desorbed during the gradual reduction of the pressure of the constant composition nitrogen–helium mixture. The peak maximum occurs for a relative pressure corresponding to a rapid lowering of the isotherm. In order to determine the desorption isotherm, the peak is divided into segments (every 2 or 3 minutes); then having taken the detector constant into account, the volume of desorbed nitrogen is calculated at pressures recorded by another instrument. The narrow peak is obtained as a result of heat desorption after having removed the Dewar flask containing liquid nitrogen from under the adsorber.

Hally and Cahen's method, despite a certain complexity of apparatus because of the high pressures involved, shows every prospect of becoming widely applied, as the results obtained agree with those from static methods. Furthermore, the determination of adsorption and desorption isotherms can be fully automated, which also means that the porosity of solids can be conveniently determined. Where one uses a method in which a change in the relative pressure of the adsorbate is obtained by changing the composition of the adsorption mixture, the necessity of experimentally determining the relationship between the recorder deflection and the percentage of nitrogen in the nitrogen–helium mixture must be taken into account. This is essential as the katharometer traces caused by a change in the composition of the mixture are non-linear.

When determining the porosity of solids chromatographically, organic compounds of various molecular dimensions are used as adsorbates [116, 117]. In accordance with the assumption that only adsorbate molecules smaller than the pores can be adsorbed in them, selective adsorption of adsorbates of different dimensions will determine the distribution of pores. If therefore we use a series of normal alkanes as adsorbates, we can determine the pore distribution rapidly and accurately, since the conductometric detector can be replaced by the far more sensitive flame-ionization detector. This method is particularly suitable for determining pores 0.3–1.5 nm in size. Within this range of dimensions, it is difficult to use the porosimetric method, capillary condensation or low-angle X-ray diffraction.

Thanks to the rapidity of measurement, their simplicity and accuracy, the above-mentioned chromatographic techniques for determining the total adsorption and desorption isotherms can be successfully applied to the study of the pore structure of solids.

4.5 General Remarks

When determining adsorption isotherms by means of chromatography, one must take the effect of diffusion on the shape of the chromatograms into consideration by introducing an appropriate correction. This is especially important when determining adsorption isotherms from the shapes of peaks. Adsorption isotherms determined from the extended front or rear profiles of a chromatogram obtained by the frontal or elution technique give approximate results. Only for sorbents with a pore size of over 4 nm do we get good agreement between the isotherms obtained by chromatographic and static methods. For fine-pored sorbents, the chromatographically obtained isotherms lie below those obtained under static conditions. In this case we get strongly broadened peaks. It is impossible to remove all the absorbed adsorbate from a fine-pored surface, even after passing the carrier gas over it for 2 hours.

The absorbed adsorbate can be removed by thermodesorption, and an additional peak then appears. These facts demonstrate that, as far as fine-pored adsorbents and catalysts are concerned, diffusion of the adsorbate into the pores is significant. At higher concentrations of adsorbate in the carrier gas, the change in the flow rate of the gas stream as a result of adsorption must be considered.

Of the chromatographic methods for determining adsorption isotherms, Helfferich and Peterson's method using labelled adsorbates is particularly worthy of note. In this way, adsorption is studied while the concentration of adsorbate on a solid surface remains constant.

By gradually altering the adsorbate concentration, a very precise determination of the adsorption isotherm over the whole range of relative pressures is possible. In this way one can also determine the rate of sorption and the sorption equilibrium as a function of the concentration of adsorbate on the surface.

References

[1] Brunauer S., *Sorption of Gases and Vapours*, Princeton Univ. Press, Princeton, New Jersey, 1945.

[2] Young D. M. and Crowell A. D., *Physical Adsorption of Gases*, Butterworths, London 1962.

[3] De Boer J. H., *The Dynamic Character of Adsorption*, The Clarendon Press, Oxford, 1953.

[4] Khan G. M., *The Rev. Sci. Instr.*, **43**, 117 (1972).

[5] Conder J. R. and Purnell J. H., *Trans. Faraday Soc.*, **64**, 3100 (1968), *ibid.*, **65**, 824 (1969).

[6] Davis R., *Chem. Ind.*, **8**, 160 (1952).

[7] Rubinstein A. M. and Afanasev V. A., *Izv. Akad. Nauk SSSR., ser. Khim.*, **11**, 1294 (1956).

[8] Stalkup F. I. and Kobayashi R., *Amer. Inst. Chem. Eng. J.*, **9**, 121 (1963).

[9] Gilmer H. B. and Kobayashi R., *Amer. Inst. Chem. Eng. J.*, **11**, 702 (1965).

[10] Koonce K. T. and Kobayashi R., *Amer. Inst. Chem. Eng. J.*, **11**, 259 (1965).
[11] Ivanova N. T. and Zhukhovitskii A. A., *Zh. Fiz. Khim.*, **43**, 2339 (1969).
[12] Wilson J. N., *J. Am. Chem. Soc.*, **62**, 1582 (1940).
[13] Weis J., *J. Chem. Soc.*, 297 (1943).
[14] De Voult D., *J. Am. Chem. Soc.*, **65**, 532 (1943).
[15] Glueckauf E., *Nature*, **156**, 748 (1945).
[16] Glueckauf E., *Nature*, **160**, 301 (1947).
[17] Glueckauf E., *J. Chem. Soc.*, 1302 (1947).
[18] Glueckauf E., *Disc. Faraday Soc.*, **7**, 199 (1949).
[19] Glueckauf E., *J. Chem. Soc.*, 3280 (1949).
[20] Wicke E., *Angew. Chem.*, **B19**, 15 (1947).
[21] Cremer E. and Prior F., *Z. Elektrochem.*, **55**, 66 (1951).
[22] Cremer E. and Müller R., *Z. Elektrochem.*, **55**, 217 (1951).
[23] James D. H. and Phillips C. S. G., *J. Chem. Soc.*, 1066 (1954).
[24] Gregg S. J. and Stock R., *Gas Chromatography*, Ed. Desty D. H., London, 1958, p. 90.
[25] Gregg S. J., *The Surface Chemistry of Solids* (2nd ed.), Chapman and Hall, London, 1961, p. 329.
[26] Schay G. and Szekely G., *Acta Chim. Akad. Sci. Hung.*, **5**, 1 (1954).
[27] Schay G., Fejes P., Halasz J. and Kiraly J., *Acta Chim. Acad. Sci. Hung.*, **11**, 381 (1957).
[28] James D. H. and Phillips C. S. G., *J. Chem. Soc.*, 1066 (1954).
[29] Huber J. F. K. and Gerritse R. G., *J. Chromatogr.*, **58**, 137 (1971).
[30] Gruber O., *XIX Chemicky Sjezd*, Brno, 1962.
[31] Roginskii S. Z., Yanovskii M. I., Lu Pei-Chan, Gaziev G. A., Zhabrova G. M., Kadenatsi B. M., Brazhnikov V. V., Neimark I. E. and Piotrowska M. A., *Kinet. Katal.*, **1**, 287 (1960).
[32] Conder J. R. and Young C. L., *Physicochemical Measurment by Gas Chromatography*, Chap. 9, J. Wiley, New York, 1979.
[33] Cremer E., *Monatsh.*, **92**, 112 (1961).
[34] Cremer E. and Huber H. F., *Angew. Chem.*, **73**, 461 (1961).
[35] Stock R., *Anal. Chem.*, **33**, 966 (1961).
[36] Eberly P. E. Jr and Kimberlin C. N. Jr, *Trans. Faraday Soc.*, **57**, 1169 (1961).
[37] Eberly P. E. Jr, *J. Phys. Chem.*, **65**, 1261 (1961).
[38] Huber J. F. K., *Gas Chromatography 1962*, Ed. Van Swaay M., Butterworths, London, 1962, p. 26.
[39] Cremer E. and Huber H. F., in: *Gas Chromatographie 1961*, Eds. Brenner N., Callen J. E. and Weiss M. D., Akademie Verlag, Berlin, 1962, p. 173.
[40] Fejes P., Fromm-Czaran E. and Schay G., *Acta Chim. Acad. Sci. Hung.*, **33**, 87 (1962)
[41] Stalkup F. I. and Deans H. A., *Amer. Inst. Chem. Eng. J.*, **9**, 106 (1963).
[42] Habgood H. W., in: *The Solid-Gas Interface*, Ed. Flood E. A., Marcel Dekker, New York, 1967, p. 640.
[43] Knözinger H. and Spannheimer H., *J. Chromatogr.*, **16**, 1 (1964).
[44] Kiselev A. V., Nikitin Yu. S., Petrova R. S., Scherbakova K. D. and Yashin Yu., *Anal. Chem.*, **36**, 1526 (1964).
[45] Owens D. R., Hamlin A. C. and Phillips T. R., *Nature*, **20**, 901 (1964).

[46] Cahen R. M., Marechal J. E. M., Della Faille M. P. and Fripiat J. J., *Anal. Chem.*, **37**, 133 (1965).
[47] Saint-Yrieix A., *Bull. soc. chim. France*, 3407 (1965).
[48] Kipping P. J. and Winter D. G., *Nature*, **205**, 1002 (1965).
[49] Vespalec R. and Grubner O., in: *Gas Chromatographie 1965*, Ed. Struppe H. G., Akademie Verlag, Berlin, 1966, p. 147.
[50] Feltl L., Grubner O. and Smolkeva E., in: *Gas Chromatographie 1965*, Ed. Struppe H. G., Akademie Verlag, Berlin, 1966, p. 169.
[51] Saffert W., Theuring D. and Schuberth H., in: *Gas Chromatographie 1965*, Ed. Struppe H. G., Akademie Verlag, Berlin, 1966, p. 471.
[52] Beebe R. A., Evans P. L., Kleinsteuber T. C. and Richards L. W., *J. Phys. Chem.*, **70**, 1009 (1966).
[53] Urone P. and Parcher J. F., *Anal. Chem.*, **38**, 270 (1966).
[54] Parcher J. F. and Urone P., *Nature*, **211**, 628 (1966).
[55] Urone P., Parcher J. F. and Bayler E. N., *Separation Sci.*, **1**, 595 (1966).
[56] Conder J. R. in: *Progress in Gas Chromatography*, Ed. Purnell J. H., Interscience, New York, 1968, p. 209.
[57] Masukawa S. and Kobayashi R., *J. Gas Chromatogr.*, **6**, 257 (1968).
[58] Sewell P. A. and Stock R., *J. Chromatogr.*, **50**, 10 (1970).
[59] Waksmundzki A., Suprynowicz Z. and Rayss J., *Chemia analit.*, **15**, 325 (1970).
[60] Dollimore D., Heal G. R. and Martin D. R., *J. Chromatogr.*, **50**, 209 (1970).
[61] Belyakova L. D., Kiselev A. V. and Kovaleva N. B., *Bull. soc. chim. France*, 285 (1967).
[62] Dzhavadov S. N., Kiselev A. V. and Nikitin Y. S., *Zh. Fiz. Khim.*, **41**, 1131 (1967).
[63] Saint-Yrieix A. and Sibut-Pinote R., *Bull. soc. chim. France*, 3433 (1971).
[64] Kropichenko O. M., Yanovskii M. I., Roginskii S. Z. and Nashivochnikov B. M., *Gazovaya khromatografiya*, Dzerzhinsk, 1966.
[65] Andreev L. V. and Kuvshinnikov V. D., *Gazovaya khromatografiya*, Izd. Nieftchim, Moskva, 1967.
[66] Gerritse R. G. and Huber J. F. K., *J. Chromatogr.*, **71**, 173 (1972).
[67] Kiselev A. V. and Yashin Y. I., *Gas Adsorption Chromatography Plenum*, New York, London, 1969.
[68] Roginskii S. Z., Yanovskii M. I. and Berman A. D., *Osnovy primenenya khromatografii v katalize*, Izd. Nauka, Moskva, 1972.
[69] Huber H. F. and Keulemans A. J. M. in: *Gas Chromatography*, Ed. Van Swaay M., Butterworths London, 1963.
[70] Gerasimov Y. I. (Ed.), *Kurs fizicheskoy khimii*, 1964 Vol. 1, p. 534.
[71] Schupp O. E., *Gas Chromatography*, John Wiley, N. Y., 1968
[72] Bachmann L., Bechtold E. and Cremer E., *J. Catal.*, **1**, 113 (1962).
[73] Pommier B. and Teichner F. J., *Bull. soc. chim. France*, 1268 (1972).
[74] Belyakova L. D., Kiselev A. V. and Kovaleva N. V., *Zh. Fiz. Khim.*, **42**, 2289 (1968).
[75] Belyakova L. D., Keybal V. L. and Kiselev A. V., *Zh. Fiz. Khim.*, **44**, 2345 (1970).
[76] Thibault S., Amouroux J. and Talbot J., *Bull. soc. chim. France*, 1319 (1968).
[77] Yanovskii M. I. and Gaziev G. A., *Gazovaya khromatografiya*, Izd. Nieftchim, Moskva, 1967, Vol. 5, p. 20.

[78] Fejes P., Fromm-Czaran E. and Schay G., in: *Gas Chromatographie 1961*, Ed. Schröter M. and Metzner K., Akademie Verlag, Berlin, 1962, p. 173.
[79] Wolf F. and Beyer H., *Chem. Technik*, **3**, 143 (1959).
[80] Cremer E., *Z. Anal. Chem.*, **B170**, 219 (1959).
[81] Kiselev A. V. and Yashin Y. I., *Gazovaya khromatografiya*, Trudy III Vses. Konf., Dzerzhinsk, 1966, p. 181.
[82] Stalkup F. I. and Kobayashi R., *Amer. Inst. Chem. Eng. J.*, **9**, 121 (1963).
[83] Helfferich F. and Peterson D. L., *Science*, **142**, 661 (1963).
[84] Kiselev A. V., *Disc. Faraday Soc.*, **40**, 205 (1965).
[85] Fejes P. and Fromm-Czaran E., *Acta Chim. Acad. Sci. Hung.*, **29**, 171 (1961).
[86] Schay G., *Theoretische Grundlagen der Gas Chromatographie*, VEB Dtsch. Verl. Wissenschaften, Berlin, 1960.
[87] Schay G., Nagy L. and Racz G., *Acta Chim. Acad. Sci. Hung.*, **71**, 23 (1972).
[88] Boreskov G. K. (Ed.), *The Porous Structure of Catalysts and Transport Processes in Heterogeneous Catalysts* (IV International Congress on Catalysis, Symposium III), Nauka Publishers, Siberian Branch, Novosibirsk, 1970, p. 183.
[89] Fedorov G. I., Tarasova G. F. and Izmailov R. I., *Zh. Fiz. Khim.*, **42**, 1036 (1968).
[90] Fedorov G. I. and Izmailov R. I., *Izv. Akad. Nauk SSSR, Ser. Khim.*, 2799 (1968).
[91] Volf J., Koubek J. and Pasek J., *J. Chromatogr.*, **81**, 9 (1973).
[92] Andreev L. V., Baiburskii V. L., Lapteva R. J. and Kuvshinnikov V. D., *Zh. Fiz. Khim.*, **44**, 2350 (1970).
[93] Andreev L. V., Baiburskii V. L. and Kuvshinnikov V. D., *Zh. Fiz. Khim.*, **46**, 80 (1972).
[94] Eberly P. E. jr, Kimberlin C. N. and Baker L. E., *J. Appl. Chem.*, **17**, 44 (1967).
[95] Pavlishenko N. M., *Zh. Fiz. Khim.*, **44**, 271 (1970).
[96] Nodzeński A., Ph. D. Thesis, AGH, Kraków, 1973.
[97] Schay G., Szekely G. and Szigetvary G., *Acta Chim. Acad. Sci. Hung.*, **12**, 299, 309 (1957).
[98] Schay G., Fejes P., Halasz J. and Kiraly J., *Anal. Chem.*, **14**, 439 (1958).
[99] Krivoruchko O. P., Yanovskii M. I., Roginskii S. Z. and Nashivochnikov B. M., *Gazovaya khromatografiya*, Trudy III Vses. Konf., Dzerzhinsk, 1966, p. 173
[100] Andreev L. V. and Kuvshinnikov V. D., *Gazovaya khromatografiya*, Izd. Nieftchim, Moskva, 1967, Vol. 6, p. 66.
[101] Van der Vlist E. and Van der Mejden J., *J. Chromatogr.*, **79**, 1 (1973).
[102] Peterson D. L. and Helfferich F., *J. Phys. Chem.*, **69**, 1283 (1965).
[103] Gilmer H. B. and Kobayashi R., *Amer. Inst. Chem. Eng. J.*, **11**, 702 (1965).
[104] Haydel J. J. and Kobayashi R., *Ind. Eng. Chem. Fundam.*, **6**, 546 (1967).
[105] Amino R., Franko J. and Keller H., *Anal. Chem.*, **43**, 107 (1971).
[106] Peterson D. L., Helfferich F. and Carr R. J., *Amer. Inst. Chem. Eng. J.*, **12**, 903 (1966).
[107] Sazonov M. L., Arenkova G. G., Selenkina M. S. and Shlakhov A. F., *Zh. Fiz. Khim.*, **42**, 2906 (1968).
[108] Vasileva V. S., Davydov V. Y. and Kiselev A. V., *Dokl. Akad. Nauk SSSR*, **192**, 107 (1970).
[109] Kiselev A. V. and Pavlova L. F., *Neftekhimiya*, **2**, 862 (1962).
[110] Davydov V. Y., Kiselev A. V. and Kuznecov B. V., *Zh. Fiz. Khim.*, **44**, 1 (1970).

[111] Gregg S. J. and Stock R., *Gas Chromatography*, 2nd Intl Symp., Amsterdam, Inostr. Lit. Moscow, 1961, p. 91.
[112] Winter D. G., *Chem. Ind.* (*London*), 233 (1969).
[113] Hally A. L., *J. Appl. Chem.*, **13**, 399 (1963).
[114] Cahen R. M. and Marechal J. E., *Analyt. Chem.*, **37**, 133 (1965).
[115] Lasoń M. and Nodzeński A., *Roczniki Chem.*, **47**, 591 (1973), *ibid.*, **49**, 357 (1975).
[116] Lyu Chzhun-Khueĭ, Yanovskii M. I. and Gaziev G. A., *Gazovaya khromatografiya*, Izd. Nauka, Moskva, 1964.
[117] Saha N. C. and Mathur D. S., *J. Chromatogr.*, **81**, 207 (1973).
[118] Dubinin M. M., Nikolaev K. M., Polyakov N. S. and Tilkunov I. N., *Zh. Fiz. Khim.*, **50**, 1039 (1976).
[119] Arenkova G. G., Lozgachev V. I. and Sazanov M. L., *Zh. Fiz. Khim.*, **48**, 375 (1974).
[120] Sazonov M. L., Arenkova G. G., Selenkina M. S. and Shlyakhov A. F., *Zh. Fiz. Khim.*, **42**, 2906 (1968).
[121] Jaroniec M., *J. Chem. Soc. Faraday*, **73**, 933 (1977).
[122] Jaroniec M., *Thin Solid Films*, **50**, 163 (1978).
[123] Jaroniec M., *Wiadomości Chem.*, **32**, 705 (1978).
[124] Jaroniec M., *React. Kinet. Catal. Lett.*, **8**, 425 (1978), *ibid.*, **9**, 309 (1978).
[125] Jaroniec M., *Vacuum*, **28**, 17 (1978).
[126] Jaroniec M., *J. Chem. Soc. Faraday*, **74**, 1292 (1978).
[127] Valentin P. and Guiochon G., *J. Chromatogr. Sci.*, **14**, 132 (1976).
[128] Conder J. R., Locke D. C. and Purnell J. H., *J. Phys. Chem.*, **73**, 700 (1969).
[129] Cadogan D. F., Conder J. R., Locke D. C. and Purnell J. H., *J. Phys. Chem.*, **73**, 708 (1969).
[130] Conder J. R., *J. Chromatogr.*, **39**, 273 (1969).
[131] Conder J. R., *Chromatographia*, **7**, 387 (1974).
[132] Edel G. and Chabert B., *C. R. Acad. Sci. Paris*, *ser. C*, **268**, 226 (1969).

Chapter 5

Determination of the Specific Surface Areas of Solids

5.1 Introduction

The most important geometrical characteristic of adsorbents and catalysts is the magnitude of their specific surface area.

Adsorption techniques have so far been the most widely adopted for determining of the specific surface areas of solids. Static volumetric and gravimetric methods are tedious and require fairly complicated vacuum apparatus. Thus there is a continual need for new methods of calculating the specific surface areas of solids which are quick, simple and accurate. GC has found application in this field as well.

5.2 Chromatographic Methods of Determining the Specific Surface Areas of Solids

The specific surface area of a solid can be determined in a number of ways [1]; GC is one of them [2–61]. Conventionally, all chromatographic methods are divided into three groups:

(1) methods in which adsorption isotherms are first determined, the specific surface area being calculated from these isotherms by means of the BET method [2–54];

(2) methods in which the specific surface area is calculated directly from the retention volume [55–61];

(3) methods in which the specific surface area is calculated from the second B_{2S} and third B_{3S} virial coefficients.

Methods chromatographically determining the adsorption isotherm were described in detail in Chapter 4. In the chromatographic determination of the specific surface areas of solids, the following methods are most frequently used:

(a) heat desorption methods [21–53];

(b) methods based on the use of the differential equation of the material balance of equilibrium chromatography to determine adsorption isotherms from the extended boundary of the chromatogram [2, 7–20];

(c) Schay's frontal method [3–6].

5.2.1 The Heat Desorption Method

Of all the existing chromatographic techniques of determining the specific surface area of a solid, the heat desorption method is the one most often used. This method was worked out by Nelson and Eggertsen in 1958 [21], and later modified by a number of workers [23–30, 38, 40, 42, 108].

The heat desorption method is so widely used because of its simplicity in measurement and its great sensitivity, which means that specific surface areas can be determined over a broad range — from 0.01 m^2/g up to 1000 m^2/g [18, 63, 103, 104, 108]. Apart from this, chromatographic equilibrium is not necessary when taking measurements for determining the specific surface areas of solids with a pore structure. In principle, the heat desorption method is based on the well-known BET technique [62] in which one determines the quantity of adsorbed gas at a temperature near its boiling point (usually N_2). By determining the adsorption at various pressures, it is possible, using the BET equation, to calculate the amount of adsorbate required for the formation of a monolayer.

In the classic example of this method, the principle of measurement is based on the adsorption of nitrogen (by a solid) from a stream of gas of given composition — N_2–He or N_2–H_2 — at the temperature of liquid nitrogen (adsorption peak *1*, Fig. 5.1), and then on its desorption after removal of the Dewar flask (desorption peak *2*, Fig. 5.1).

The mixture containing a known composition of nitrogen and helium or nitrogen and hydrogen (usually 5, 10, 15, 20% N_2) is obtained earlier, or is prepared by mixing the streams of adsorbate and carrier gas.

The quantity of adsorbed nitrogen, a, at an appropriate relative pressure is calculated from the desorption peak because this is more symmetrical. Each experiment performed for a given concentration of adsorbate in the mixture gives one point on the adsorption isotherm.

The magnitude of the adsorption a is calculated from the formula

$$a = kS_{\text{peak}} \frac{F_{\text{m}}}{F_{\text{cal}}}, \tag{5.1}$$

where k is the detector constant (see Chapter 4 for the method of determination), S_{peak} is the area of the desorption peak, F_{m} is the volumetric

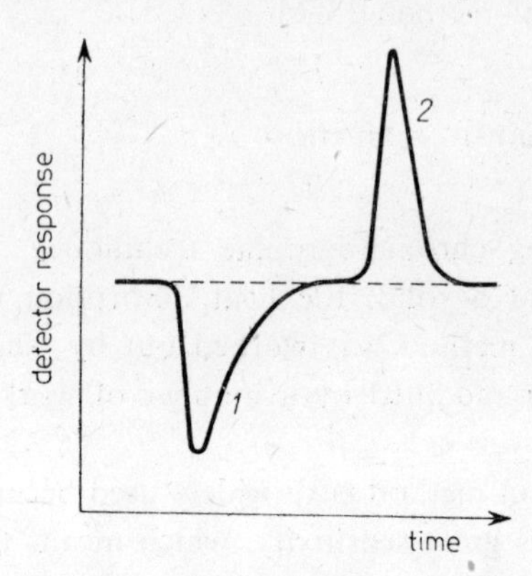

Fig. 5.1 Adsorption peak *1* and desorption peak *2* obtained by the heat desorption method.

flow rate of the mixture during measurement, and F_{cal} is the volumetric flow rate of the mixture during calibration.

For a mixture of adsorbate and carrier gas, the partial pressure of adsorbate can be calculated from

$$p = \frac{F_{\text{ads}}}{F_{\text{m}}} p_{\text{b}}, \tag{5.2}$$

where F_{ads} is the volumetric flow rate of the adsorbate, and p_{b} is the barometric pressure.

The quantity of nitrogen needed to cover the adsorbent with a monolayer is given by the BET equation

$$\frac{\dfrac{p}{p_{\text{s}}}}{a\left(1-\dfrac{p}{p_{\text{s}}}\right)} = \frac{1}{a_{\text{m}}C} + \frac{C-1}{a_{\text{m}}C} \cdot \frac{p}{p_{\text{s}}}, \tag{5.3}$$

where a is the quantity of adsorbed species (mmol/g), a_{m} the amount of species needed to cover completely a surface with a monolayer (mmol/g),

p the equilibrium pressure of adsorbate, p_s the saturated vapour pressure of adsorbate at the experimental temperature, and C a constant depending on the adsorption energy and temperature, defined by the following equation:

$$2.3 \log C = Q_1 - Q_c , \tag{5.4}$$

where Q_1 is the heat of adsorption in the first layer, and Q_c is the heat of condensation of the adsorbate.

The constant C is determined graphically (Fig. 5.2). We can determine the specific surface area of the adsorbent S if we know the magnitude

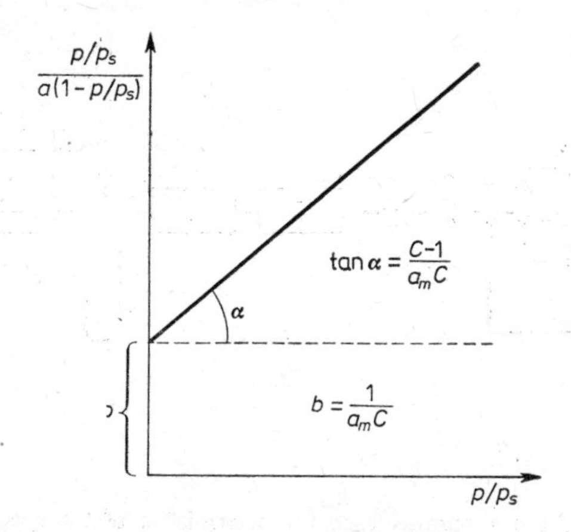

Fig. 5.2 Determination of constants for the BET adsorption isotherm equation.

of a_m and the area occupied by a molecule of adsorbate in the monolayer ω_m — the sitting surface

$$S = a_m N_A \omega_m , \tag{5.5}$$

where N_A is the Avogadro number.

The apparatus for measuring the specific surface areas of solids by means of the heat desorption method, illustrated in Fig. 5.3, enables us to work with a prepared mixture of adsorbate and carrier gas (cylinder *1*), or to prepare the required mixture by mixing the streams of adsorbate and carrier gas in the mixer *4*. The flow rate of the adsorbate–carrier gas mixture is regulated by means of a fine control valve *2*, and is usually from 10 to 60 cm^3/min. The gas stream then flows through the rotameter *3*, the drying filter *5*, *6*, the empty U-tube *7*, the comparative cell of the katharometer *9*, the U-tube *8* containing the test adsorbate or catalyst, and from there to the measurement cell of the katharometer *10* and gas flow-meter *12*. It is best to install the empty U-tube *7*, which is the same size as the adsorber *8*, before the comparative cell of the katharometer *9*, so as to reduce interference caused by changes in temperature and gas flow rate during adsorption and desorption. Dewar vessels containing liquid nitrogen are simultaneously placed under and removed from U-tubes *7* and *8*. The streams of gas entering the comparative cell *9* and

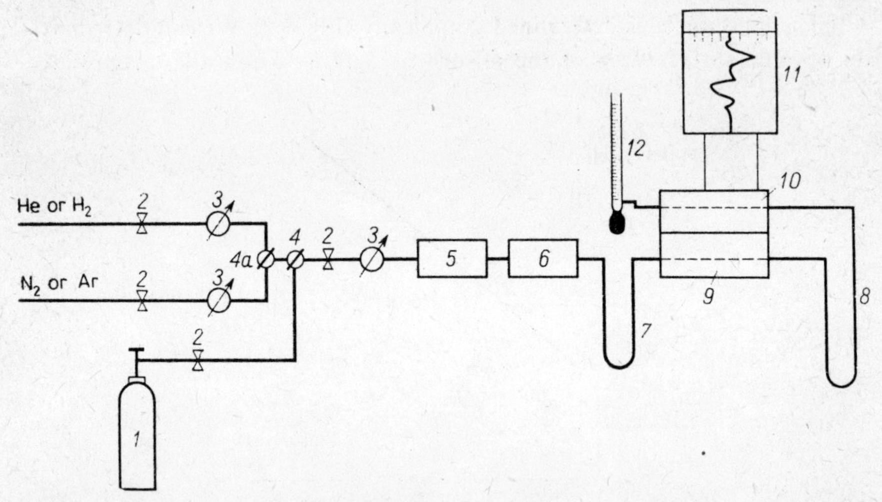

Fig. 5.3 Diagram of the apparatus used for determining of the specific surface areas of solids by means of the heat desorption method:

1 — cylinder with gaseous mixture of known composition, 2 — control valves, *3* — rotameters, *4* — three-way valve, *4a* — four-way valve, *5, 6* — drying filter, *7* — empty U-tube, *8* — U-tube containing test adsorbent or catalyst, *9, 10* — comparative and experimental katharometer cells, *11* — recording device, *12* — flow-meter.

measurement cell *10* of the katharometer are at about the same temperature. The test samples should be placed in the adsorber *8* in such quantities that the gas mixture can flow over them freely; if this is not done, resistance builds up in the system, the comparative and measurement cells of the katharometer will be at different pressures, and considerable error will ensue. Where solids with a very small specific surface area are being tested, the lower part of adsorber *8* should be suitably enlarged. If a gas mixture of the same composition flows through both comparative and measurement cells of the katharometer, the pen of the recording device *11* draws the base line. A constant volume flow rate, and equilibrium between the surface of the solid and the gas at room temperature having been attained, column *8* containing adsorbent and column *7* are placed in liquid nitrogen. The nitrogen or argon in the gas mixture is adsorbed on the surface of the solid in U-tube *8*. The concentration of adsorbate in the gas mixture flowing through the recording element of the detector is reduced. This change in composition of the gaseous mixture is recorded as an adsorption curve on the chromatogram (Fig. 5.1). Adsorption equilibrium is said to have been reached when the line on the recorder tape has returned to zero. Once equilibrium has been established, the liquid nitrogen is removed from under U-tubes *7* and *8*. This causes the adsorbent to warm up to room temperature and the nitrogen is almost totally desorbed. The composition of the gaseous mixture in the comparative cell of the katharometer changes, and this is recorded as a desorption peak (Fig. 5.1). In order to accelerate desorption and obtain a more symmetrical desorption peak, the U-tube is placed in a vessel containing water at room temperature.

Cahen and Marechal [47] indicated the possibility of determining the specific surface areas of 4 samples simultaneously, and Karnaukhov and Buyanova [49] produced a system for the simultaneous determination of the specific surface areas of six samples of adsorbent. The samples were pre-prepared for measurement by passing carrier gas through them at a suitable temperature.

Standard adsorbates can be used in the heat desorption method. The right choice of adsorbate is very important when determining the specific surface area of a solid. Even nitrogen, which is most often used for measurements of specific surface area, is not an ideal adsorbate because of its considerable quadrupole moment. A nitrogen molecule can occupy different sitting surfaces depending on the chemical properties of the adsorbent surface [65–68]. At the same time, it is important to remember that partial chemisorption of nitrogen on some metals is possible [69–71]. If this takes place, it may lead to errors in the estimation of the surface area. The sitting surface of organic molecules can vary even more widely [72–76]. The relatively large size of organic molecules may further restrict the extent of the specific surface area of a solid with a fine-pored structure.

The noble gases argon, krypton and xenon are good adsorbates for estimating the specific surface areas of catalysts and adsorbents [39, 40, 66, 68, 77–79, 88, 91]. Krypton is normally used for estimating the specific surface area of solids below 100 m^2/g, although in the opinion of some authors its usefulness is questionable [80–82]. In this heat desorption method, it is nitrogen [7, 22–24, 26, 28, 31, 38, 106], krypton [25], argon

[9, 36, 39, 40] and organic compounds such as acetone, benzene and hexane [83–86] which have mainly been used as adsorbates. The question of which adsorbate should be regarded as a standard has not been decided yet. The adsorbate most closely approaching the requirements of a standard is argon [9, 18, 36, 40, 49, 68]. The area occupied by an argon molecule is the smallest of all the usual adsorbates and in a densely-packed monomolecular layer depends little on the chemical properties of the solid surface. As regards argon, the possibility of its undergoing phase transitions tn the adsorption layer can be neglected, since its critical temperature of iwo-dimensional condensation is much lower than the temperature of

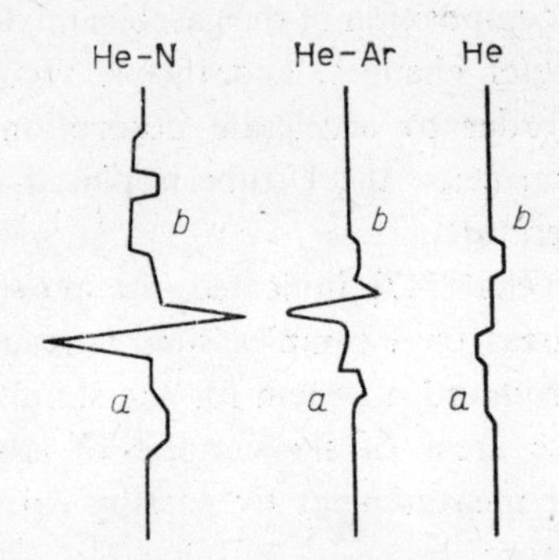

Fig. 5.4 Fluctuations in the katharometer base line when using an empty adsorber for various mixtures of gases (after N. E. Buyanova *et al.* [40]):

a — when cooling the adsorber with liquid nitrogen, *b* — after removal of the Dewar flask from under the adsorber.

liquid nitrogen. The sensitivity of chromatographic estimations with argon as adsorbate is higher than with nitrogen [39–40]. This is because lower concentrations of argon (1.5–8%) than of nitrogen (5–20%) are required in the gaseous mixture to obtain the relative pressure of $p/p_s = 0.05\text{–}0.35$ necessary for the determination of the specific surface area using the BET method. Using argon therefore reduces the deviations of the katharometer readings from linearity with respect to concentration and reduces the fluctuations of the base line while the empty adsorber is being heated and cooled (Fig. 5.4) [40]. In the heat desorption method, the katharometer base line may fluctuate widely as a result of thermodiffusion. The effects of this can be lessened by thoroughly mixing the gas mixture in a special mixer [110] placed before the measurement cell of the katharometer (in this method a mixture of adsorbate and carrier gas), or by using an adsorber with a minimal gas holdup [32].

In order to reduce the influence of changes in the rate of gas flow on the basc line as a result of cooling (adsorption) and heating (desorption), an additional adsorber *7* (Fig. 5.3), having the same dimensions as the adsorber proper *8* (Fig. 5.3), should be placed in front of the comparative cell of the katharometer. The changes in the gas flow rates during adsorption and desorption will be the same in both cells, which makes it easier to keep the base line stable. In this way, interference resulting in the appearance of an additional peak, and adsorption on the inner surface of the adsorber can be minimized [108]. Thus, any fluctuations of the base line will be due entirely to the adsorption and desorption of the adsorbate on the surface of the solid being tested.

The measurement of the specific surface area by heat desorption can be simplified to the determination of only two or even one single point on the isotherm, and the quantity of adsorbate needed to cover the adsorbent with a monolayer a_m, assuming the constancy of C, can be calculated from Temkin's formula [87], applicable to adsorbents having diverse chemical properties

$$a_m = a\left(1 - \frac{p}{p_s}\right)\left[1 + \frac{(p_s/p) - 1}{C}\right]. \tag{5.6}$$

The constant C, estimated as an average value for different adsorbents and catalysts, is about 50 ± 15 [88].

It is evident from equation (5.6) that changes in the value of C barely affect the value of a_m. A two-fold change in the value of C at a relative pressure of 0.2 causes an error in the estimated value of a_m of only 5%. Calculations according to equation (5.6) should be done for two points on the isotherm as a check of the readings and calculations. Knowing a_m, the specific surface area can be calculated from equation (5.5).

Gavrilova and Kiselev [38] described another method of determining the approximate value of the specific surface area of any solid on the basis of one isotherm point; nitrogen was used as adsorbate. It was assumed that for a sufficiently strongly adsorbing surface, a monolayer a_m is obtained at the temperature of liquid nitrogen and a pressure $p/p_s = 0.05$. The surface concentration of nitrogen in the monolayer is 10.6 $\mu mol/m^2$.

Figure 5.5 shows the adsorption isotherms of nitrogen on the surfaces of solids having different chemical properties. The surface concentrations on graphitized carbon black, silica gel and titanium dioxide at around a relative pressure of $p/p_s = 0.05$ are very similar and are equal to 10.6 $\mu mol/m^2$. When estimating the adsorption, a, of nitrogen, its concentration in the carrier gas (helium, hydrogen) being 5%, the specific surface area can be calculated from equation (5.7)

$$S = \frac{a\,\mu\mathrm{mol/g}}{10.6\ \mu\mathrm{mol/m^2}}. \tag{5.7}$$

Easy and rapid estimation of the specific surface area of a solid is achieved using the comparative method, in which we use the proportional

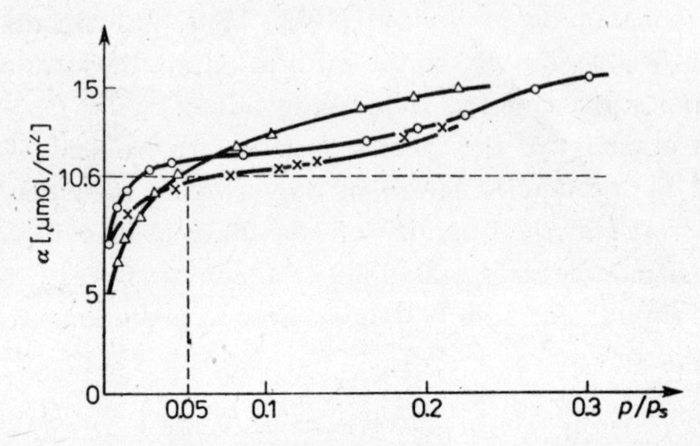

Fig. 5.5 Isotherms of the surface concentration of nitrogen on various adsorbents (after T. B. Gavrilova and A. V. Kiselev [38]):
○ — graphitized carbon black, △ — wide-pored silica gel, × — titanium dioxide.

relationship between the peak area and the specific surface area of the adsorbent [26]. In this case, we must know the specific surface area of a similar standard species. The specific surface area is then determined from the equation

$$S = \frac{S_{st} m_{st} S_{peak} F_c}{S_{peak\,st} m F_{c\,st}}, \tag{5.8}$$

where S is the specific surface area of the standard (m^2/g), m_{st} is the mass of the standard (g), $S_{peak\,st}$ is the peak area of the standard (mm^2), $F_{c\,st}$ is the volumetric flow rate of the gas mixture when estimating $S_{peak\,st}$ (cm^3/min), S_{peak} is the peak area of the tested adsorbent (mm^2), F_c is the volumetric flow rate of the gas mixture when estimating S_{peak} (cm^3/min), and m is a weighed sample of sorbent (g).

If the peaks are symmetrical, the peak heights h can be used instead of their areas. The optimum weights of samples are from 0.01 to 20 g, depending on their specific surface area and are selected in such a way that the surface area of the weighed sample is about 5 m^2.

Grubner and co-workers [83] and others [85, 86] used the vapours of organic compounds (benzene, hexane, heptane, acetone) as adsorbate, thus eliminating the liquid nitrogen which has so far been essential in the heat desorption method. Adsorption of the organic vapours took place at room temperature (293 or 298 *K*), desorption at 413–423 K. Since hydrogen may react with some organic adsorbates on solid surfaces at higher temperatures during desorption, neutral gases should be used as

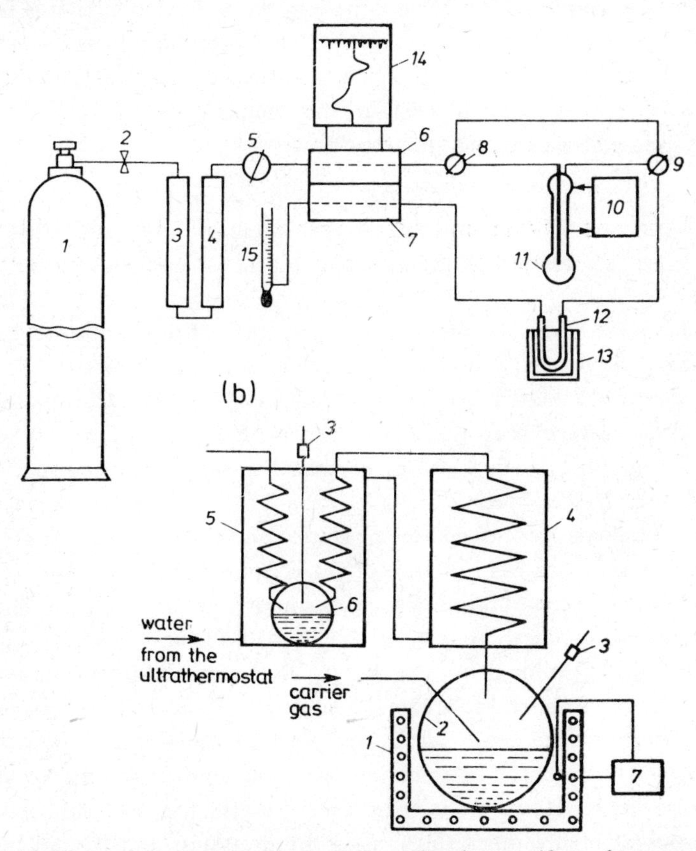

Fig. 5.6 (a) Diagram of the apparatus used the estimating specific surface areas by the heat desorption method using organic vapours as adsorbate:

1 — carrier gas cylinder, *2* — fine control valve, *3, 4* — filters for purifying and drying the carrier gas, *5, 15* — flow-meters, *6, 7* — comparative and measurement cells of the katharometer, *8, 9* — three-way valves, *10* — ultrathermostat *11* — saturator with cooler, *12* — sorption vessel, *13* — oil bath, *14* — recording device.

(b) diagram of saturator:

1 — oven, *2* — adsorbate container, *3* — adsorbate feed, *4, 5* — coolers, *6* — collector for condensing adsorbate, *7* — temperature control.

carrier gas. The carrier gas stream (helium, nitrogen, argon) is saturated with the vapours of organic compounds in the saturator. It is essential to choose appropriate carrier gas flow rates and saturator temperatures (heater and cooler) so as to achieve a constant adsorbate concentration in the carrier gas. Figure 5.6 illustrates the apparatus used [83]. The saturator ensures the complete saturation of the carrier gas with adsorbate, and if the temperature of the cooler is set at about 5° below room temperature, condensation of adsorbate in the following tubing is rendered impossible. This method is very valuable where liquid nitrogen is unavailable, or for estimating the specific surface areas of species whose properties are radically altered at the temperature of liquid nitrogen, e.g. cellulose, leather, and other polymers.

5.2.2. Methods Involving the Determination of the Adsorption Isotherm from the Extended Chromatogram Boundary

These methods are used to estimate the adsorption isotherm from the extended boundary of a chromatogram, after which the specific surface area can be calculated by the BET method [2, 7–20]. Chromatographic methods of determining the adsorption isotherm, based on the material balance equation of equilibrium chromatography, were discussed in detail in Chapter 4. The specific surface areas obtained in this manner agree well with the results obtained in the static conditions of vacuum apparatus, so long as the pore radii of the solid are greater than 4–5 nm [7, 8]. The requirements of equilibrium chromatography are difficult to fulfil with fine-pored adsorbates because of the slow diffusion of the adsorbate in the pores of the solid; this is the case especially in elution chromatography. This leads to considerable errors when estimating the adsorption isotherm and specific surface area, particularly at low temperatures. This method is not widely used for determining the specific surface area of catalysts and adsorbents. However, it is extremely useful for determining sorptive properties at high temperatures using both elution and frontal methods.

5.2.3 Schay's Frontal Method

Schay and co-workers [3–5] put forward two ways of estimating the adsorption isotherm — these were presented in detail in Chapter 4. Even assuming the equilibrium concentration c_0 in advance (which in practice cannot be done using static methods), adsorption can be estimated from the area contained between the chromatogram fronts of the adsorbate and non-adsorbing gas (Figs 4.7 and 4.8). The method takes diffusion into account since the adsorption is calculated from the relative position of both chromatogram fronts, assuming that any broadening of the fronts is identical for the adsorbing and non-adsorbing gas.

The specific surface areas estimated in this way differ from those obtained under static conditions by 5–13% [9]. This difference increases as the area between the fronts of the adsorbing and non-adsorbing gas diminishes. This area can be enlarged by increasing the adsorbent content in the adsorber, but this causes a greater pressure drop and change in the gas flow rate [10, 14, 89]. Schay's other method of determining adsorption, and the calculation of the specific surface area from it, are given in Chapter 4 (Fig. 4.10).

5.2.4 The Retention Volume Method

It was Cremer [55, 56] and Wolf and Beyer [57] who, in 1959, first suggested the possibility of estimating the specific surface area from the retention volume. This method has since been developed and modified by other workers. The principle of the technique is derived from the theory of ideal equilibrium chromatography, which states that specific retention volumes V_g are proportional to the magnitude of the surface area S of the adsorbent in the column

$$V_g = AS, \tag{5.9}$$

where A is a constant for a given adsorbate–adsorbent system at a constant temperature and characterizes the adsorption energy within the applicability of Henry's law. The method is therefore suitable only for adsorbents of a similar chemical nature and texture.

The value of A can be determined from the independent estimation of the specific surface area and retention volume of a standard sample

$$A = \frac{V_{gst}}{S_{st}} = V_s, \tag{5.10}$$

where V_s is the net retention volume with respect to unit area. The specific surface area can be determined by a comparative method

$$S = \frac{V_g}{V_s}. \tag{5.11}$$

The essence of Cremer's reasoning [55, 56] will be outlined here because of its significance not only when estimating the specific surface area but also when determining the thermodynamic functions of adsorption. His reasoning is based on the kinetic-molecular theory. As a single adsorbate molecule moves along the column with the carrier gas, it is successively adsorbed and desorbed at the active sites of the adsorbent. The number of collisions Z of the adsorbate molecules with the surface of the adsorbent S during a passage time through the column t_M is

$$Z = \frac{1}{4} N \bar{u}_c S t_M , \quad (5.12)$$

where $\bar{u}_c$ is the average velocity of adsorbate molecules at the experimental temperature, N is the number of molecules of adsorbate in 1 cm^3. Assuming uniform packing of the adsorbent, the number of collisions in every section of the column will be the same. The adjusted retention time t'_R is equal to the time τ that an adsorbate molecule remains at the adsorption site, multiplied by the total number of adsorption acts Z_a which, on average, one molecule undergoes while moving through the adsorbent layer

$$t'_R = Z_a \tau , \quad (5.13)$$

where Z_a is the number of collisions of the molecule with the surface which lead to adsorption.

The retention time depends on the size of the adsorption surface (number of collisions with the surface) and the free energy of adsorption. Where Henry's law is applicable, that is when the adsorbent is covered with adsorbate only to a small extent, it may be assumed that every collision of a molecule leads to adsorption. The value of Z_a is then calculated from equation (5.12).

The number of adsorbate molecules N_g in the gas space of the column is given by

$$N_g = N L \varepsilon q , \quad (5.14)$$

where L is the column length, q is the column cross-section and ε is that part of the cross-section not occupied by the stationary phase.

If we divide equation (5.12) by N_g (equation (5.14)), and substitute the value of Z_a obtained (range of applicability of Henry's law) in equation (5.13) we get

$$t'_R = \frac{1}{4} \alpha \frac{\bar{u}_c \tau t_M S}{L \varepsilon q} , \quad (5.15)$$

where $\alpha < 1$ is a coefficient allowing for diffusion and the fact that not every collision of a molecule with the surface leads to adsorption. For a constant carrier gas flow rate (t_M = const), constant experimental temperature ($\bar{u}_c$ = const), and for small differences between the heats of adsorption of the test sample and the standard (τ = const), equation (5.15) enables us to estimate the specific surface area of a solid from the following relationship:

$$\frac{t'_{R_2}}{t'_{R_1}} = \frac{S_2}{S_1}, \tag{5.16}$$

where t'_{R_2} and t'_{R_1} are the adjusted retention times of the test sample and standard, S_1 and S_2 are the specific surface areas of the test sample and standard respectively.

The specific surface area can be determined correctly for small concentrations of adsorbate, that is to say, within the applicability of Henry's law, which was emphasised while deriving equation (5.15). This equation can be rewritten

$$t'_R \frac{\varepsilon q L}{t_M} = \tfrac{1}{4} \alpha \bar{u}_c \tau S, \tag{5.17}$$

where $\varepsilon q L / t_M$ is the volumetric flow rate of the carrier gas in the column F_c (cm^3/min). The temperature affects the average velocity of adsorbate $\bar{u}_c$ in the column only to a small extent; this may be seen from the expression

$$\bar{u}_c = \sqrt{\frac{8RT}{\pi M}}, \tag{5.18}$$

where M is the mass of 1 mole of adsorbate.

On the other hand, the time spent by a molecule at an adsorption site increases exponentially with the coefficient λ/RT, where λ is the energy of desorption.

If the rate of desorption proceeds according to a first-order equation, τ is the reciprocal of the desorption rate constant k_d

$$\tau = \frac{1}{k_d}. \tag{5.19}$$

The rate constant k_d is linked with the free energy of desorption by the Eyring equation

$$k_d = \gamma_p \frac{\bar{k}T}{\bar{h}} \exp\left(-\frac{\Delta G}{RT}\right) = \gamma_p \frac{\bar{k}T}{\bar{h}} \exp\left(-\frac{\Delta H}{RT}\right) \exp\left(\frac{\Delta S}{RT}\right), \tag{5.20}$$

where ΔG, ΔH, ΔS are the free energy, enthalpy and entropy of adsorption, $\bar{k}$ is Boltzmann's constant, $\bar{h}$ is Planck's constant, and γ_p is the transition coefficient ($\gamma_p < 1$).

An expression for the specific retention volume can be derived from equations (5.19), (5.20) and (5.15), viz.

$$V_g = \tfrac{1}{4}\bar{u}_c \sigma \frac{\bar{h}}{\bar{k}T} \exp\left(-\frac{\lambda}{RT}\right) S, \tag{5.21}$$

where $\sigma = \alpha/\gamma_p \exp(-\Delta S/RT)$, $\lambda = \Delta H$.

Substituting values which are constant at a temperature of 273 K in equation (5.21), we obtain an equation from which we can calculate the specific surface area

$$S = 6 \times 10^7 \frac{1}{\sigma} 10^{-\lambda/4.57T} V_g. \tag{5.22}$$

All the magnitudes in equation (5.22) can be determined independently, with the exception of the coefficient σ. The value of σ is calculated by estimating the surface area of this type of adsorbent by some other, independent method.

Having determined the value of V_{gst} and S_{st}, and keeping the remaining conditions constant, the relative specific surface area can be estimated from equation (5.21), i.e.

$$\frac{V_{g1}}{V_{g2}} = \frac{S_1}{S_2}, \tag{5.23}$$

where V_{g1}, V_{g2} are the specific retention volumes of the sample and standard, and S_1, S_2 are the specific surface areas of sample and standard.

The value of λ is determined on the basis of the specific retention volume obtained for the sample at two temperatures

$$\lambda = \frac{T_1 T_2}{T_2 - T_1} R \ln \frac{V_{g1}}{V_{g2}}. \tag{5.24}$$

Because of the low dependence of the average velocity $\bar{u}_c$ on the temperature (equation (5.18)), the heat of adsorption can be determined for sufficiently high temperatures from the linear dependence of $\log V_g$ on $1/T$.

Gaziev, Yanovskii and Brazhnikov [61] assumed that the values of S and λ (equation (5.22)) for chemically different adsorbents differed little, and they thus took the constant A in equation (5.9) to be invariable for adsorbents consisting of any given chemical surface. These authors confirmed that this assumption is reasonable for a whole range of adsorbents and catalysts.

The specific retention volumes they determined were approximately proportional to the specific surface areas determined by independent

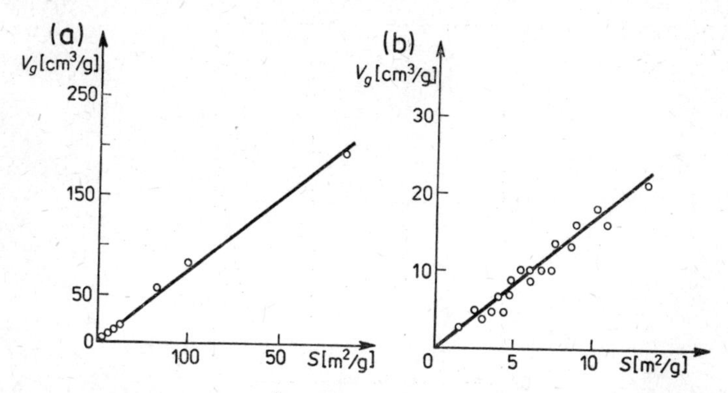

Fig. 5.7 Relationship between the specific retention volume V_g of *n*-heptane and the specific surface areas *S* of different adsorbents and catalysts: (a) 0–100 m²/g; (b) 0–10 m²/g (after G. A. Gaziev *et al.* [61]).

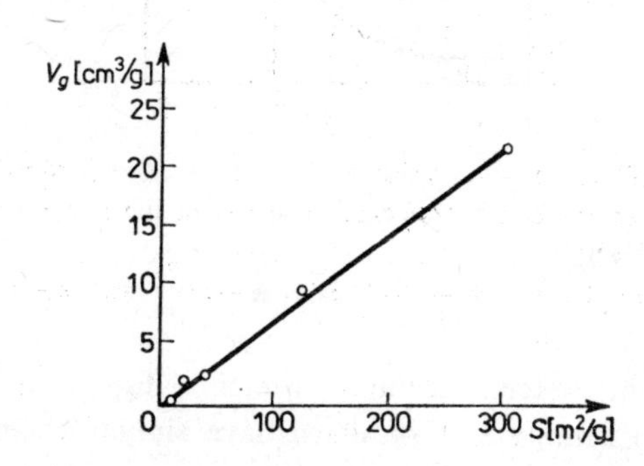

Fig. 5.8 Relationship between the specific retention volume V_g of *n*-hexane and the specific surface areas *S* of wide-pored silica gels at 373 K; surface coverage 0.001–0.1 (after A. V. Kiselev *et al.* [58]).

methods (Fig. 5.7). Kiselev *et al.* [58] (Fig. 5.8) got a similar linear relationship between the specific surface area of wide-pored silica gels and the retention volume. The tangent of the gradient of the straight lines in Figs 5.7 and 5.8 is equal to the net retention volume V_s. The maximum variation of constant *A* for samples having different chemical properties is about 30%. Such a variation is understandable, since the adsorption energy, and thus also the value of the net retention volume V_s, depends to a large extent on the chemical and geometrical nature of the surface. The suggestion of Kiselev and his co-workers [15, 38, 58, 59, 92–94] that the net retention volumes V_s should be assumed equal only for certain

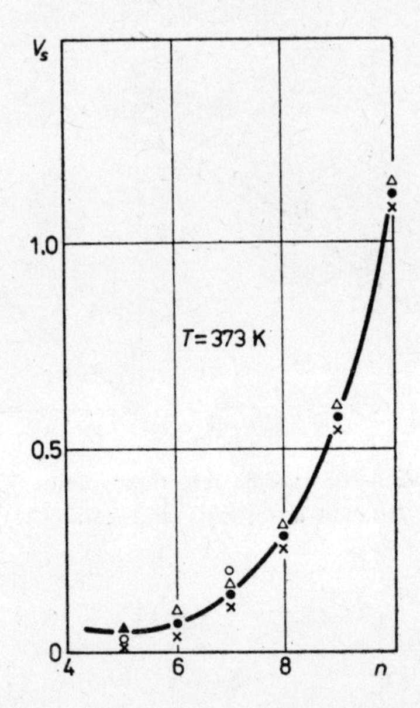

Fig. 5.9 Net values of the retention volume V_s of *n*-alkanes on silica gels of different surfaces with respect to the number of carbon atoms in the *n*-alkane molecule (after A. V. Kiselev *et al.* [58]):
○ — s = 300 m²/g, ▲ — s = 117 m²/g, △ — s = 31 m²/g, ● — s = 9 m²/g, × — s = 9 m²/g.

adsorbate–adsorbent systems accounts for this. Equation (5.11) can be applied only when sample and standard have similar chemical and geometrical surface properties, and similar degrees of coverage.

Kiselev proposes that V_s be accepted as a physicochemical constant characterizing the adsorbate–adsorbent system (Fig. 5.9). Knowing V_s for a given adsorbate–adsorbent system, it is easy to calculate the specific surface area of a sufficiently wide-pored adsorbent from equation (5.11) by estimating only V_g. The mass of adsorbent, the kind of adsorbate and the column temperature should be so chosen as to obtain narrow, symmetrical peaks which enable the retention times to be estimated with sufficient accuracy.

Buyanova, Karnaukhov and Rybak [60] also suggested determining the specific surface area from the retention volume, but with large coverages, corresponding to the second linear section of the isotherm above the so-called point *B*. These authors found that over the range of the

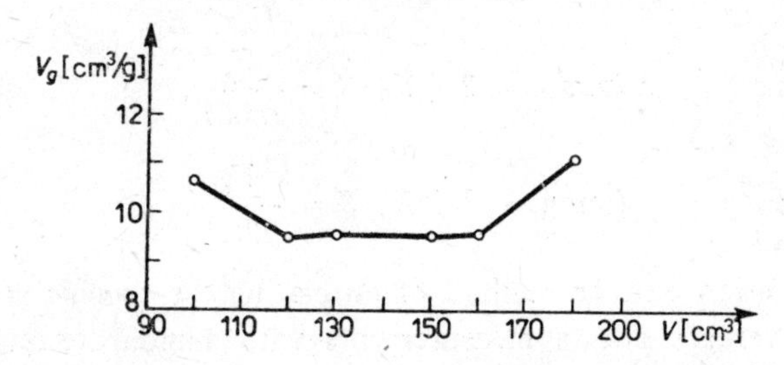

Fig. 5.10 Relationship between the specific retention volume V_g of *n*-pentane on silica gel at 314 K and the size of the injected sample (after N. E. Buyanova *et al.* [60]).

large coverages they were testing, the chemical nature and the non-homogeneity of the adsorbent surface did not affect the magnitude of the retention volume because the surface was screened with a layer of adsorbate.

The relationship between the retention volume and the size of an introduced sample of n-pentane on silica gels is shown in Fig. 5.10.

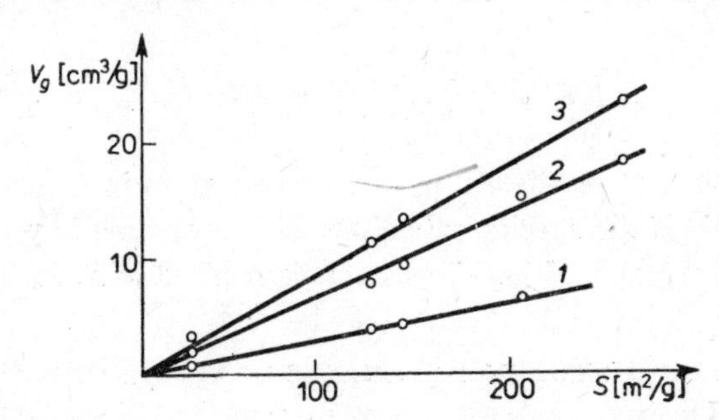

Fig. 5.11 Relationship between V_g and the specific surface area S of the adsorben (after N. E. Buyanova *et al.* [60]):
1 — *n*-pentane (temp. 319 K), *2* — *n*-pentane (temp. 314 K), *3* — chloroform (temp. 345 K).

Over a certain range of adsorbate sample sizes, V_g remains unchanged, which indicates that a monolayer has been formed, and that we have now entered the range of the linear section of the isotherm corresponding to the coverage of a second and further layers. Over this range of surface concentrations, the values of the specific retention volumes of n-pentane and chloroform alter linearly with respect to the specific surface areas estimated by an independent method (Fig. 5.11).

Simple formulae for determining the specific surface area of chloroform and n-pentane as adsorbates are given below:

$$\text{chloroform} \qquad (\text{temp.} = 345\ \text{K}) \quad S = \frac{V_g}{0.095}, \tag{5.25}$$

$$n\text{-pentane} \qquad (\text{temp.} = 314\ \text{K}) \quad S = \frac{V_g}{0.067}, \tag{5.26}$$

$$n\text{-pentane} \qquad (\text{temp.} = 319\ \text{K}) \quad S = \frac{V_g}{0.031}. \tag{5.27}$$

The retention volume method of estimating the specific surface area for large coverages allows measurements with standard samples to be restricted to a minimum. The basic faults of this method are its lower sensitivity as compared with the heat desorption method, and the time-consuming procedure for establishing the size of the adsorbate sample at the start of the experiment.

According to Wolf and Beyer [57], the specific surface area can be estimated from the relationship between the heat of adsorption of a homologous series of alkanes and the number of carbon atoms in the molecule n, viz.

$$\log V_g^0 = \frac{\Delta\lambda}{RT} n + \ln (\text{const } S), \tag{5.28}$$

where $\Delta\lambda$ is the heat of adsorption per carbon atom in a molecule of adsorbate, and V_g^0 is the specific retention volume obtained by extrapolation to $n = 0$ on the graph of $\log V_g$ vs. n. This method is not much used.

5.2.5 A Method Based on the Change in Peak Shape with Change in Sample Size

Kuge and Yoshikawa [54] described an interesting method of estimating the specific surface area based on the change in peak shape with respect to the size of the adsorbate sample introduced into the column (Fig. 5.12). They noticed that as one goes from adsorption of a largely monomolecular layer to adsorption in polymolecular layers, a characteristic kink appears in the apex of the peak (Figs 5.12 and 5.13). This corresponds to point B on isotherms of type II in the Brunauer classification [96]. Figure 5.14 shows the change in retention time with change in sample size. We can see from Fig. 5.13 that we get a symmetrical peak for the linear part of

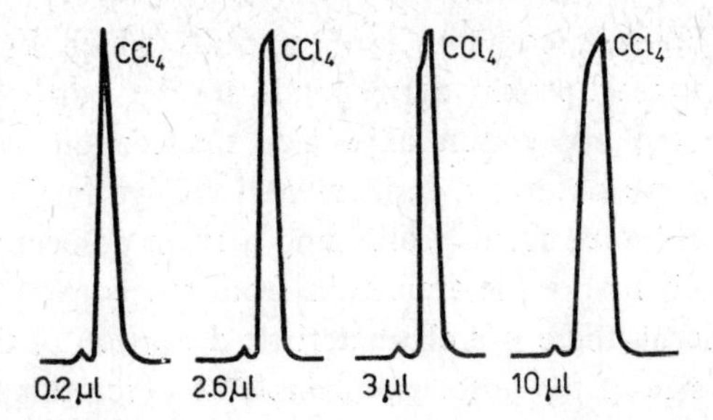

Fig. 5.12 Change in peak shape with respect to the size of the adsorbate sample; adsorbent $Cu(Py)_2(NO_3)_2$ (after Y. Kuge and Y. Yoshikawa [54]).

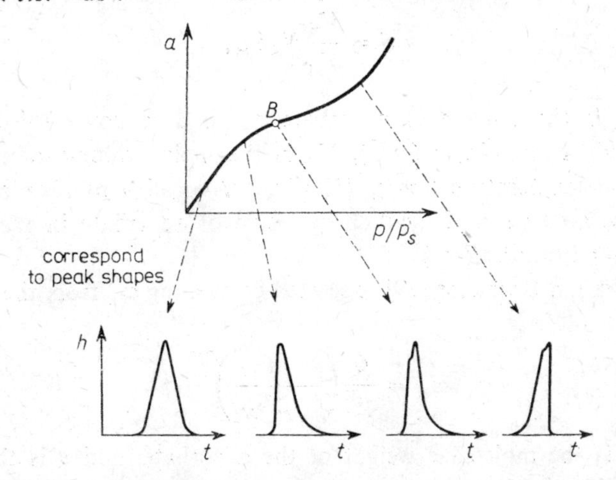

Fig. 5.13 The second type of adsorption isotherm according to the Brunauer classification and the peak shapes corresponding to it (after Y. Kuge and Y. Yoshikawa [54]).

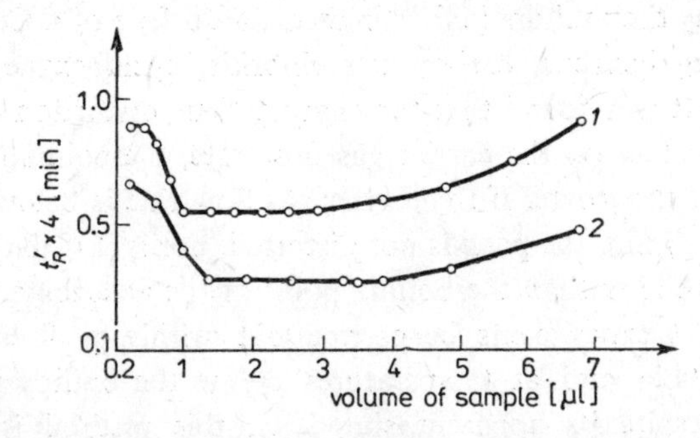

Fig. 5.14 Changes in retention time with increase in adsorbate sample size (after Y. Kuge and Y. Yoshikawa [54]):

(*1* — benzene, *2* — carbon tetrachloride; adsorbent $Cu(Py)_2(NO_3)_2$, gas flow rate 57.7 cm^3/min, column temp. 323 K).

the isotherm. The most common type of peak, which has a steep front and an extended rear profile corresponds to the part of the isotherm convex towards the adsorption axis. For the section convex towards the pressure axis, we observe a fundamental change in the peak shape — we now get an extended front profile and a steep descent from the apex. At point B, which marks the transition from the convex to the concave part of the isotherm, there is a characteristic distortion of the peak's apex. If we know the size of the adsorbate sample at which this peak distortion takes place, we can determine the surface area of the adsorbent in the column, S

$$S = \frac{V_m}{V_M} N_A \omega_m, \tag{5.29}$$

where V_m is the volume of adsorbate required to cover the adsorbent surface with a monolayer (cm^3), V_M is the molar volume of the gas at the column temperature (cm^3), N_A is the Avogadro number and ω_m is the surface area covered by each molecule of adsorbate in the coherent monolayer (sitting surface).

Emmet and Brunauer [97] suggested calculating ω_m from the following equation:

$$\omega_m = \frac{6}{\sqrt{3}} \left(\frac{M}{4\sqrt{2} N_A d} \right)^{2/3}, \tag{5.30}$$

where M is the molecular weight of the adsorbate, and d is the density of the liquid adsorbate at the temperature of adsorption. Table 5.1 gives the values of ω_m for a number of adsorbates.

In this way the authors [54] estimated the surface of a $Cu(Py)_2(NO_3)_2$ adsorbent using benzene, carbon tetrachloride, cyclohexane and hexane as adsorbates. It was found that the characteristic distortion of the peak's apex was dependent on the carrier gas flow rate, the column temperature and the type of adsorbate. If the carrier gas flow rate is below 20 cm^3/min or above 60 cm^3/min, the peak is not distorted, nor is it if the experimental temperature is higher than the boiling point of the adsorbate. The authors recommend that experiments be carried out within a flow rate range of 20–60 cm^3/min and at temperatures below the boiling points of the adsorbates. Despite its apparent simplicity, this method is more time-consuming than other chromatographic techniques of estimating the specific surface area. Another reason for its restricted use is the fact that the experimental conditions must be adhered to precisely.

Table 5.1 VALUES OF THE ACTIVE SURFACE OF ADSORBATE MOLECULES ω_m

Adsorbate	*Adsorption temperature* T[K]	*Generally accepted value of* ω_m [nm²]	*Range of values of* ω_m *in various papers depending on the nature of the adsorbent surface* [nm²]
N_2	78	0.162	0.13–0.20
Ar	78	0.138	0.13–0.18
Kr	78	0.200	0.15–0.22
Xe	78	0.250	0.18–0.27
O_2	90	0.144	0.14–0.18
CO	90	0.168	0.15–0.19
NO	123	0.125	–
H_2O	298	0.250	0.20–0.35
CO_2	216.4	0.170	–
SO_2	273	0.192	–
NH_3	237	0.129	–
CH_4	133	0.181	–
C_2H_6	78	0.210	0.20–0.24
n-C_4H_{10}	273	0.320	0.30–0.55
n-C_5H_{12}		0.450	–
n-C_6H_{14}		0.510	0.51–0.72
n-C_7H_{16}		0.570	0.57–0.80
n-C_8H_{18}		0.610	–
CH_3OH	298	0.250	0.15–0.30
C_6H_6	298	0.400	0.30–0.50

5.2.6 DETERMINATION OF THE SPECIFIC SURFACE AREA BY THE ADSORBED LIQUID PHASE METHOD

Serpinet's method. Serpinet *et al.* [33, 111–118] have worked out a new chromatographic method, independent of the BET adsorption model, for determining the specific areas of solids with hydroxyl groups on their surface (e.g. silica gels, alumina and diatomite). The BET method requires estimation of the amount of adsorbate necessary for a complete monolayer coating of the solid whose area is being determined. Difficulties in determining precisely the adsorbate packing density in the monolayer and on adsorbents whose surfaces are chemically different often lead to incorrect assumptions about the molecular area of, ω_m, the monolayer (sitting surface).

Serpinet's adsorbed liquid layer method takes into account the monolayer of the supported phase, that is actually formed.

The idea of using an adsorbed liquid layer for determining specific surface area instead of adsorption from solution has been known for a long time [1c]. Serpinet's method has helped to overcome the considerable theoretical and practical difficulties which prevented this idea from being implemented earlier.

The method is based on the decomposition of a liquid phase (generally long-chain alcohols such as octadecanol), supported on a hydroxyl surface, into two states: a "compact monolayer" (two-dimensional state), and a "normal liquid phase" (three-dimensional state) which is in excess in relation to the monolayer and characterized by properties (e.g. chromatographic) completely different from those of the monolayer.

The molecules of octadecanol in the monolayer are orientated parallel to each other and almost at right angles to the surface (like the hair in a carpet or a brush). The outer part of the monolayer consists of relatively big CH_3 groups, little polarized, with a very small surface energy and at a considerable distance (0.25 nm^2) from the solid surface. The area occupied by one molecule in the monolayer at 331 K is 0.21 nm^2 (the cross-section of an aliphatic chain) and is completely independent of the chemical nature of the solid surface provided this contains hydroxyl groups. An identical value (0.21 nm^2) is obtained on the surface of ethylene glycol (ethane 1,2-diol) and water [33, 111, 114].

Serpinet [33, 111] suggests two variants of the method:

(a) a change in the amount of supported liquid phase (at constant temperature);

(b) a change in temperature (with a constant amount of supported liquid phase).

Change in the amount of supported liquid phase. A series of columns containing different amounts of supported stationary phase per gram of the test adsorbent τ is prepared. The columns serve to determine the retention volume V_s^0 (n-alkane, n-C_5 to n-C_8 are recommended), and a plot of V_s^0/τ against $1/\tau$ is made (Fig. 5.15).

The plot consists of two straight lines crossing at the critical point τ_c, which corresponds to the monolayer formed. The point on the y-axis corresponding to the point of intersection of the two straight lines is the specific retention volume V_g^* on the monolayer formed, and point V_g^0 corresponds to the specific retention volume of the stationary phase (three-dimensional state). The specific surface area S can be easily estimated from the value of τ_c obtained from the plot (Fig. 5.15)

$$S = \frac{\tau_c N_A \omega'_m}{M}, \tag{5.31}$$

where N_A is the Avogadro number, ω'_m is the surface area of a liquid phase molecule in the monolayer at the column temperature (0.21 nm² for 1-octadecanol at 331 K), M is the molecular weight of the liquid phase.

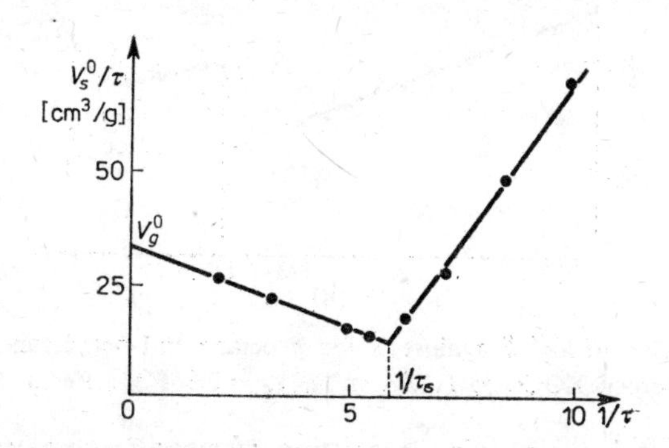

Fig. 5.15 Dependence of V_s^0/τ against $1/\tau$ for *n*-pentane on 1-octadecanol supported on silica gel at the melting point of the stationary phase (331 K) (after J. Serpinet [33]).

Temperature change. In order to determine the specific surface area by this method, only one column containing a small excess of the supported phase τ_b (10–20%) in relation to τ_c — the amount necessary for monolayer formation — can be used. This excess τ_b takes the "normal liquid" form (three-dimensional state). The increase in retention of the test substance at the melting point of the "normal" supported phase allows this excess to be determined (Fig. 5.16).

It is recommended that four measurements of retention volume be carried out above and below the melting point of the supported phase. Extrapolation of the linear range to the melting point enables ΔV_s^0 to be determined (Fig. 5.16): note that

$$\Delta V_s^0 = V_{s2}^0 - V_{s1}^0 . \tag{5.32}$$

From the increase in retention volume ΔV_s^0, the "excess" of the liquid phase τ_b can be determined

$$\tau_b = \frac{\Delta V_s^0}{V_g^0}, \tag{5.33}$$

and

$$\tau_c = \tau - \tau_b \,. \tag{5.34}$$

Estimation of τ_c allows the specific surface area to be determined from the formula (5.31).

The value of V_g^0 (if unknown, say, from Fig. 5.15) can be found by carrying out identical measurements with another chromatographic column.

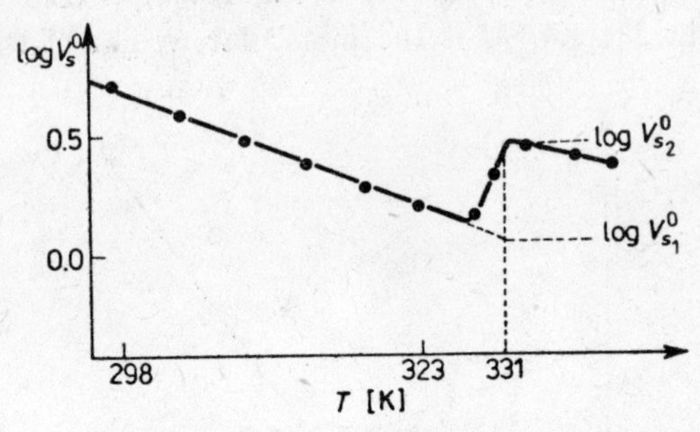

Fig. 5.16 Dependence of $\log V_s^0$ against T for n-octane on 1-octadecanol ($\tau = 2.70\%$) supported on Spherosil XOCOO5 (11.08 m²/g, $\tau_c = 2.36\%$) (after J. Serpinet [33]).

The column contains a packing consisting of some stationary phase supported on the hydrophobic surface of the support (e.g. the hydrophobization of silica with silicones).

No orientated monolayer is formed on the hydrophobic surface. Only the "normal" stationary phase is observed. The change in retention volume at melting point is characteristic of the whole supported stationary phase τ:

$$V_g = \frac{(\Delta V_s^0)_{sil}}{\tau} \,. \tag{5.35}$$

Comments. In both variants of the method, Serpinet recommends the use of long-chain alcohols such as 1-octadecanol ($\omega_m' = 0.21$ nm^2) if the pore diameters of the solid are bigger than 20 nm. When the pore diameter is from 6 to 20 nm, dibutyl sulphone ($\omega_m' = 0.428$ nm^2) (But–SO_2–But), may be used.

n-Alkanes (from C_5 to C_8) are recommended for determining retention volumes.

While supporting the stationary phase dichloromethane (CH_2Cl_2) is usually used as solvent, which is then removed by evaporating under vacuum at a temperature between the melting point of the monolayer and that of the "normal" supported phase (three-dimensional phase).

It is very important to use an accurate thermostat in the chromatograph maintaining the measurement temperature to within at least 0.1 K.

Table 5.2 presents a comparison of the values of the specific surface area obtained by BET and Serpinet's method.

Table 5.2 COMPARISON OF THE SPECIFIC SURFACE AREA DETERMINED BY THE BET METHOD [84] AND SERPINET'S METHOD [33, 112–118]

Adsorbent	S[m²/g] BET	S[m²/g] Serpinet
I Stationary phase 1-octadecanol		
Chromosorb P	3.6	3.60
Spherosil XOC005	11.1	11.08
Spherosil XOB015	26.2	25.5
α-Al_2O_3 (I)	6.5	7.04
α-Al_2O_3 (II)	14.5	14.4
α-Al_2O_3 (III)	28	27.6
Chromosorb G	—	0.41
II Stationary phase dibutyl sulphone (But–SO_2–But)		
Chromosorb P	3.6	3.58
Spherosil XOC005	11.1	11.08
Spherosil XOA200	162.5	162.8
α-Al_2O_3 (III)	28	26.2

As can be seen, the agreement between both methods is excellent. The same value of the area occupied by one molecule in the monolayer for 1-octadecanol (0.21 nm^2) and butyl sulphone (0.428 nm^2) has been assumed in all respective examples. Serpinet's method is much more precise than those described earlier, although in practice it is more troublesome than, say, the thermal desorption method.

5.2.7 Determination of the Specific Surface Area from the Second B_{2S} and Third B_{3S} Virial Coefficients [120]

The following relationship exists between the net retention volume V_N and the number of adsorbed molecules N [119]:

$$V_N = j \frac{\partial N}{\partial d_0}, \tag{5.36}$$

where j is the pressure gradient correction factor, and d_0 is the density of the adsorbate in the gaseous phase.

In the virial description of physical adsorption, the number of adsorbed molecules is given by the power of the activity z^n

$$N = \sum_{n=1}^{\infty} B_{nS} z^n , \tag{5.37}$$

where B_{nS} is the n-th gas–solid virial coefficient. When $d_0 \to 0$, $d_0 \to z$. This is the case when the concentrations of adsorbate are small. We can then write equation (5.37) in the form

$$V_N = j \frac{\partial}{\partial d_0} \sum_{n=1}^{\infty} B_{nS} d_0^n = j \sum_{n=1}^{\infty} n B_{nS} d_0^{(n-1)} . \tag{5.38}$$

If we fit the above equation to the measured retention value, we can find the value of B_{nS}. To this end, the relationship $V_N = f(d_0)$ for various concentrations of adsorbate is measured graphically (Fig. 5.17).

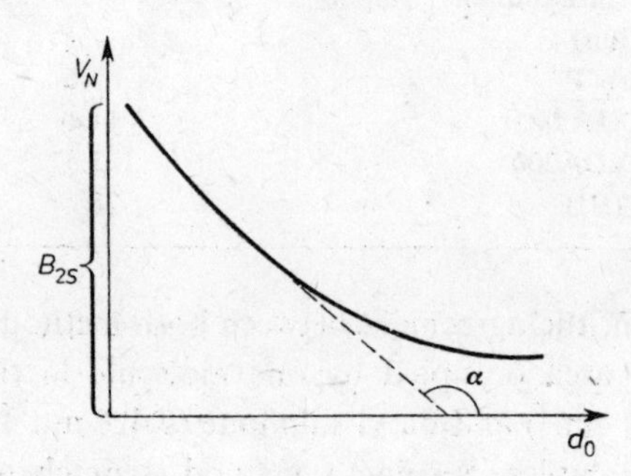

Fig. 5.17 The net retention volume V_N as a function of the adsorbate density in the gaseous phase d_0.

By extrapolating the experimental curve, we can estimate the section equal to B_{2S}, and $\tan\alpha = B_{3S}$.

The number of adsorbed molecules can be expressed by the equation

$$N = B_{2S} d_0 + B_{3S} d_0^3 + ... \tag{5.39}$$

The first derivative of equation (5.39) gives the value of V_N

$$V_N = B_{2S} = 2 d_0 B_{3S} . \tag{5.40}$$

If we know the values of B_{2S} and B_{3S}, we can determine the specific surface area from the following equation:

$$S = -\pi D^2 \frac{B_{2S}^2}{B_{3S}}, \tag{5.41}$$

where D is the diameter of the collision area of adsorbate with adsorbent; this is effectively the diameter of the adsorbate molecule.

As this method is far more tedious and time-consuming than the other methods described, it has not found much favour.

5.2.8 Catalyst Surface Area Measurements under Reaction Conditions

Investigations of the properties of catalysts are particularly valuable in conditions similar to those of a catalytic reaction. With the static method, it is difficult to estimate the adsorption of reagents at high temperatures since they are in contact with the catalyst for a long time, and a chemical reaction often takes place. The flow technique is best suited to this purpose as the period of contact between the adsorbate and the surface of the catalyst can be controlled. The specific surface area of catalysts under conditions similar to those obtaining during a catalytic reaction is usually estimated from the adsorption isotherm obtained chromatographically at a high temperature [98]. At high temperatures, diffusion effects are much reduced, and adsorption equilibrium is rapidly achieved, thus the fundamental conditions of equilibrium chromatography are satisfied. Tamaru [99–102] was one of the first to study adsorption and estimate the specific surface areas of catalysts during a heterogeneous reaction while simultaneously measuring its rate. The estimation is based on the elution-frontal method (see Section 1.2.3). Instead of carrier gas, the reaction mixture (or reacting component) is passed through the catalyst bed in the column at the temperature of the reaction. Having established the rate constant (plateau obtained), various samples of the reacting gas are introduced into the gas stream at the top of the column (see Section 2.3.4). The adsorption on the surface of the catalyst during a run and the rate of reaction can be determined by analysing the reaction product in the out-flowing gas. The necessary conditions for the successful use of this technique are the rapid, reversible adsorption of the test component and a sufficiently slow chemical reaction.

5.2.9 Survey of the Chromatographic Techniques for Determining the Specific Surface Areas of Solids

All the chromatographic techniques described above for determining the specific surface area yield plausible results under conditions approaching those of real adsorbent and catalyst operation. Using the static method, for example, the specific surface area of a solid is usually estimated by means of the low-temperature adsorption of nitrogen or the noble gases krypton, argon or xenon. The use of low temperatures in chromatographic techniques would lead to considerable diffusion effects. These substantially reduce the accuracy of such methods which require the conditions of equilibrium chromatography to be satisfied (retention volume method, use of adsorption isotherms). Estimation of the specific surface area of solids from the adsorption isotherm, obtained by both elution and frontal methods, is very quick. The frontal technique determines in a simple manner both the total surface area of the adsorbent or catalyst and that part of it which reversibly and irreversibly sorbs adsorbate molecules. This is very significant when determining, for example, the acidity of a surface. The principal limitation of both the elution and the frontal techniques is the need to preserve the conditions of equilibrium chromatography during the estimation, which in practice are difficult to maintain in their entirety. Errors are also possible in Schay's method which involves the determination of retention times and the pressure drop along the column. Hence the agreement between estimations of the specific surface area obtained by these methods and the static method is not so good (Table 5.3). Results which are in good agreement are obtained only for catalysts and adsorbents whose pore radius exceeds 4 nm. This method is particularly convenient for determining small specific surface areas [108]. The technique is, however, irreplaceable for determining specific surface areas at higher temperatures, under catalytic reaction conditions. It can also be applied to the study of the adsorption of substances capable of reacting, and when investigating highly labile compounds at high temperatures, because of the short, controlled period of contact with the adsorbent or catalyst.

The retention volume technique gives good results in conditions approaching those of ideal equilibrium chromatography, i.e. for adsorbents with a fairly homogeneous surface, at high temperatures and for small surface coverages — within the applicability of Henry's law. This method is quick and easy, but not very accurate — it can only give an approximate estimate of the surface area of a solid. It is especially useful

Table 5.3 THE ESTIMATION OF THE SPECIFIC SURFACE AREAS [m²/g] OF CATALYSTS USING DIFFERENT METHODS — A COMPARISON [9, 108]

Catalyst	Effective pore radius [nm]	*Static method*	*Heat desorption method*		*Frontal method*		*Estimation* *from retention volume*		*Estimation* *from chromatogram isotherm*	
		S_{ST}	S_{HD}	$\frac{S_{ST}-S_{HD}}{S_{,T}}100$	S_{FR}	$\frac{S_{ST}-S_{FR}}{S_{ST}}100$	S_R	$\frac{S_{ST}-S_R}{S_{ST}}100$	S_I	$\frac{S_{ST}-S_I}{S_{ST}}100$
Iron-molybdenum	100	7.5	7.5	0	7.1	+5	10.1	—35	6.6	+12
Silica	18	85	80	+6	96	—13	94	—11	53	+37
gel	5	294	315	—7	325	—10	284	+3.5	151	+50
Alumino-silicate	2	336	336	0	320	+5	—	—	138	+60
Adsorbent	—	2.5* 2.3**	3.4		—	—	—	—	—	—

* — volumetric method,
** — gravimetric method.

when assessing changes on the surface of a catalyst during a run, and also for rapidly determining the surface areas of adsorbents and catalysts of the same type. The retention volume method for large coverages appears to be promising, because of its greater accuracy and the possibility of using a universal standard which facilitates the estimation of the surface areas of solids with diverse chemical properties and geometrical structures. The method based on the change in peak shape with change in sample size is not widely applied in spite of its simplicity.

The greatest precision in estimating specific surface areas (the least differences with respect to the static method) is obtained with the heat desorption method. The specific surface areas of solids with various chemical properties and geometrical structures can be determined; besides this, the conditions of equilibrium chromatography need not be satisfied. This method gives us equilibrium values of adsorption, because the recorder pen returns to the base line only when adsorption equilibrium is also attained in fine pores. The method is very simple, highly sensitive and universal — it can be used to estimate specific surface areas from 0.01 to 1000 m^2/g. Using krypton as adsorbate, a total surface area of barely 6 cm^2 was measured in one sample [25]. In such a case the inner surface of the sample container must also be taken into consideration [108]. The size of the adsorbent sample in this method is not really important, whereas in other techniques, and in the static method, it is of primary significance. If liquid nitrogen is unavailable, organic compounds can be used as adsorbates. Argon is the recommended adsorbate in the heat desorption method. A number of companies manufacture standard sorptometers which use the heat desorption method [107, 109].

References

[1] Anderson R. B., Ed., *Experimental Methods in Catalytic Research*, Academic Press, New York and London, 1968.

[1a] Flood E. A., Ed., *The Solid–Gas Interface*, E. Arnold Publishers Ltd., London, Marcel Dekker Inc., New York, 1967.

[1b] *Surface Area Determination*, Butterworths, London, 1970.

[1c] Gregg S. J. and Sing K. S. W., *Adsorption Surface Area and Porosity*, Academic Press, London and New York, 1967.

[1d] Czanderna A. W., Ed., *Methods and Phenomena* **1**, *Methods of Scientific Analysis*, Elsevier Scientific Publishing Company, Amsterdam, Oxford, New York, 1975.

[2] Glueckauf E., *J. Chem. Soc.*, 1302, 1321 (1947).

[3] Schay G. and Szekely G., *Acta Chim. Acad. Hung.*, **5**, 1 (1954).

[4] Fejes P., From-Czaran E. and Schay G., *Gazovaya khromatografiya*, Izd. Gostontekhnizdat, Moskva, 1963.

[5] Fejes P., Fromm-Czaran E. and Schay G., *Acta Chim. Acad. Hung.*, **33**, 87 (1962).

[6] Schay G., *Theoretische Grundlagen der Gas Chromatographie*, VEB Dtsch. Verl. Wissenschaften, Berlin, 1960.

[7] Roginskii S. Z., Janovskii M. I., Lu Pejchan, Gaziev G. A., Neimark I. E., Zharbova G. N., Kagenatsi B. I., Brazhnikov V. V. and Piotrovska M. A., *Kinet. Katal.*, **1**, 287 (1960).

[8] Lyu-Chzhun-Khuei, Yanovskii M. I. and Gaziev G. A., *Gazovaya khromatografiya*, Trudy II Vses. Konf., Izd. Nauka, Moskva, 1964, p. 84.

[9] Buyanova N. E., Gudkova G. B. and Karnaukhov A. P., *Kinet. Katal.*, **8**, 428 (1967).

[10] Beebe R. A., Evans P. L., Kleinstuber T. C. and Richards L. W., *J. Phys. Chem.*, **70**, 1009 (1966).

[11] Gregg S. J., *The Surface Chemistry of Solids*, Chapman and Hall, London, 1961, p. 329.

[12] Gregg S. J. and Stock R., *Gazovaya khromatografiya*, Izd. Inostr. Lit., Moskva, 1961, p. 90.
[13] Zhukhovitskii A. A. and Turkeltaub N. M., *Gazovaya khromatografiya*, Izd. Gostontekhnizdat, Moskva, 1962.
[14] Grubner O., *Gazovaya khromatografiya*, Izd. Gostontekhnizdat, Moskva, 1963, p. 79.
[15] Kiselev A. V. and Yashin Y. I., *Gas Adsorption Chromatography*, Plenum, New York, London, 1969.
[16] Roginskii S. Z., Yanovskii M. I. and Berman A. D., *Osnovy primenenya khromatografii v katalize*, Izd. Nauka, Moskva, 1972.
[17] Vigdergauz M. S. and Izmaílov R. I., *Primenenie gazovoy khromatografii dlya opredelenya fizikokhimicheskich svoystv veshchestv*, Izd. Nauka, Moskva, 1970.
[18] Sakodynskii K. I., Ed., *Fizikokhimicheskie primenenie gazovoy khromatografii*, Izd. Khimya, Moskva, 1973.
[19] Kipping P. J. and Winter D. G., *Nature*, **205**, 1002 (1965).
[20] Roginskii S. Z., Yanovskii M. I. and Lu-Pey Chan, *Dokl. Akad. Nauk SSSR* **133**, 878 (1960).
[21] Nelson F. M. and Eggertsen F. T., *Anal. Chem.*, **30**, 1387 (1958).
[22] Nelson F. M., *Anal. Chem.*, **30**, 1387 (1958).
[23] Grubner O., *Z. phys. Chem.*, **216**, 287 (1961).
[24] Stock R., *Anal. Chem.*, **33**, 966 (1961).
[25] Wise K. V. and Lee E. H., *Anal. Chem.*, **34**, 301 (1962).
[26] Daeschner H. W. and Stross F. H., *Anal. Chem.*, **34**, 1150 (1962).
[27] Ettre L. S. Brenker W. and Ciepliński W. E., *Z. phys. Chem.*, **219**, 17 (1962).
[28] Atkins H., *Anal. Chem.*, **36**, 579 (1964).
[29] Grubner O., **3** *Internationale Analytische Konferenz in Prag*, Section *Gas Chromatographie*, 1959.
[30] Suprynowicz Z., Gorgol A. and Wójcik J., *J. Chromatogr.*, **148**, 151 (1978).
[31] Haley A. L., *J. Appl. Chem.* **13**, 392 (1963).
[32] Cremer E. and Huck H., *Glas-Techn. Ber.*, **37**, 511 (1964).
[33] Serpinet J., *J. Chromatogr.*, **119**, 483 (1976).
[34] Paryjczak T., Lewicki A. and Witekowa S., *Przemysł Chem.*, **49**, 819, 495 (1970).
[35] Paryjczak T., *Wiadomości Chem.*, **22**, 481 (1968).
[36] Scharf E., Berak J. M. and Kehl B., *Przemysł Chem.*, **48**, 407 (1969).
[37] Staszewski R. and Pompowski T., *Chem. Anal.*, **10**, 1123 (1965).
[38] Gavrilova T. B. and Kiselev A. V., *Zh. Fiz. Khim.*, **39**, 2582 (1965).
[39] Buyanova N. E., Gudkova G. B. and Karnaukhov A. P., *Metody Issled. Katal. Katal. Reakt.*, Sibir. Otd. Akad. Nauk SSSR, Novosibirsk, 1965, Vol. 2, p. 55.
[40] Buyanova N. E., Gudkova G. B. and Karnaukhov A. P., *Kinet. Katal.*, **6**, 1085 (1965).
[41] Bogomolov V. I., Minachev Kh. M. and Romanova N. V., *Molekulyarnaya khromatografiya*, Izd. Nauka, Moskva, 1964, p. 18.
[42] Derby J. V. and La Mont B. D., *Pittsburgh Conference on Anal. Chem. and Appl. Spectroscopy*, 1960.
[43] Ettre L. S., *J. Gas Chromatogr.*, **4**, 166 (1960).
[44] Anonymous, *Electronic Review*, **3**, 6 (1962).
[45] Ettre L. S., *Pittsburgh Conference on Anal. Chem. and Appl. Spectroscopy*, 1960.

[46] Ettre L. S., Carotti A. A., *Chim. Ind.*, **8**, 864 (1960),
[47] Cahen R. M. and Marechal J. E. M., *J. Anal. Chem.*, **35**, 259 (1963).
[48] Saint-Yrieix A., *Bull. soc. chim. France*, 3407 (1965).
[49] Karnaukhov A. P. and Buyanova N. E., *International Union of Pure and Applied Chemistry Surface Area Determination*, Butterworths, London, 1969, p. 165.
[50] Kourilova D. and Krejci M., *J. Chromatogr.*, **65**, 71 (1972).
[51] Krejci M. and Kourilova D., *Chromatographie*, **4**, 48 (1971).
[52] Datar A. G. and Romanathan P. S., *J. Chromatogr.*, **114**, 29 (1975).
[53] Kourilova D. and Krejci M., *Chem. Listy*, **65**, 742 (1971).
[54] Kuge Y. and Yoshikawa Y., *Bull. Chem. Soc. Japan*, **38**, 948 (1965).
[55] Cremer E., *Z. anal. Chem.*, **70**, 219 (1959).
[56] Cremer E., *Angew. Chem.*, **71**, 512 (1959).
[57] Wolf F. and Beyer H., *Chem. Techn.*, **11**, 142 (1959).
[58] Kiselev A. V., Petrova R. S. and Shcherbakova K. D., *Kinet. Katal.*, **5**, 526 (1964).
[59] Kiselev A. V., Nikitin Y. S., Petrova R. S., Shcherbakova K. D. and Yashin Y. I., *Anal. Chem.*, **36**, 152b (1964).
[60] Buyanova N. E., Karnaukhov A. P. and Rybak V. T., *Kinet. Katal.*, **12**, 670 (1971).
[61] Gaziev G. A., Yanovskii M. I. and Brazhnikov V. V., *Kinet. Katal.*, **1**, 548 (1960).
[62] Brunauer S., Emmett P. H. and Teller E., *J. Am. Chem. Soc.*, **69**, 309 (1938).
[63] Ellis J. F., Forrest C. W. and Howe D. D., *Anal. Chim. Acta*, **22**, 27 (1960).
[64] Choudhary V. R. and Daraiswamy L. K., *Ind. Eng. Chem. Prod. Res. Develop.*, **10**, 218 (1971).
[65] Walner W. L. and Zettlemoyer A. E., *J. Phys. Chem.*, **57**, 182 (1953).
[66] Kaganer M. Ch., *Dokl. Akad. Nauk SSSR*, **138**, 405 (1961).
[67] Kiselev A. V. and Poschkus D. P., *Kolloid. Zh.*, **21**, 590 (1959).
[68] Aristov B. G. and Kiselev A. V., *Zh. Fiz. Khim.*, **37**, 2520 (1963), **38**, 18 (1964).
[69] Izokes R. J. and Emmett P. H., *J. Am. Chem. Soc.*, **80**, 2082 (1958).
[70] Elrich G., Hichmott T. and Hudda E. G., *J. Phys. Chem.*, **28**, 506 (1958).
[71] Maciver D. C and Tobin H. H., *J. Phys. Chem.*, **64**, 451 (1960).
[72] Kiselev A. V., Krasilnikov K. G. and Soboleva L. N., *Dokl. Akad. Nauk. SSSR*, **94**, 85 (1954).
[73] Belyakova L. D. and Kiselev A. V., *Dokl. Akad. Nauk SSSR*, **119**, 298 (1958).
[74] Kiselev A. V., *Usp. Khim.*, **25**, 705 (1956).
[75] Zhdanov S. P. and Kiselev A. V., *Zh. Fiz. Khim.*, **31**, 2213 (1957).
[76] Avgul N. N., Berezin G. I., Kiselev A. V. and Lygina I. A., *Izd. Akad. Nauk SSSR, ser. Khim.*, 787 (1956), 1034 (1957), 1021 (1959).
[77] Karnaukhov A. P., *Kinet. Katal.*, **3**, 583 (1962).
[78] Haul R. A., *Angew. Chem.*, **68**, 238 (1956).
[79] Saines G. L. and Cannon P., *J. Phys. Chem.*, **64**, 997 (1960).
[80] Malden J. P. and Match J. O. F., *J. Phys. Chem.*, **63**, 1309 (1959).
[81] Thomas J. M., *Nature*, **189**, 134 (1961).
[82] Ross S. and Winkler W., *J. Colloid Sci.*, **10**, 330 (1955).
[83] Smolkova E., Feltl L. and Grubner O., *Gazovaya khromatografiya*, Trudy III Vses. Konf., Moskva, 1966, p. 151.

[84] Waksmundzki A., Suprynowicz Z. and Rayss J., *Chemia analit.*, **15**, 325 (1970).
[85] Pospisil M., Dolezal J. and Cobicar J., *Coll. Czechosl. Chem. Comm.*, **32**, 3757 (1967).
[86] Paryjczak T. and Gebauer A., *Prace Instytutu Przemysłu Skórzanego*, **19**, 131 (1975).
[87] Temkin M. I., *Zh. Fiz. Khim.*, **29**, 1610 (1955).
[88] Buyanova N. E., Karnaukhov A. P. and Anabuzhev I. A., *Opredelenie udelnoy poverkhnosti dispersnykh i poristykh materialov*, Sibir. Otd. Akad. Nauk SSSR, Novosibirsk, 1978.
[89] Krige G. I. and Pretorius V., *Anal. Chem.*, **37**, 1186, 1191 (1965).
[90] Cremer E. and Roselius L., *Angew. Chem.*, **70**, 42 (1958).
[91] Adamson A. W., *Physical Chemistry of Surfaces*, 3rd ed., Wiley, New York, 1976.
[92] Kiselev A. V., Paskonova E. A., Petrova R. S. and Shcherbakova K. D., *Zh. Fiz. Khim.*, **38**, 161 (1964).
[93] Belyakova L. D., Kiselev A. V. and Kovaleva N. V., *Zh. Fiz. Khim.*, **40**, 1494 (1966).
[94] Belyakova L. D., Kiselev A. V. and Kovaleva N. V., *Dokl. Akad. Nauk SSSR*, **157**, 646 (1964).
[95] Buyanova N. E., Karnaukhov A. P., and Chernyavskaya O. N., *Gazov. Khromatogr.*, **9**, 113 (1969).
[96] Brunauer S., *Sorption of Gases and Vapours*, Princeton University Press, Princeton, N. J., 1945.
[97] Emmett P. H. and Brunauer S., *J. Am. Chem. Soc.*, **59**, 1553 (1937).
[98] Eberly P. E., *J. Phys. Chem.*, **65**, 1261 (1961).
[99] Tamaru K., *Bull. Chem. Soc. Japan*, **31**, 666 (1958).
[100] Tamaru K., Catalysts Meeting, Tokyo, April 1957.
[101] Tamaru K., *Nature*, **183**, 319 (1959).
[102] Tamaru K., *Advan. Catalysis*, **14**, 65 (1964).
[103] Krejci M. and Kourilova D., *Chromatographia*, **4** (2), 48 (1971).
[104] Kourilova D. and Krejci M., *J. Chromatogr.*, **65**, 71 (1972).
[105] Ghosh Samir K., Sarkow H. S. and Saha N. C., *J. Chromatogr.*, **74** (2), 171 (1972).
[106] Mursyan I. L., Pishilina S. L., Rafalkes I. S., Snegireva T. D. and Borodina L. N., *Zavod. Lab.*, **1**, 41 (1971).
[107] Kulakov M. V., Schkatov E. F. and Khanerg V. A., *Gazovye khromatografy*, Izd. Energya, Moskva, 1968.
[108] Nieto M. I., Diez-Masa J. C., Oteo J. L. and Dabrio M. V., *Chromatographia*, **12**, 111 (1979).
[109] Ettre L. S., 1966 *Sorptometer Applications*, Anal. Div. Perkin Elmer Corp. SO-AP-002.
[110] Angely L., Guiochon G., Levart E. and Peslerbe G., *Analysis*, **1**, 103 (1972).
[111] Serpinet J., Untz G., Gachet C., de Morugues L. and Perrin M., *J. Chim. Phys.*, **71**, 949 (1974).
[112] Serpinet J., *J. Chromatogr.*, **68**, 9 (1972).
[113] Serpinet J., *Chromatographia*, **8**, 18 (1975).

[114] Serpinet J., *J. Chromatogr. Sci.*, **12**, 832 (1974).
[115] Serpinet J., *J. Chromatogr.*, **77**, 289 (1973).
[116] Serpinet J., *Anal. Chem.*, **48**, 2264 (1976).
[117] Untz G. and Serpinet J., *Bull. Soc. Chim. France*, 1591 (1973).
[118] Serpinet J. and Robin J., *C. R. Acad. Sci.*, **272**, 1765 (1971).
[119] Conder J. R. and Purnell J. H., *Trans. Faraday Soc.*, **64**, 3100 (1968).
[120] Waksmundzki A., *Physicochemical Applications of Gas Chromatography*, Ossolineum, PAN, 1974, p. 99 (in Polish).

Chapter 6

Determination of the Dispersion and Selective Surface Area of Metals and Metal Oxides in Compound Catalysts

6.1 Principles

Compound catalysts, especially mono- and bi-metals deposited on oxide supports are nowadays often used in technological processes. It is important to know the degree of dispersion of these metals and their selective surface area, as regards both the efficient use of the precious metals from Group VIII of the periodic table, and the elucidation of a number of theoretical problems involving the properties of these metals, the high degree of dispersion and, in particular, their catalytic activity.

Metal dispersion in compound catalysts is mostly estimated using chemisorption (static and dynamic), gas titration (oxygen–hydrogen and vice versa), electron microscopic methods, magnetic susceptibility and low-angle *X*-ray diffraction [1].

The static chemisorptive methods, and with the recent development of GC also the dynamic ones, have become widely applied; only these will be discussed in detail.

Chemisorptive techniques are the most universal since they facilitate the estimation of metal dispersion over the whole range of crystallite magnitudes. The GC methods used to estimate the dispersion of the active phase in compound catalysts include pulse techniques [2–23], frontal chromatography [24–28] and heat desorption [29–32].

The following factors may fundamentally affect chemisorption:

(1) contaminants on the surface and in the adsorbate or carrier gas;

(2) slow adsorption, especially under static conditions;

(3) the crystallographic heterogeneity of the surface;

(4) absorption or solution of the adsorbate;

(5) the presence of a support;

(6) metal-support interaction;

(7) the effects of small metal molecules;

(8) the spillover effect of hydrogen or oxygen from the metal on the support.

The influence of these factors depends on the research method used, the type of system and the conditions of measurement.

From the methodological point of view, the use of chemisorption to estimate the selective surface area of compound catalysts must take into account [33]:

(a) the choice of optimum chemisorption conditions;

(b) the selection of a suitable adsorbate;

(c) the choice of method for calculating the surface area and the degree of dispersion of the metal.

Every compound catalyst requires special conditions for chemisorption, e.g. the range of temperature and pressure must be chosen in such a way that adsorption equilibrium can be attained, the given gas must be minimally sorbed on all the components except the one being estimated, and it must not be absorbed by the component. Physical adsorption should be eliminated during chemisorption.

Chemisorption should therefore be carried out at the highest possible temperature at the lowest possible pressure, using an adsorbate with a low boiling point.

The adsorbate and chemisorption temperatures are selected from the sorption isobars of all the components in the compound catalyst. Unfortunately, there is in the literature a lack of exhaustive sorption data for a wide range of temperatures and pressures even for the metals most frequently used in catalysis. This is why before commencing the measurements proper, the sorption isobars of a given adsorbate on the various components of the catalyst must be determined. The choice of a suitable temperature for the chemisorption of hydrogen on a Pt/SiO_2 catalyst is illustrated in Fig. 6.1 [40], from which it can be seen that for a Pt/SiO_2 catalyst, we get maximum sorption of hydrogen on platinum at around 313 K, while adsorption reaches a minimum on SiO_2 at 523 K. Chemisorption was carried out at 523 K, at which temperature the sorption of hydrogen on the support is minimal, but sufficiently great on platinum. This temperature also guarantees minimal solubility of hydrogen in the platinum (curve *3*, Fig. 6.1).

Figure 6.2 illustrates the effect of temperature and pressure on the sorption of hydrogen on palladium black [55]. It is evident from this figure that, in agreement with Aben [69], the chemisorption of hydrogen

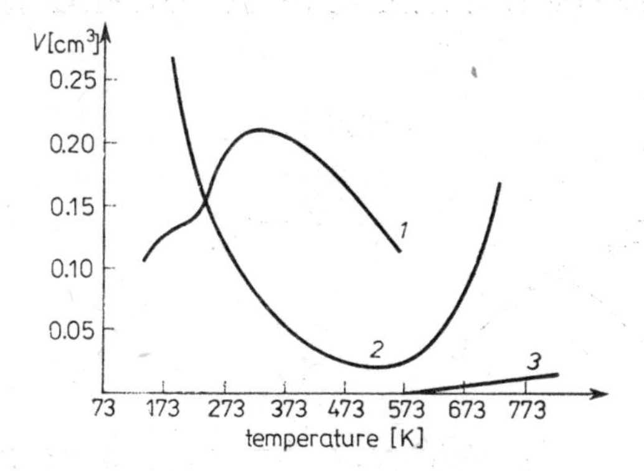

Fig. 6.1 Sorption isobars of hydrogen on Pt (curve *1*) and SiO_2 (curve *2*) with respect to temperature; curve *3* gives the solubility of hydrogen in Pt with respect to temperature (after G. K. Boreskov and A. P. Karnaukhov [40]).

should be carried out at a temperature above 343 K in order to avoid considerable absorption of hydrogen in the mass of the palladium. Alternatively, the process can be carried out at a lower temperature and the values extrapolated back to zero pressure.

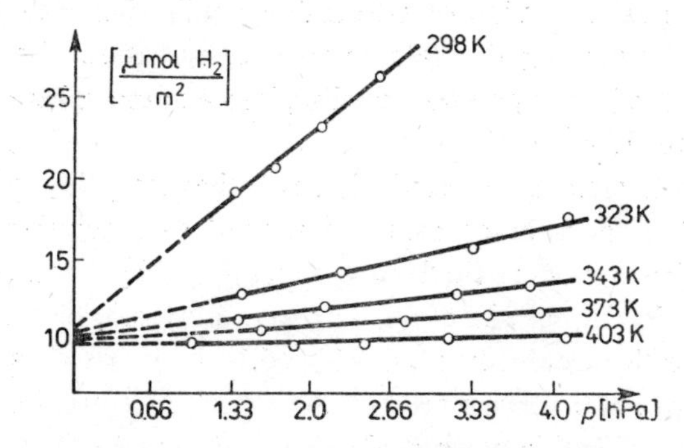

Fig. 6.2 Sorption isotherms of hydrogen on palladium black (after T. Paryjczak and S. Karski [55]).

The adsorption isobars of hydrogen on the deposited metals comprise, over a certain range of temperature, two curves: an upper equilibrium curve, and a lower one, in which equilibrium is not fully achieved (Fig. 6.3) [52]. The inflection point of the curve depends on the nature and dispersion of the metal, the nature of the support, and the state of their surfaces. Figure 6.3 shows the isobars of hydrogen on highly dispersed platinum deposited on SiO_2 and platinum black. For the deposited platinum, the isobar curves cut at 273 K, for the black, at 423 K. Equilibrium

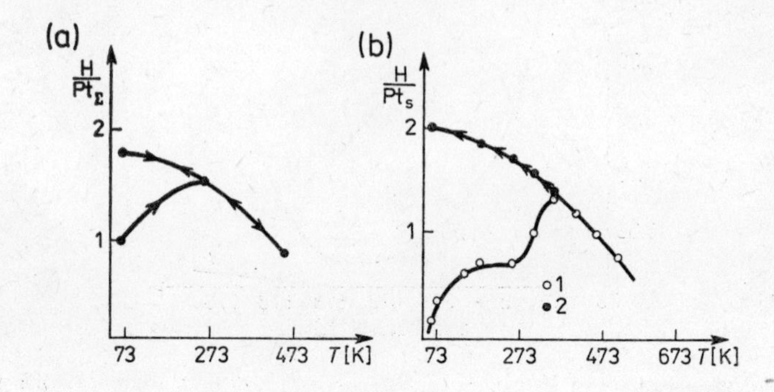

Fig. 6.3 Chemisorption isobars of hydrogen on: (a) Pt/SiO_2; (b) Pt-black (pressure 0.066–0.133 kPa) (after V. S. Boronin *et al.* [52]):

(1 — chemisorption of hydrogen during 10 h on clear platinum surface, 2 — chemisorption of hydrogen during 2 h after cooling in hydrogen).

values of adsorption can be obtained only at temperatures higher than these. The temperature range of adsorption equilibrium can be considerably extended by heating the sample to a temperature above the point of inflection on the isobar and then cooling it in an atmosphere of hydrogen (for Pt down to 77 K).

We obtain a similar isobar during the chemisorption of oxygen on Pt/SiO_2 [70]. The adsorbates most often used to determine the specific surface area of metals deposited on a support are hydrogen, oxygen and carbon monoxide. In certain cases, nitrogen, ethylene, acetylene (ethyne) and carbon dioxide can also be used (Table 6.1). Nitric oxide is also used for estimating the specific surface area of the oxides of chromium [130], iron [131], nickel [132] and copper [133] deposited on Al_2O_3. Furthermore, it has been used to determine the surface area of platinum [38]. All these gases have a low boiling point and have a high affinity for metals.

These gases are adsorbed on to the surfaces of metals over a wide range of temperature (from 78 K to 573 K) and pressure (from 1.33×10^{-5} to 1.33×10^{2} kPa).

The purity of the surface is of major importance in chemisorption.

The purer the surface of a metal, the lower the pressure required for the formation of a monolayer. This depends on the metal-support system, the metal content and its dispersion, and at 293 K is not always achieved, even at atmospheric pressure.

Table 6.1 THE CLASSIFICATION OF METALS AND SEMI-CONDUCTORS ACCORDING TO THE CHEMICAL REACTIVITY OF THEIR SURFACES WITH RESPECT TO VARIOUS GASES [39]

Li	Be											B	C
Na	Mg											Al	Si
								d					
K	Ca	(Sc)	Ti	(V)	Cr	Mn	Fe	Co	Ni	Cu	Zn	Ga	Ge
Rb	Sr	(Y)	Zr	Nb	Mo	(Tc)	(Ru)	Rh	Pd	Ag	Cd	In	Sn
Cs	Ba	La	(Hf)	Ta	W	Re	(Os)	Ir	Pt	Au	Hg	Tl	Pb
	c		a			b		e					

Metals	Reacting gases						
	O_2	C_2H_2	C_2H_4	CO	H_2	CO_2	N_2
Group a	3	3′	3	3	3	3	3
Group b	3	3	3	3	3*	3	2
Group c	3	3	3	3	2–3	3	2
Group d	3	3	3	3	3	3	1
Group e	3	3	3	3	3	1–0	1–0
Cu	3	3	3	1	0	?	0
Ag	2–3	1	1	0	0	?	0
Au	0	3	3	1	0	?	0
B	3–2	?	?	3–2	3–2	?	3–2
Al	3	2	2	3	0	?	0
Si, Ge	3	?	?	0	2	2–3	0
K	3	3	0	0	0	?	0
Other metals	3	0	0	0	0	?	0

* The adsorption of hydrogen on Mn is activated at 300 K.
3 — rapid and probably unactivated adsorption of gas, detectable at 300 K and a pressure of 1.33×10^{-5} kPa.
2 — slow and sometimes activated adsorption of gas detectable at 300 K and 1.33×10^{-5} kPa.
1 — detectable adsorption of gas at 195 K but undetectable at 300 K.
0 — undetectable adsorption of gas at 195 K and 300 K at 1.33×10^{-5} kPa.
? — no data available.

In the case of the Group VIII metals, used in the form of foil, powders, blacks, and deposited on supports, it is equilibrium chemisorption that mainly takes place at room temperature [71–74]. The correction for adsorption on the support at room temperature is not great (5–10%), even for small quantities of metal (under 1%), but it does increase with pressure.

It is not only the correction for adsorption by the carrier that increases with pressure, but also the solubility of the adsorbate, its diffusion into the crystal lattice, and the spillover effect. Quite often, high adsorbate pressures of 26.6–79.8 kPa have been used in the estimation of metal dispersion but, for the reasons just mentioned, it would be better to use a lower range of pressures, from 1.33×10^{-3} to 1.33 kPa [87].

Hydrogen is a frequently-used adsorbate in the estimation of Pt [14–17, 33, 40–47, 51–55], Ni [54, 56–63], Co [62, 65, 66] and Fe [67, 68] surface areas. The results of determinations of metal surface areas by means of hydrogen chemisorption probably give the most acceptable results because of the simple stoichiometry of the hydrogen–metal surface atom (H/Me_s) which is 1 : 1 for a wide range of metal dispersion [1, 14–18, 71, 75, 76–78]. It should be borne in mind, however, that when selecting the experimental conditions, a number of metals such as aluminium, chromium, molybdenum, tungsten, iron, cobalt, nickel, manganese, copper, silver and platinum absorb hydrogen to give real solutions or metallic hydrides [1, 39]. There are a number of metals forming hydrides of variable stoichiometry: they include titanium, zirconium, hafnium, thorium, vanadium, niobium, tantalum, cerium, lanthanum, the rare earth metals and palladium [64]. The solubility of hydrogen in these metals may be considerable, though decreasing with temperature-increase (Fig. 6.2). Other noble metals like rhodium, ruthenium, iridium and osmium sorb quantities of hydrogen which are comparable to its solubility in platinum [1].

The chemisorption of oxygen on metals is a complicated process, and depends to a large extent on the temperature, the oxygen pressure and the dispersion of the metal [14–17, 77–83]. Oxygen sorption at higher temperatures is much greater as multilayer adsorption is possible [42, 84]. At room temperature, it is mainly irreversible chemisorption that takes place, leading to the formation of a monolayer of atomic oxygen on the surface of most metals (molybdenum, tungsten, rhodium, palladium, platinum) [2, 3, 5, 11, 14–17, 27, 84].

The initial heats of oxygen adsorption are much greater than the corresponding heats of formation of oxides in the mass. Often, the rapid chemisorption of oxygen is accompanied by slow sorption, whose rate and extent is dependent on the temperature. Slow sorption does not normally take place at a temperature of 77 K, though it does occur to a slight extent at room temperature. Such metals as manganese, iron and titanium sorb oxygen in much larger quantities than are required for a monolayer. Partial oxidation of these metals in the mass takes place already at room temperature. Even at a temperature of 77 K, iron sorbs enough oxygen to form six monolayers [85]. On the other hand, chromium, cobalt, nickel, niobium and tantalum sorb sufficient oxygen for 2–3 monolayers, and oxide formation in the mass at room temperature does not take place.

Carbon monoxide sorbed on to the surface of metals can, in theory, form various structures [86]:

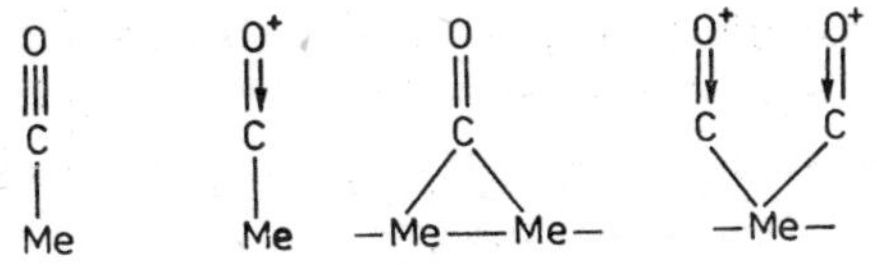

I *II* *III* *IV*

V *VI*

However, the linear (I) or bridge (III) structures, or both together are formed most often [87, 88].

Which structure is formed depends on the sorption conditions, metal dispersion and the nature of the support [42, 87, 88]. If we use carbon monoxide as adsorbate, we must carry out an accurate determination of the quantities of each structure present by means of additional infra-red tests.

6.2 Determination of the Dispersion and Specific Surface Area of a Supported Metal

The specific surface area of a supported metal can be calculated from chemisorption in two ways: either by comparing the chemisorption on a pure metal of known surface area (standard), or by estimating the chemisorptive monolayer. In the first method, it is assumed that the adsorptive properties of the pure metal and that deposited on the support are the same, so that the magnitude of chemisorption per unit area α is identical in both cases for a given set of experimental conditions. The specific surface area of a metal can be determined from the equation

$$S = \frac{a}{\alpha}, \tag{6.1}$$

where a is the chemisorption on 1 g of supported metal.

This method of calculating the surface area can be applied in accordance with our assumption that the supported metal occurs in the form of sufficiently large crystals [88]. Obviously, as a "one-point" method, it is open to the criticism that the results may not be reliable. However, if we ensure identical conditions of measurement (pressure, temperature, time, method of sample preparation), the chemisorptive method can be extended to "one-point" adsorption values. Assuming that the metal crystallites are cubic with one side in contact with the support, the average dimension $\bar{d}_k$ can be calculated from

$$\bar{d}_k = \frac{5}{Sd}, \tag{6.2}$$

where S is the specific surface area of the metal, and d is its density.

The sizes of the crystallites, obtained by chemisorptive methods, are in closer agreement with those obtained by the electron microscope method if we assume they are spherical [55, 89, 90].

If the metal on the carrier occurs in a highly dispersed form, the specific surface area has to be calculated on the basis of a chemisorptive monolayer from the following equation:

$$S = a_m \omega N_A, \tag{6.3}$$

where a_m is the amount of adsorbate in gram-atoms or gram-molecules required to cover 1 g of metal with a monolayer, ω is the mean surface area of 1 surface atom of metal, and N_A is the Avogadro number.

Equation (6.3) is reasonable if the following assumptions are satisfied:

(a) a chemisorptive monolayer is formed under experimental conditions;

(b) the mechanism of the chemisorption of the adsorbate on to the metal is known (known stoichiometry);

(c) the equal probability that all the crystallographic planes of the metal will occur on the surface, which means that an average value of ω can be determined.

The value of ω is difficult to define if the dispersion of the metal on the support is high (no crystalline form). The specific surface area can be estimated only formally. In this case, the dispersion of the metal is defined as the ratio of the number of atoms available for chemisorption, Me_s, to the total number of metal atoms Me ($Me_s/Me = d_\varepsilon$).

The expression for dispersion in absolute units (Me_s/Me) is the most common one, as it permits the dispersibility of various metals to be compared regardless of their atomic weight, density, crystalline structure and other parameters. From d_ε it is easy to calculate the number of active sites N_a per gram of metal if this is equal to the number of surface atoms

$$N_a = Me_s = Me d_\varepsilon = \frac{N_A}{A} d_\varepsilon, \tag{6.4}$$

where A is the atomic weight (relative atomic mass) of the metal.

The specific surface area of the metal and the average dimension of the crystallites $\bar{d}_k$ can be calculated from d_ε via the expressions

$$S = \frac{N_A}{A} \omega d_\varepsilon , \tag{6.5}$$

$$\bar{d}_k = \frac{5A}{N_A \omega d d_\varepsilon} . \tag{6.6}$$

The stoichiometry of the interactions between the adsorbate and the surface atoms of a metal over a wide range of dispersions, experimental temperatures and pressures still causes some difficulty today. It can be generally expressed as

$$\chi = \frac{n_a}{Me_s} = \frac{\beta a N_a}{n} = \beta a N_A \omega , \tag{6.7}$$

where n_a is the number of atoms or molecules chemisorbed on the surface of a metal, β is the number of atoms in one molecule of adsorbate, a is the adsorption in moles per gram of metal, and n is the number of atoms of metal per square metre of surface.

At the same time

$$d_\varepsilon = \frac{n_a}{Me \chi} , \tag{6.8}$$

$$\chi = \frac{n_a}{Me} \cdot \frac{1}{d_\varepsilon} . \tag{6.9}$$

As d_g cannot be greater than 1, i.e. $d_g \leqslant 1$, we have

$$\chi \geqslant \frac{n_a}{\mathrm{Me}}. \tag{6.10}$$

Only if all the atoms are available for chemisorption does

$$\chi = \frac{n_a}{\mathrm{Me}}. \tag{6.11}$$

As is evident from equation (6.8) for calculating dispersion, a monolayer does not have to be formed; any value of adsorption at any temperature and pressure can be used for this purpose. It is, however, essential to know the value of χ under given conditions; χ varies within the range

$$0 < \chi < \chi_m, \tag{6.12}$$

where χ_m is the stoichiometry in the monolayer.

The relationship between χ and temperature may be obtained from the isobars.

During the chemisorption of hydrogen on platinum it was assumed that total coverage was obtained at a temperature of 423 K ($\chi_m = 1$) [40, 42, 43], a over the range 273–298 K [27, 44, 78]. It is assumed that at 423 K one atom of hydrogen really is chemisorbed on to each surface atom of platinum, but that a monolayer is not yet obtained [42, 43, 52]. When the temperature is lowered to 298 K, χ increases to 1.7 and at 78 K, to 2.0 [52].

Tables 6.2 and 6.3 set out the stoichiometry of hydrogen and oxygen sorption on various metals under different conditions.

As a result of the small molecules' effect, many authors [79, 124, 127, 128] obtained a much higher adsorption per atom of metal for concentrations of metal on the support than should result from a monolayer: $n_a/\mathrm{Me} \geqslant 2$. The small molecules' effect is due, i.a. to the rapid increase of coordinately unsaturated metal atoms at edges, corners and apices which are capable of further adsorption. These changes in properties may also be linked with changes in electron levels in small metal molecules, which should be reflected in the chemisorptive properties. This applies to molecules, two-dimensional clusters and discrete atoms.

According to Anderson [1], anomalies in chemisorption should be observed with metal atoms smaller than 1 nm, though Karnaukhov puts

Table 6.2 THE STOICHIOMETRIC COEFFICIENTS OF THE CHEMISORPTION OF HYDROGEN ON VARIOUS METALS

Metal	*Form of sample*	T [K]	p [kPa]	χ	*References*
Pt	black	77–523	0.133	1.9–1.1	[52]
	black	77–473	0.133	2.0–1.1	[52]
	black	523	13.3	0.94	[42]
	black	523	6.65–31.9	0.58–0.76	[43]
	black	523	0.2–85	0.35–1.22	[40]
Pd	black	343	0.133	1.0	[69]
	black	298–398	0.06–3.32	2.5–1.0	[55]
Rh	black	298	—	1.13	[91]
	powder	293	0.26–26.6	0.82–1.0	[91]
	black	298–573	6.65–79.8	1.7–0.5	[91]
	film	77–298	1.33×10^{-3}	1.25–0.5	[74, 92]
Ni	film	77–298	1.33×10^{-3}	1.7–1.4	[72, 74]
	film	288	2.66×10^{-3}–3.6×10^{-2}	0.31–0.46	[93, 95]
	film	296	1.33×10^{-2}	1.0	[94]
Ir	black	296	0.133–17.9	1.46–2.24	[22]
	black	77–573	0.133–4.78	2.2–1.7	[22]
	black	473	1.33–39.9	0.52–1.0	[113]
Fe	film	77–298	1.33×10^{-3}	1.5–1.0	[72, 74]
Cu	powder	423–523	5.98–106.4	1.1–1.0	[96]
Ru	powder	373	—	0.90	[111]
	powder	294	6.65–26.6	0.97–1.0	[112]
	powder	195–773	26.6	0.86–0.51	[73]

this minimum size at 1.5 nm [127]. However, these authors neglected the effect of the support and its chemical nature.

For platinum deposited on carbon, H/Pt = 8–10 [124] and for iridium supported on Al_2O_3, H/Ir = 3 [88]. This can be explained by the migration of activated hydrogen from the metal on to the support: this is the so-called spillover effect. This effect increases together with the pressure of hydrogen and the experimental temperature. Sermon and Bond [79] report a number of cases of abnormally high chemisorption of hydrogen on metals deposited on supports as a result of the spillover effect.

Table 6.3 THE STOICHIOMETRIC COEFFICIENTS OF THE CHEMISORPTION OF OXYGEN ON VARIOUS METALS

Metal	*Form of sample*	T [K]	p [kPa]	χ	*References*
Pt	Pt/SiO_2 Pt/Al_2O_3 powder	298–523	pulse technique	1.0	[16]
	film	298	1.33×10^{-5}	0.65	[97]
	powder	298	1.33	0.7	[98]
Pd	Pd/SiO_2	298–423	pulse technique	1–1.3	[16]
	film	298	1.33×10^{-3}	0.50	[104]
	frame	373	6.65×10^{-3}	0.65	[105]
	black	298	66.5	0.91	[106]
	black	293	6.65	0.84	[107]
	black	298	1.33	0.5	[98]
	powder	298	1.2	0.76	[108]
Rh	film	77	1.33×10^{-3}	0.85	[99]
	film	298	1.33×10^{-5}	0.84	[97]
	black	298	1.33	0.90	[98]
	black	195–473	—	1.1	[100]
	black	298–573	6.65–85.1	1.32–1.47	[100]
	Rh/Al_2O_3	195–373	pulse technique	1–1.1	[14]
Ni	film	77	1.33×10^{-3}	2.2	[99]
	film	298	1.33×10^{-5}	1.65–1.95	[97]
	powder	195–295	1.33–13.3	1.95–2.08	[101]
	powder	195	0.13–66.5	2.1	[83]
	powder	298	1.33	1.6	[98]
	powder	293–673	1.33	1.0	[102]
Ir	black	298	1.33	1.5	[88]
Fe	film	77	1.33×10^{-3}	3.2	[74]
	film	298	1.33×10^{-5}	3.39	[97]
	powder	293	1.33×10^{-4}–0.01	3.4	[103]
	powder	298	1.33	3.6	[98]
Co	film	298	1.33×10^{-5}	1.45	[97]
Ru	powder	293	2.66–26.6	1.5	[116]
	powder	296	—	0.80	[111]
	powder	293–623	6.65–85.1	1.32–1.47	[100]
	powder	298	1.33	0.90	[98]
Ag	powder	473	0.01–0.66	0.3–1.0	[109]
	powder	195–673	1.33	0.6–1.1	[110]
	powder	383	0.02–0.05	0.58–0.94	[114]
	powder	323–473	0.03–16	0.1–1.3	[115]

6.3 The Pulse Technique

Pulse GC has found widespread application in the estimation of the specific surface areas of metals deposited on supports. In this method, precisely-measured small portions of adsorbate are injected into the carrier gas (helium, argon, nitrogen). The first samples of adsorbate are sorbed irreversibly until the surface of the metal is completely covered with a monolayer. When the metal surface has become saturated with adsorbate, and further samples injected, peaks of the same height (area) appear on the chromatogram (Fig. 6.4). The quantity of adsorbate

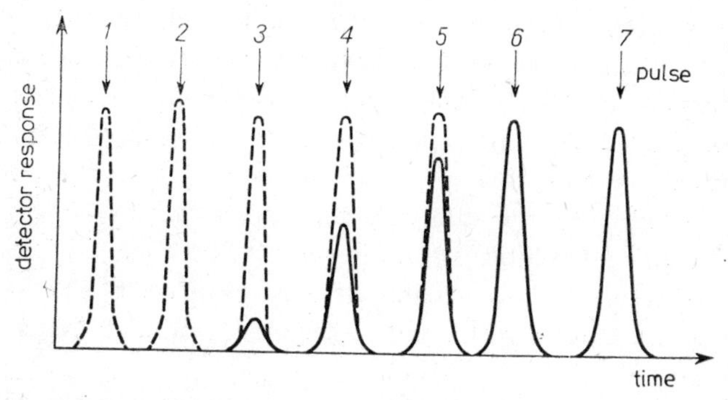

Fig. 6.4 A typical chromatogram showing the first seven consecutive pulses of hydrogen, oxygen or carbon monoxide on a pure metal surface.

uptaken by the catalyst is given by the sum of all the adsorbed samples. If the area of the first peak to appear on the chromatogram is less than that of the next ones, it should be included in the summed quantity of sorbed adsorbate.

Hydrogen, oxygen and carbon monoxide are used as adsorbates in pulse GC.

Using hydrogen, the specific surface areas of platinum, nickel, iridium and palladium have been established [2, 5, 48, 117]. The dispersion of platinum has also been determined from the changes in retention time of hydrogen on a Pt/Al_2O_3 catalyst. A freshly-prepared catalyst demonstrated a much greater dispersion than one roasted at 1023 K, the retention time falling from 190 to 130 s. This enabled the rate of recrystallization of platinum on the support to be calculated.

The use of hydrogen as adsorbate requires further methodological investigations, as it does cause problems. These arise from having to determine the reversible and irreversible sorption of hydrogen on the surface of metals. We assume, however, that only irreversible sorption takes place under chromatographic conditions. Slow sorption processes do not occur in pulse GC either. On the other hand, in order to get a monolayer on the metal surface, we usually need higher partial pressures of hydrogen than those obtained in pulse GC, which means that adsorptions have to be extrapolated to higher pressures [2, 5, 7].

In the opinion of Buyanova, Karnaukhov and others [3, 11–13, 118], oxygen is the most suitable adsorbate for determining the surface areas of Group VIII metals by means of the pulse technique. The extent of the fast chemisorption of oxygen corresponds to a given stoichiometry characteristic of each metal over a wide range irrespective of its dispersion. In order to avoid overheating the catalyst, the oxygen should be injected in small portions of 0.05–0.1 cm^3. As the adsorbate is in contact with the catalyst for only a short time, a distinction can be made between irreversible, reversible and slow sorption. The reversibly-sorbed part of the oxygen is eluted from the catalyst's surface by the carrier gas stream. The slow sorption, which takes place in such a short time, may be ignored. Only the oxygen bound irreversibly at a temperature of 298 K remains as a layer on the surface of the metal. Figure 6.5 shows a diagram of the apparatus used.

The catalyst (particle size 0.25–0.5 mm) is placed in U-tube *14* and is reduced in a stream of deoxygenated and dehumidified hydrogen (0.0015–0.003 m^3/h). The reduction temperature depends on the type of metal deposited: it is 573–623 K for nickel and palladium, 673 K for iron, ruthenium and rhodium, and 773 K for platinum. The flow of hydrogen is interrupted after 2–3 hours and carrier gas (helium or argon) is passed through at a rate of 0.001–0.002 m^3/h. While the carrier gas is flowing, the catalyst is cooled to room temperature. Having established a stable base line on the recorder, that is, total removal of hydrogen, samples of oxygen are introduced through the four-way valve *13*. The amount of sorbed oxygen is calculated from the sum of samples uptaken by the catalyst (Fig. 6.4). The magnitude of the metal surface area is calculated by the comparative method using equation (6.1) and dispersion from equation (6.2). If the determinations are to be successful, the carrier gas and the hydrogen must be thoroughly purged of even trace amounts of oxygen: this can be done by using a MnO/support catalyst (see Chapter 1). Table 6.3 gives the adsorption of oxygen on samples of metals at 298 K.

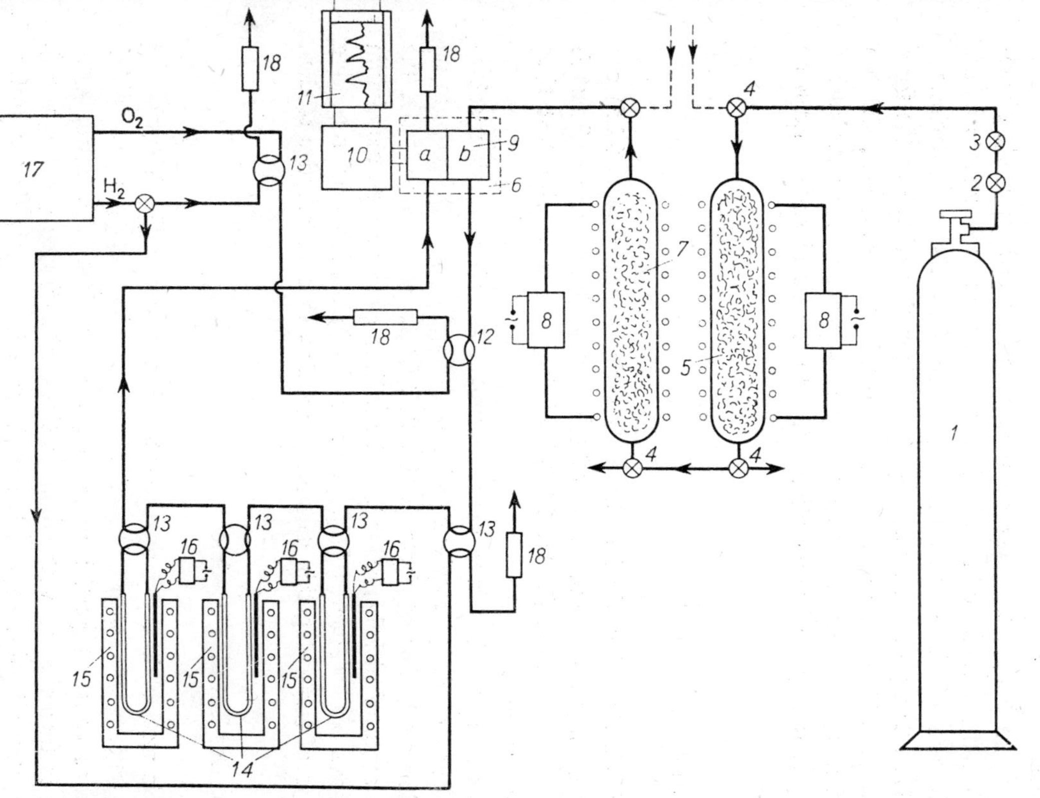

Fig. 6.5 Apparatus used in the estimation of the surface area of metals deposited on supports (after T. Paryjczak and W. K. Jóźwiak [66]):

1 — carrier gas cylinder (helium, argon), *2* — reducing valve, *3* — fine control valve, *4* — three-way valves, *5* — deoxygenating columns ($Cu/\gamma\text{-}Al_2O_3$ and MnO/support catalysts), *6* — thermostat, *7* — drying column 5 A molecular sieve), *8* — autotransformers, *9* — katharometer (*a* — measurement cell, *b* — comparative cell), *10* — katharometer power supply, *11* — recorder, *12* — feeder valve, *13* — four-way valves, *14* — reactors with test samples of catalysts, *15* — furnaces with controlled temperature, *16* — temperature controllers with thermocouples, *17* — electronic system with system for purifying oxygen and hydrogen, *18* — flow-meters.

Although in Table 6.3 the formal stoichiometric coefficients of oxygen chemisorption on Me_s are given, they can be used in calculations of the surface area and dispersion of metals on supports if the metals occur as crystallites.

At room temperature, carbon monoxide is also irreversibly chemisorbed on the surfaces of metals. It has been used as adsorbate in the determination of the surface area of a metal by the pulse technique [5–10, 117]. The previously mentioned chemisorption of CO in the form of linear or bridge structures does present difficulties. However, CO can be used in the comparative method. When calculating the chemisorbed monolayer, the type of bond joining CO to the metal surface must be known.

6.4 The Frontal Method

Schay's frontal method in both its variants (see Section 4.3.5) can also be applied to the estimation of the specific surface areas of metals deposited on supports [2, 11, 24–26], although to a lesser extent than the pulse method.

This technique has been used to estimate the chemisorption isobars of hydrogen on nickel catalysts [24], and the surface area of platinum on reforming and other catalysts [2, 11, 25]. Using radioactive ^{14}CO, the surface areas of nickel, platinum and rhodium supported on aluminium oxide have been estimated [26]. The remarks in Section 4.3.5 regarding the ways of improving this method apply also to chemisorptive studies.

6.5 The Gas-Titration Method

This method is based on the saturation of the catalyst's surface at room temperature with oxygen from a stream of gas containing oxygen at constant partial pressure (or pulse-wise). The chemisorbed oxygen is then titrated with small portions of hydrogen (or vice versa). As was stated before, oxygen is chemisorbed irreversibly on the surface of Group VIII metals at room temperature, in most cases forming a monolayer. This method was put forward by Weindenbach and Fürst [27] and has become widely applied in the estimation of the surface of platinum deposited on supports, both by the static method [28, 75, 77, 107, 119] and chromatography [4, 18, 66, 84, 120–122]; it has also been used in the estimation of the surface area of rhodium [100], palladium [16, 66, 69, 91] and iridium [17, 123].

In general, the titration reaction in an oxygen-hydrogen system can be described by the following equations:

$$Me_sO_x+(x+y/2)H_2 \rightarrow Me_sH_y+xH_2O\,, \tag{6.13}$$

$$Me_sH_y+(x/2+y/4)O_2 \rightarrow Me_sO_x+y/2H_2O, \tag{6.14}$$

where Me_s denotes the surface atom of the metal, and x, y are coefficients defining the stoichiometry of the surface interactions of the metal with oxygen and hydrogen respectively.

Titration reactions are usually carried out at temperatures approaching room temperature. The water forming as a result of the reaction is adsorbed on hydrophilic supports [91] (SiO_2, Al_2O_3, zeolites) or is weakly adsorbed on the metal if the reaction is carried out on unsupported metals.

As can be seen from the above reactions, the ratio of the amount of hydrogen consumed in reaction (6.13) to the amount of oxygen consumed in reaction (6.14) is equal to 2 and does not depend on the stoichiometry of the interactions between the oxygen x or the hydrogen y and the metal surface. The value of 2 for this ratio may serve as a check to see if the interactions of the oxygen and hydrogen with the metal are simple and rapid chemisorptive processes. If the experimental values deviate from 2, this may mean that subsidiary processes are occurring (weak adsorption, absorption, formation of compounds in the mass, spillover effects, and others). A certain influence may also be exerted by the contamination of the metal sample or adsorbate.

If we take $x = 0$ in reaction (6.13) and $y = 0$ in reaction (6.14), we get an equation describing the chemisorption of hydrogen and oxygen on pure metal surfaces

$$Me_s+y/2\,H_2 \rightarrow Me_sH_y\,, \tag{6.15}$$

$$Me_s+x/2\,O_2 \rightarrow Me_sO_x\,. \tag{6.16}$$

Titration reactions offer a number of advantages:

(1) Greater sensitivity; smaller weighed samples or a lower metal content in the catalyst can be used.

(2) The surface area can be measured without having to purify it specially; this eliminates sintering of the metal which sometimes takes place during purification (this applies in particular to strongly dispersed

blacks and catalysts). The possibility of sintering as a result of exothermic titration reactions has to be borne in mind.

(3) Rapidity and reproducibility. Titration reactions are fairly simple to carry out in a dynamic system; series of measurements are possible.

The stoichiometries of oxygen and hydrogen interactions with metals are the same for adsorption processes and titration reactions [100, 106]. During the reaction, attention should be paid to the water formed, the presence of which may affect the titration results in the case of metal blacks and pure, unsupported metals [15, 28]. Exothermic reactions may also affect the state of the surface.

When estimating the dispersion of platinum on supports using the oxygen–hydrogen titration method, we assume the following set of reactions:

$$Pt_s + \tfrac{1}{2}O_2 = Pt_sO_{ads}\,, \qquad (6.17)$$

$$Pt_sO_{ads} + nH_2 = Pt_s(n-1)H_{2ads} + H_2O\,. \qquad (6.18)$$

The stoichiometric coefficient n changes from 1 to 2 depending on the temperature of titration [18, 27, 75, 77, 84, 120, 121]. At room temperature, n takes on the value 3/2, in accordance with the reactions [18, 77, 84, 121)

$$Pt_s + \tfrac{1}{2}H_2 \xrightarrow{298\,K} Pt_sH_{ads}\,, \qquad (6.19)$$

$$Pt_s + \tfrac{1}{2}O_2 \xrightarrow{298\,K} Pt_sO_{ads}\,, \qquad (6.20)$$

$$Pt_sO_{ads} + 3/2H_2 \xrightarrow{298\,K} Pt_sH_{ads} + H_2O\,. \qquad (6.21)$$

The water formed in the reaction is usually bound by the support (Al_2O_3, SiO_2). The oxygen–hydrogen titration method should be three times as sensitive as the method based merely on the chemisorption of hydrogen [77]. The stoichiometry of the reverse titration of sorbed hydrogen by oxygen at room temperature gives the equation

$$Pt_sH_{ads} + \tfrac{3}{4}O_2 \xrightarrow{298\,K} Pt_sO_{ads} + \tfrac{1}{2}H_2O\,. \qquad (6.22)$$

Between 623 K and 773 K hydrogen is not chemisorbed on the surface of platinum

$$Pt_sH_{ads} \xrightarrow{>623\,K} Pt_s + \tfrac{1}{2}H_2\,, \qquad (6.23)$$

where Pt_s denotes a surface atom of platinum.

The method has been used to estimate the surface areas of other metals such as palladium [66].

The technique used in estimating the surface area of palladium on Pd/Al_2O_3 catalysts will be discussed in somewhat greater detail. Measurements were carried out in the apparatus depicted in Fig. 6.5. Oxygen or hydrogen was introduced through the four-way tap *12*. The volume of samples fed in was 0.139 or 0.0689 cm^3.

Samples of catalyst containing 4.2% Pd, of mass 1.5–3 g, were placed in the glass U-tube *14* (Fig. 6.5) which was 20 cm high with an internal diameter of 3 mm. Having placed the catalyst in the U-tube in order to remove moisture, carrier gas (helium or argon) was passed through at a rate of 40 cm^3/min at 573 K. The catalyst was reduced with hydrogen for 2 hours at 443 K. The flow rate of hydrogen was about 20 cm^3/min. Reduction being complete, carrier gas at 573 K was passed for 2 hours to remove the hydrogen. The sample was cooled in a stream of carrier gas to room temperature. The surface of the catalyst prepared in this way was treated as a "pure" surface. This catalyst was used in the measurement of the chemisorption of oxygen or hydrogen, and also in gas titration.

The chemisorption of oxygen and hydrogen, and the oxygen–hydrogen and hydrogen–oxygen titrations on a palladium surface can be described by the following reactions:

$$Pd_s + \tfrac{1}{2}O_2 \rightarrow Pd_sO; \qquad O/Pd_s = 1\,, \tag{6.24}$$

$$Pd_s + \tfrac{1}{2}H_2 \rightarrow Pd_sH; \qquad H/Pd_s = 1\,, \tag{6.25}$$

$$Pd_sO + \tfrac{3}{2}H_2 \rightarrow Pd_sH + H_2O; \qquad H/O = 3\,, \tag{6.26}$$

$$Pd_sH + \tfrac{3}{4}O_2 \rightarrow Pd_sO + \tfrac{1}{2}H_2O; \qquad O/H = 3/2\,, \tag{6.27}$$

where Pd_s denotes a surface atom of palladium.

The results are presented in Table 6.4. These results (columns *3* and *5*) cannot be interpreted quantitatively because at this experimental temperature hydrogen is absorbed in the mass of the palladium during a process which is difficult to control.

Experiment shows that the hydrogen absorbed in the mass of the palladium can be removed by passing carrier gas at 393 K for 2 hours. At this temperature absorption of hydrogen in the mass of palladium is eliminated without affecting its chemisorption on the surface (extrapolation to zero pressure) [55]. Thus only the hydrogen chemisorbed on the surface remains, and this can be titrated against oxygen (reaction (6.27)). The results of this study are given in column *6*. If the quantity of oxygen chemisorbed on the pure surface (column *2*) is then sub-

Table 6.4 THE CHEMISORPTION OF OXYGEN AND HYDROGEN AND THE RESULTS OF GAS

Pd *content* [%]	$V_{O_2}^{p}$ [cm³/g cat.]	$V_{O_2}^{red}$ [cm³/g cat.]	$V_{H_2}^{p(298\,K)}$ [cm³/g cat.]	$V_{H_2}^{ox}$ [cm³/g cat.]
1	*2*	*3*	*4*	*5*
0.86	0.112	0.362	0.466	0.730
1.05	0.181	0.450	0.483	0.875
1.37	0.200	0.520	0.600	1.029
1.82	0.232	0.995	1.540	2.030
4.21	0.397	1.040	1.390	2.270

$V_{O_2}^{p}$ — volume of oxygen sorbed by the "pure" surface of the catalyst at 298 K (reaction (6.24)).

$V_{O_2}^{red}$ — volume of oxygen consumed in the reaction with the reduced surface of the catalyst at 298 K (reaction (6.27)).

$V_{H_2}^{p}$ — volume of hydrogen sorbed by the "pure" surface of the catalyst at 298 K (reaction (6.25)).

$V_{H_2}^{ox}$ — volume of hydrogen consumed on the oxidized surface of the catalyst at 298 K (reaction (6.26)).

$V_{O_2}^{red(393K)}$ — volume of oxygen consumed in the reaction with the reduced surface of the catalyst at 298 K (reaction (6.27)); in this reaction, the hydrogen which was not desorbed during the 2-hour passage of carrier gas at 393 K, was titrated.

$V_{H_2}^{p(393K)}$ — volume of hydrogen chemisorbed at 393 K on the surface of the catalyst.

tracted from the results of the oxygen titration (column *6*), we get the quantity of oxygen consumed to titrate the hydrogen. The amount of hydrogen reversibly sorbed at 298 K under dynamic conditions (column *8*) can be calculated from the difference between the values shown in columns *4* and *7* (Table 6.4).

The H/O ratio in reaction (6.26) and the O/H ratio in reaction (6.27) were established from the data set out in Table 6.4. These values are to be found in columns *9* and *10*. In principle, they agree well with theoretical data.

Table 6.5 presents values for the dispersion and specific surface area of palladium on Pd/Al_2O_3 catalysts, estimated by pulse GC directly using oxygen and titrating oxygen with the hydrogen irreversibly bound at 393 K. The results are in good agreement.

For a quick estimation of the dispersion of palladium the chemisorption of oxygen should be carried out at room temperature, but the titration with hydrogen at higher temperatures.

If the catalyst is bimetallic, containing platinum metals and other

TITRATIONS ON A PALLADIUM SURFACE IN A Pd/Al_2O_3 CATALYST [66]

$V_{O_2}^{red(393 K)}$ [cm³/g cat.]	$V_{H_2}^{p(393 K)}$ [cm³/g cat.]	$V_{H_2}^{rev}$ [cm³/g cat.]	H/O	O/H
6	*7*	*8*	*9*	*10*
0.173	0.122	0.344	3.44	1.56
0.273	0.184	0.299	3.18	1.64
0.293	0.186	0.414	3.08	1.68
0.346	0.225	1.315	3.08	1.50
0.582	0.370	1.020	3.15	1.43

$V_{H_2}^{rev}$ — volume of hydrogen reversibly bound to the surface of the catalyst ($V_{H_2}^{rev} = V_{H_2}^{p} - V_{H_2}^{p(393K)}$).

H/O — ratio of volume of hydrogen to volume of previously chemisorbed oxygen (reaction (6.26))

$$\frac{H}{O} = \frac{V_{H_2}^{ox} - V_{H_2}^{rev}}{V_{O_2}^{p}}.$$

O/H — ratio of volume of oxygen to volume of previously chemisorbed hydrogen (reaction (6.27))

$$\frac{O}{H} = \frac{V_{O_2}^{red} - \frac{1}{2} V_{H_2}^{rev}}{V_{H_2}^{p(393K)}}.$$

inactive metals, e.g. rhenium, lead, tin and others, we can assess the surface of any metal during a titration reaction by comparing the results of chemisorption and gas adsorption titration, provided, of course, that

Table 6.5 THE SPECIFIC SURFACE AREA AND DISPERSION OF PALLADIUM ON Pd/Al_2O_3 CATALYSTS DETERMINED BY PULSE GC [66]

Pd *content* [%]	O/Pd	S_{O_2} [m²/g Pd]	H/Pd	S_{H_2} [m²/g Pd]	$\frac{S_{O_2}-S_{H_2}}{S_{O_2}}$ [%]
0.32	0.210	93.6	0.196	89.4	+4.5
0.75	0.147	69.37	0.149	70.44	—1.5
1.0	0.133	62.42	0.130	61.17	+2.0
1.37	0.125	58.72	0.116	54.60	+6.7
1.82	1.09	51.27	0.105	49.72	+3.0
4.21	0.081	37.94	0.075	35.33	+6.9

H — irreversibly bound hydrogen, determined by titrating against oxygen at 393 K.

the metals do not form an alloy. The adsorption of oxygen or hydrogen gives us the summed area, while from the gas titration we can estimate the surface area of the metal active in this reaction.

The surface areas of Pt and Re in the bimetallic catalyst Pt–Re/Al_2O_3 were determined using this oxygen–hydrogen titration [122]. Oxygen chemisorbed on the surface of Re at room temperature does not react with hydrogen — unlike oxygen sorbed on Pt. In the first stage, oxygen is introduced pulse-wise at 298 K to form a monolayer on Pt and Re. The oxygen chemisorbed by Pt is titrated against hydrogen at room temperature in accordance with equation (6.21). After this, oxygen is introduced pulse-wise and becomes chemisorbed on Pt only in accordance with equation (6.22). From the difference between the amounts of oxygen sorbed by Pt and Re (first stage) we can determine the amount of oxygen chemisorbed on Re, then its specific surface area and crystallite size.

Several authors [78, 125, 126] have considered the titration reaction of the oxidized surface of platinum supported on Al_2O_3 with carbon monoxide from the gaseous phase for estimating the dispersion of platinum

$$O_{(s)}+2CO_{(g)} \rightarrow CO_{(s)}+CO_{2(g)} . \tag{6.28}$$

The problems involved in this reaction are in principle analogous to those of the oxygen–hydrogen system considered above, and concern the variability of the stoichiometry with respect to the dimensions of the platinum crystallites, and also to the temperature of the process.

Bond and Sermon [124] used the titration of the hydrogenated surface of Pt/SiO_2 catalysts with alkenes (1-pentene) to demonstrate the spillover of hydrogen on to the support during the adsorption of hydrogen.

6.6 Determination of the Selective Surface Area of Metal Oxides in Compound Catalysts

There are not many papers dealing with this topic. Farrauto reviewed the available ones on the determination of the active surface areas of metal oxides [129].

The supports of oxide catalysts are usually those used for metal catalysts, and include silica, aluminium oxide, aluminosilicates, chromium oxide, magnesium oxide and carbon.

As there is no distinct difference between the chemisorptive capabilities of the support and the active oxide phase, great difficulties are encountered when attempting to perfect a chemisorptive method of estimating the selective surface area of an active oxide. Adsorption on metal oxides may occur simultaneously at two types of sites: cations and oxygen ions. At both sites, adsorption may take place at varying rates and may be reversible or irreversible.

The stoichiometry of interactions may vary over a wider range than is the case with metal catalysts; it depends on the nature of the support, the concentration of the active component and its dispersion. Furthermore, the correction for adsorption by the support is large in comparison with metal catalysts. The preparation of a "pure" surface on the active oxide phase also causes many more problems than does a metal phase.

Despite these difficulties, Shelef *et al.* [130–134] worked out a method of determining the specific surface areas of a series of active oxides: Fe_2O_3, NiO, CuO, Cr_2O_3, MnO — using nitric oxide as adsorbate.

NO was adsorbed over a temperature range from 273 to 423 K and at pressures from 0.133 to 26.6 kPa. The isotherms of adsorption on both supported and non-supported oxides were as given by the Freundlich equation. The amount of NO adsorbed as a monolayer on all the oxides tested corresponded to the stoichiometry $NO/Me_x = 0.5$. The correction for adsorption by the support ranged from 10 to 60% depending on the oxide content of the sample.

The chemisorptive method was also used to estimate the surface concentration of nickel cations in NiO–MgO solid solutions containing from 2 to 20% nickel [135]. NO was adsorbed at pressures from 0.013 to 1.6 kPa and temperatures from 273 to 393 K. The correction for adsorption by the support was less than 30%. Bunina and Sazanova [135] showed that the concentrations of nickel cations at the surface and in the body of the solution were identical.

Recently [136], the selective surface area of MoO_3 in compound cobalt–molybdenum catalysts was estimated using the pulse chemisorptive technique with oxygen as adsorbate at 195 K.

The kinetic method is also used in the estimation of the selective surface area of metal oxides [137–139]. The rate of any heterogeneous process taking place at a surface (reduction, oxidation, solution, etc.) is proportional to the distribution surface.

One kinetic method recently adopted was for estimating the surface area of CuO deposited on silica by reducing the catalyst with carbon monoxide [137, 138]. The reduction was carried out at 523 K and 1.33×10^{-3} kPa, the temperature and pressure being kept constant throughout the experiment. The rate at which the standard sample of pure CuO was reduced, with respect to the specific surface area determined by the BET technique, is given by the straight line passing through the origin of the coordinates [138]. The surface area of CuO in compound catalysts was estimated from this standard curve.

An interesting kinetic method was suggested by Lee [139]. He reduced bismuth–molybdenum catalysts with hydrogen in a continuous system at a temperature of 773 K for a given time and then oxidized them by introducing small portions of oxygen into the carrier gas. He then established the graphic relationship between the amount of sorbed oxygen and the period of reduction with hydrogen. After an initial period of induction, the curve becomes a straight line corresponding to the reduction proceeding at a constant rate. According to the author, the rate constant for the reduction involves the diffusion of oxygen from the body to the surface; this is a limiting process. By comparing the process for supported and non-supported systems and assuming the invariability of the oxidation-reduction stoichiometry, the selective surface areas of oxides can be determined.

6.7 Temperature-Programmed Desorption (TPD)

Temperature-programmed desorption (TPD) is a very useful method of studying physicochemical surface phenomena, including adsorbate–adsorbent interactions. The essence of the method is based on the chemisorption of a gas on the surface of a solid at a given temperature, followed by its desorption at a result of a temperature rise.

During desorption, the desorbed gas is estimated as a function of temperature and time. The temperature changes are in accordance with a definite programme. Linear temperature rise programmes are the most frequently used. The linear increase of temperature as a function of time can be expressed thus

$$T_t = T_0 + \beta t \,, \tag{6.29}$$

where T_t is the sample temperature at time t, T_0 is the temperature at time $t_0 = 0$, t is the time, and β is the rate of heating.

Catalysts tested by TPD can be used in various forms:

(a) crystals with given crystallographic faces;

(b) polycrystalline films and wires;

(c) polycrystalline powders (most often metal) deposited or non-deposited on a support (e.g. metal/support catalysts).

At first, TPD was used only for studying metal wires and strips. The temperature rise is obtained by rapid resistance heating. The rate of temperature increase was 10^6K/s in extreme cases [31, 140]. This method was therefore called flash desorption.

Various thermal desorption methods have been described by Amenomiya and Cvetanovic [141–145].

Thermodesorption can be carried out under different conditions:

(1) in a closed system (the pressure after TPD is higher than at the start);

(2) in a continuous flow system (the gas is desorbed into the carrier gas stream, e.g. He, Ar, N_2);

(3) in an open system (the gas is continuously pumped away, the pressure is the same at the end of the process as at the start).

Different kinds of detector for measuring the quantities of the desorbed gases are used in each of the above-mentioned thermodesorption systems. In a closed system any kind of manometer is suitable, so long as the temperature is also appropriate. Katharometers are usually used in continuous flow systems. In principle, the mass spectrometer can be used in all systems; it is the most suitable detector for thermodesorption studies.

The curves obtained by desorption (thermodesorption spectra) can be divided into two basic groups: TPD spectra (non-isothermic — Fig. 6.6) and isothermic desorption (Fig. 6.7).

The quantitative analysis of the kinetics of gas desorption (defining the order of reaction, rate constant, activation energy of desorption) is complicated. A serious difficulty standing in the way of a description of thermodesorption processes on heterogeneous surfaces is the lack of a fully developed theory of adsorption on heterogeneous surfaces.

Most of the papers [140–149] on the analysis of TPD are limited to a kinetic compilation of data for first- and second-order reactions and for a linear change in temperature.

For first-order desorption reactions, assuming that the activation energy of desorption is independent of the degree of coverage, the temperature, the form of the Arrhenius rate constant and the linear increase in temperature with time, we can use the expression [150]

$$\frac{\mathrm{d}\theta}{\mathrm{d}t} = -A\theta \exp\left(-\frac{E_\mathrm{d}}{RT}\right), \qquad (6.30)$$

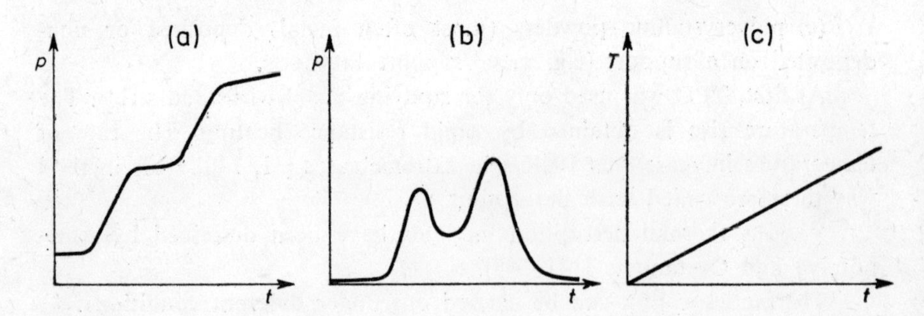

Fig. 6.6 Diagrammatic course of thermoprogrammed (non-isothermic) desorption: (a) pressure change as a function of time in a closed system; (b) pressure change as a function of time in a pumped-out open system; (c) temperature change as a function of time.

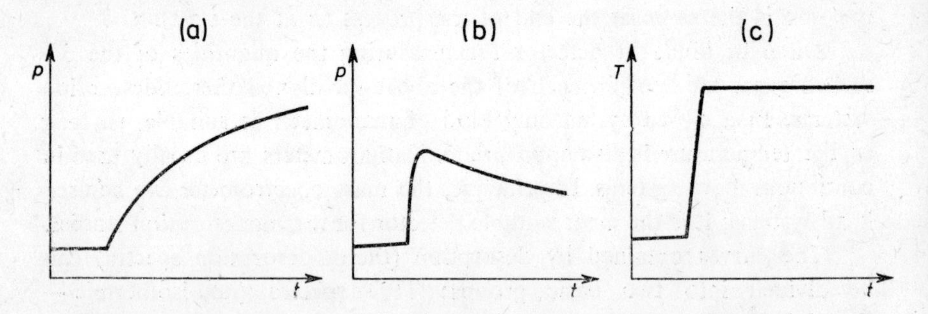

Fig. 6.7 Diagrammatic course of isothermic desorption: (a), (b), (c) as in Fig. 6.6.

where θ is the degree of coverage, A is the pre-exponential Arrhenius coefficient, and E_d is the activation energy of desorption.

From equation (6.29) we can see that $dT = \beta\, dt$, so that substituting this in equation (6.30) we get

$$\frac{d\theta}{dT} = -\frac{A}{\beta}\theta \exp\left(-\frac{E_d}{RT}\right). \tag{6.31}$$

In TPD we usually measure the partial pressure P of the desorbed gas. In an experiment where readsorption can be neglected (rapid flow of carrier gas), the peak maximum occurs when

$$\frac{dP}{dT} = 0 = \frac{d}{dT}\left[A\theta \exp\left(-\frac{E_d}{RT}\right)\right]. \tag{6.32}$$

After differentiating and taking equation (6.31) into consideration, equation (6.32) takes the form

$$2\ln T_m - \ln\beta = \frac{E_d}{RT_m} + \ln\left(\frac{E_d}{AR}\right), \tag{6.33}$$

where T_m is the peak maximum temperature.

The activation energy of desorption E_d can be calculated from the gradient of $(2\ln T_m - \ln\beta)$ versus $1/T_m$. This method of analysing thermo-desorption spectra, based on the Polanyi–Wigner model [150] and developed by Redhead [147] requires the heating rates to vary by at least one order of magnitude. As can be seen from Fig. 6.8, the rate of heating β has no great effect on the peak maximum temperature T_m.

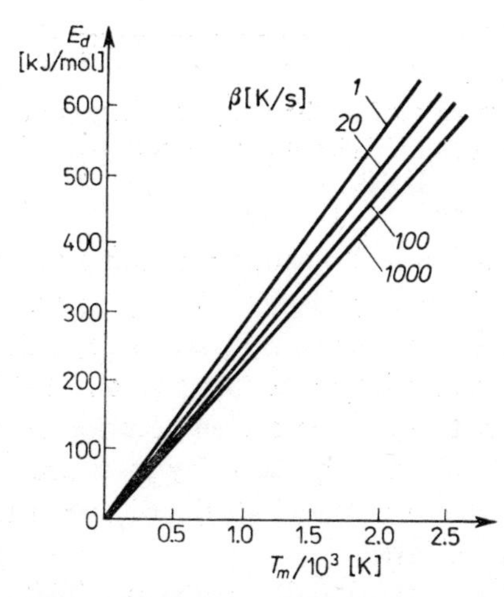

Fig. 6.8 The change of the activation energy of desorption, E_d, as a function of the peak maximum temperature T_m for a first-order reaction and linear temperature-increase β; $A = 10^{13}\ s^{-1}$ (after P. A. Redhead [147]).

Lord and Kittelberger [151] discussed this method in detail to see whether the activation energy of desorption E_d could be read off from the relationship of $(2\ln T_m - \ln\beta)$ and $1/T_m$ while ignoring the order of reaction. They found (Fig. 6.9) that the reading error increases with a decrease in E_d, the coefficient A and the initial degree of coverage θ_0. The result clearly suggests that the activation energy of desorption for reactions of second and higher orders can be determined from equation (6.33). When using this method, it is important to keep the initial degree of coverage θ_0 the same for various sample heating rates.

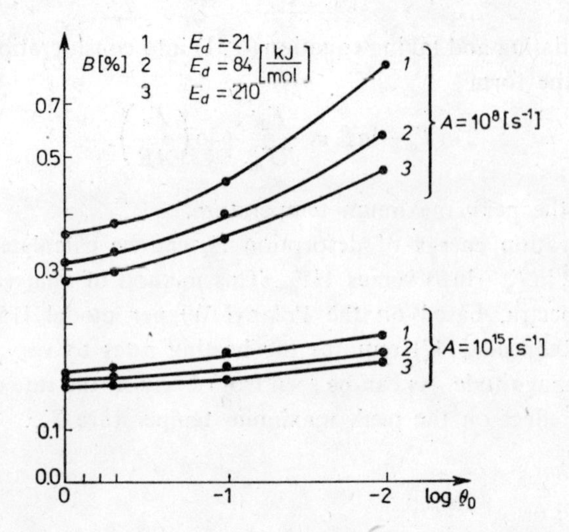

Fig. 6.9 The error B when reading the activation energy of desorption, E_d, from the graph of $(2\ln T_m - \ln\beta)$ against $1/T_m$ for a second-order desorption process (after F. M. Lord and J. S. Kittelberger [151]).

Analysis of equation (6.33) shows that every ten-fold increase in the value of A causes an increase of E_d by only 6%, and for an error in reading off the peak maximum temperature T_m equal to 1, the activation energy of desorption E_d increases by about 3.35 kJ/mol. That is why the authors [152] draw attention to the need for an accurate reading of T_m, which may be considerably affected by the delay in thermocouple readings, by inaccurate corrections for the hold-up time between the reactor and detector, and diffusion delays.

Charlamov *et al.* [153a] indicate the possibility of calculating E_d and A from one experiment with a constant temperature-rise. By expressing equation (6.30) in logarithmic form, taking the quantity of desorbed substance N_d instead of the degree of coverage θ, they obtained the relationship

$$\ln\left(-\frac{dN_d}{dT}\frac{1}{N_d}\right) = \ln\left(\frac{A}{\beta}\right) - \frac{E_d}{RT}. \tag{6.34}$$

The rate of desorption is proportional to the detector signal, and the quantity of desorbed compound can be found by integrating the expression

$$N_d = \int_{T}^{T_k} P(T)\,dT, \tag{6.35}$$

where T_k is the temperature at which desorption of the compound from the catalyst's surface is complete, and $P(T)$ is a function corresponding to the form of the desorption peak obtained. By assuming constant values for E_d and A and zero readsorption, and by integrating approximately equation (6.30), Kollen and Czanderna [153b] expressed it linearly for first- and second-order desorption processes taking place in isothermic conditions and with programmed heating:

isothermal conditions

first-order reaction

$$\ln(\theta_s/\theta_{so}) = -k\Delta t\,, \qquad (6.36a)$$

second-order reaction

$$1/\theta_{so} - 1/\theta_s = -k\Delta t\,, \qquad (6.36b)$$

programmed heating

first-order reaction

$$\ln\frac{\ln\theta_{so}/\theta_s}{T^2} = \ln(AR/\beta E_d) - E_d/RT\,, \qquad (6.37a)$$

second-order reaction

$$\frac{\ln(1/\theta_s - 1/\theta_{so})}{T^2} = \ln(AR/\beta E_d) - E_d/RT\,, \qquad (6.37b)$$

where θ_{so} is the original degree of surface coverage with the adsorbed species, and θ_s is the degree of surface coverage with the adsorbed species.

In order to define the order of the desorption reaction, graphs of

$$\ln\frac{\ln\theta_{so}/\theta_s}{T^2} \quad \text{against} \quad 1/T,$$

or

$$\ln(1/\theta_s - 1/\theta_{so}) \quad \text{against} \quad 1/T$$

were drawn.

By maintaining the linear relationship between these magnitudes, the order of reaction was defined. The activation energy of desorption was read from the gradient of the straight line ($\tan\alpha = -E_d/R$), the coefficient A from the point where the straight line cuts the y-axis. The heterogeneity of the surface of nickel black, for example, was determined in this way [154].

Recently [155], a relationship between the activation energy of desorption E_d and a "retention" parameter of the given adsorption form has been derived for homogeneous surfaces; this would be a quick and simple method of estimating E_d for spectra with well-resolved peaks.

6.7.1 Thermodesorption of Hydrogen from Group VIII Metals

TPD has been used to study hydrogen–metal interaction in recent years [156–165]. A number of papers deal with the thermodesorption of hydrogen from the surface of nickel [154, 157, 163–168]. Analysis of the thermodesorption graphs shows up significant differences in the number of forms of desorbed hydrogen and in the ranges of temperature over which adsorption takes place. The shape of the desorption curve depends upon:

(a) the conditions under which adsorption takes place (temperature, pressure of hydrogen, degree of surface coverage);

(b) the conditions under which adsorption takes place (open or closed system, neutral gas atmosphere, rate of sample heating);

(c) the form of the catalyst sample (wires, films, blacks, metal/support deposited systems, bimetallic systems);

(d) the technique of catalyst preparation (kind of salt used, temperature and conditions of decomposition and reduction).

A detailed comparison of the thermodesorption curves obtained by various authors is difficult. Certain temperature ranges of desorption do however occur with particular forms of hydrogen adsorbed on metal surfaces. In principle, three ranges of hydrogen desorption can be distinguished, regardless of the type of nickel catalyst (films, wires, blacks and nickel deposited on a support). Figure 6.10 illustrates a typical desorption spectrum of hydrogen from nickel black.

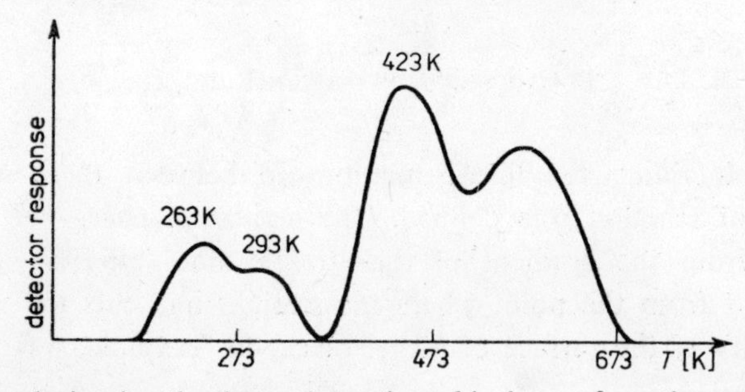

Fig. 6.10 Graph showing the thermodesorption of hydrogen from the surface of nickel (after L. V. Babenkova *et al.* [165]).

It was found that the kinetics of hydrogen desorption are second-order [167]. The activation energies of the peaks are 41.9, 81.7, and 123.6 kJ/mol [168]. The deposition of nickel on a support may, according to its nature, alter both the content and the temperature areas of hydrogen desorption. In general it is assumed that the presence of a support favours the shift of hydrogen desorption areas towards higher temperatures. On the other hand, activating nickel with platinum or palladium increases the overall sorption of hydrogen. Much attention has been devoted to the thermodesorption of hydrogen from the surface of platinum [169–172].

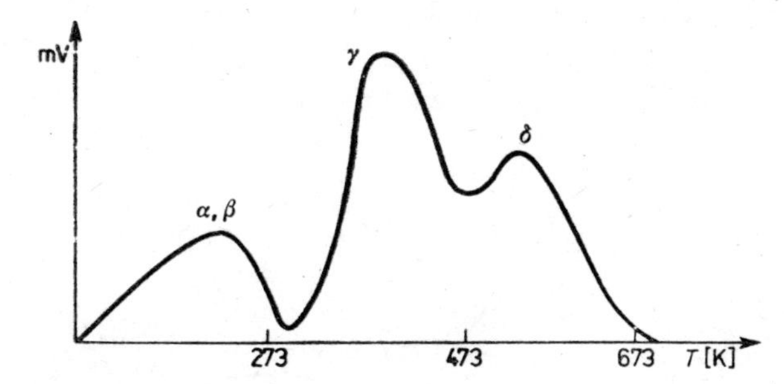

Fig. 6.11 Graph showing the thermodesorption of hydrogen from the surface of platinum (after S. Tsuchiya *et al.* [173]).

Four forms of hydrogen have been found to occur on platinum [173] (Fig. 6.11).

The low-temperature forms α and β desorb from the platinum surface during outgassing at room temperature. The other forms, γ and δ, desorb at temperatures up to 873 K.

The desorption of hydrogen from palladium takes place over three basic temperature areas [159, 176]. In the first one, above room temperature, the hydrogen dissolved in the mass of the palladium desorbs. This peak disappears if the palladium crystallites are smaller than 1 nm.

Between 373 and 673 K, desorption of the adsorbed hydrogen proceeds approximately according to a first-order equation, with an average activation energy of desorption of around 25.1 kJ/mol. The third desorption peak (673–873 K) represents hydrogen desorbing with a high activation energy of desorption: 104.7–159.2 kJ/mol. Within this range, desorption takes place according to a second-order reaction. Figure 6.12 shows the thermodesorption of hydrogen from rhodium black [175].

On the basis of research into the adsorption of hydrogen on metals carried out by various methods (emission work, surface potential measurement, electrical conductivity, TPD), Sokolskii [174] proposed that four forms of hydrogen adsorbed on the surface of Group VIII metals should be distinguished

$$\begin{array}{ccccccccc} H_{2\,ads} & \rightleftharpoons & (H\ldots H)_{ads} & \rightleftharpoons & (H\ldots H)^{+}_{ads} & \rightleftharpoons & 2(H)^{+}_{ads} & \rightleftharpoons & Me\,Me\,. \\ | & & |\quad\;\; | & & |\quad\;\; | & & | & & \diagdown\;\diagup \\ Me & & Me\;\;Me & & Me\;\;Me & & Me & & H^{(-)}_{ads} \\ & T_m & & T_m & & T_m & & T_m & \\ & 173\text{–}248\,K & & 233\text{–}323\,K & & 256\text{–}508\,K & & 573\text{–}683\,K & \end{array} \quad (6.38)$$

The most weakly-bound molecules of hydrogen (linear structure) are present only where $\theta \to 1$, and are held in place by Van der Waals forces. In the molecular hydrogen bridge structure, each hydrogen is

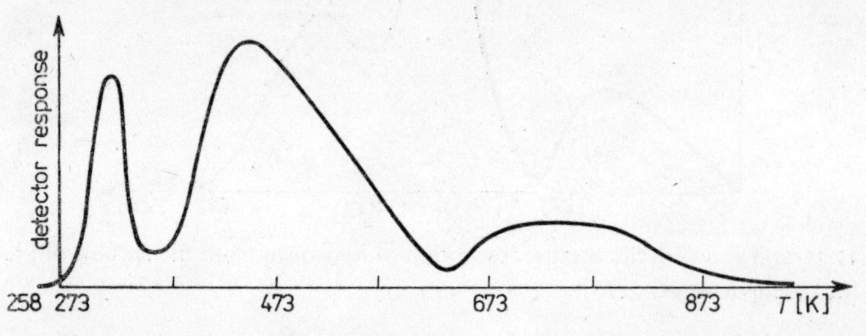

Fig. 6.12 Graph showing the thermodesorption of hydrogen from rhodium black (after V. K. Solnyshkova *et al.* [175]).

bound to a metal atom; the hydrogen–hydrogen bond is weakened though not broken. This form of hydrogen may pass into the strongly polarized ionized state H_2^+ [177, 178]. It does not take direct part in hydrogenation reactions, although it may serve as an active source of atomic hydrogen, especially at high pressures [179]

$$H_2^+ \rightleftharpoons H^+ + H_{ads}\,.$$

Experimental data indicate that the principal catalytically-active forms of adsorbed hydrogen are atoms joined by a linear or bridge bond to the surface. The dissociated hydrogen adsorbed at the surface forms a dipole, which in the extreme case becomes a proton bound atomically to a metal atom [173]. It is this form of hydrogen which desorbs from the surface of nickel and palladium blacks with an average activation energy of desorption decreasing from 70 (Ni) and 100 (Pd) to around 33.5 kJ/mol [180, 181]. It is generally assumed that this form of dissociated hydrogen is adsorbed on the surfaces of all the metals of Group VIII.

The strongest polycentric adsorption of hydrogen takes place where the adsorbed hydrogen mutually interacts with the energetically most unsaturated metal atoms. These hydrogen atoms become located between two metal atoms in the surface layers and form negatively charged particles [182–185]. Thc formation of this form of hydrogen in the metal lattice proceeds slowly and may be classified as a type of activated adsorption. Heats of adsorption are high, from 83.8 to 125.7 kJ/mol [169, 185, 186]. The negatively charged hydrogen atoms are capable of migrating to parts of the surface where the heat of adsorption is lower; they settle there as the linear form of atomically adsorbed hydrogen [187].

Sokolskii's interpretation [174] of the form of adsorbed hydrogen, though useful, seems to be too general; moreover, it does not take into account certain factors which influence the means by which hydrogen is bound to the surface of a metal, and the energy involved in this process. The most important of these factors include the so-called "small particles effect", metal-support interaction (hydrogen spillover), changes involved in the use of bimetallic systems, the possibility of hydrogen being adsorbed on to contaminants. The small particles' effect occurs in strongly dispersed metal systems, e.g. in metal-support type catalysts. The surfaces of large crystallites have properties analogous to those of solid metals, whereas the surfaces of small metallic particles are highly unsaturated, and thus the surface atoms have a lower coordination number. The surface atoms of small crystallites show a greater electronic affinity than do the atoms of large crystallites. It has been found that as the crystallite size decreases, not only does the amount of hydrogen in the form strongly bound to the surface increase, but its activation energy of desorption is also distinctly greater.

One significant indication of metal-support interactions could be the lower susceptibility to reduction of the supported metal [188–192]. This is especially the case with nickel supported on aluminium oxide where a nickel–aluminium spinel has been found to occur [193–195]. It should be inferred from this that the nickel crystallite is strongly bound to the carrier by oxide bonds. Depending on the extent to which the metal phase has been reduced, quantitative and qualitative changes in the adsorption of hydrogen may be expected, and these should be reflected in its desorption spectrum.

Another manifestation of metal-support interactions, not considered by Sokolskii, is the spillover of hydrogen [79, 196]. This is the migration of hydrogen atoms from the supported metal, which is active in the dis-

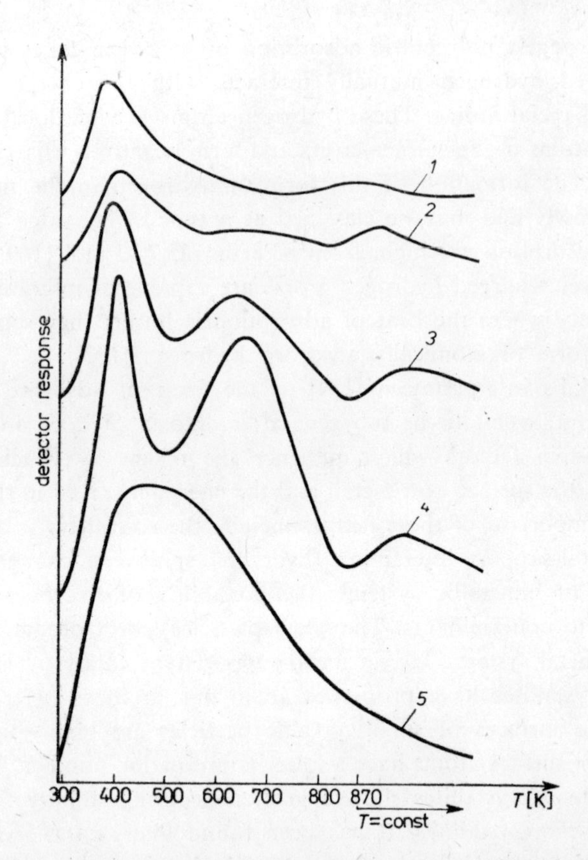

Fig. 6.13 Curves showing the TPD of hydrogen from 2% Pd–Ni/Al_2O_3 catalysts after adsorption in a stream of hydrogen at room temperature. The numbers of the curves refer to the percentages by weight of the catalyst components (after J. M. Farbotko [176]):
1 — 100% Ni, *2* — 30% Pd, 70% Ni, *3* — 50% Ni, 50% Pd, *4* — 70% Pd, 30% Ni, *5* — 100% Pd.

sociative adsorption of hydrogen, on to the support which is incapable of hydrogen, dissociation. This effect is favoured by a rise in temperature, and also by the presence of contaminants such as oxygen, carbon and water [172, 197]. This process may furthered by oxygen bridges between a metal atom and the support.

Under favourable conditions of adsorption and desorption, the TPD method can be used to record ths effect. It has been found that the rate of spillover increases together with rises in hydrogen pressure, the temperature of adsorption, and the dispersion of the metal.

In bimetallic systems it is difficult to define unequivocally the changes in the forms of adsorbed hydrogen. The nature of these changes depends a great deal on the abilities of the different components of an alloy to adsorb hydrogen. The admixture of a metal incapable of chemisorbing hydrogen will reduce the overall adsorption. This effect may be intensified by the surface segregation of the alloy. More complex effects are observed in bimetallic systems where both metals are capable of adsorbing hydrogen, e.g. Pd–Ir [162], Pd–Pt [198]. Adding another metal to palladium, e.g. nickel or platinum, markedly influences the palladium–hydrogen interactions: one of these effects is that the palladium is rendered incapable of adsorbing hydrogen. Figure 6.13 shows the TPD curves for 2% Pd–Ni/Al_2O_3.

There are a number of contaminants which can affect the adsorption of hydrogen on metals. The most common include oxygen, carbon, sulphur and chlorine [199, 200].

It is essential to prepare in a suitable way the samples on which the adsorption and desorption of hydrogen is to be measured. A necessary step in the purification of the sample is to heat it in oxygen, and then to reduce it in hydrogen.

6.7.2 Thermodesorption of Carbon Monoxide from the Surface of Group VIII Metals

The thermodesorption of carbon monoxide from the surface of Group VIII metals has been studied by a number of authors, mostly from the point of view of interactions of carbon monoxide with hydrogen and oxygen, and the nature and strength of the bonds between the adsorbed CO and the metal surface.

Stephan [201] found that three forms of carbon monoxide adsorbed on different metals occur:

(1) weakly adsorbed CO — the maximum rate of desorption of this form takes place at about 113 K. The quantity of CO desorbing at this temperature exceeds that to be expected from pure Van der Waals adsorption;

(2) moderately strong adsorption of carbon monoxide, desorbing within the temperature range 323–413 K. Morgan and Somorjai [202] suggest that this form covers two states of bound CO with different desorption energies;

(3) strongly adsorbed CO — maximum rate of desorption at about 503 K.

Winterbottom [203] proposed a description of the thermodesorption of carbon monoxide using six different basic forms having activation energies of desorption from 104.7 to over 167.6 kJ/mol and a maximum desorption temperature of over 673 K.

According to Stephan *et al.* [204], the thermodesorption characteristics of CO from a palladium surface are analogous to those from platinum. It was found that at higher temperatures (above 573 K) there exist two forms of CO on nickel whose maximum rates of desorption occur at 653 K and 803 K. These forms involve a recombination of the carbon and oxygen atoms during desorption [205, 206].

Physically-adsorbed CO is thermodesorbed from silver between 23 K and 423 K [201]. There are three temperature ranges for CO desorption from iridium supported on aluminium oxide [207]. The high temperature peak in this case ($T_m \approx 873$ K) represents at least in part the dissociatively-bound CO.

For unsupported iridium, the carbon monoxide all desorbs up to about 673 K.

The desorption of carbon monoxide from Rh after previous adsorption at room temperature is recorded as a single peak where the maximum rate of desorption occurs at 523 K [208, 209]. CO was only slightly dissociated, especially at high temperatures. The degree of purity of the rhodium surface markedly affects the extent of dissociation. If contaminants such as oxygen are present, a second desorption peak appears with a maximum temperature of the order of 823 K. This peak is attributed to a dissociative form of carbon monoxide [209].

Sexton and Somorjai [210] maintain that in order to obtain a pure surface from which desorption would be exclusively molecular, the surface would have to be bombarded with argon ions at 1073 K. If this procedure is omitted, two carbon monoxide peaks are obtained; in these authors' opinion, the high temperature peak ($T_{max} = 973$ K) is due to the dissociative form (Fig. 6.14).

Yates *et al.* [211] do not agree with this. With the aid of isotope exchange measurements and thermodesorption they found that the probability of a dissociation reaction taking place is equal to about 10^{-3}.

Thermodesorption with simultaneous chromatographic analysis of desorption products and application of spectrographic methods can provide information regarding the forms of adsorption, the state and structure of surface bonds, also the nature of the heterogeneity of adsorbent and catalyst surfaces. The method cannot always be used as the adsorbate molecules are in contact with the active surface sites for a long period at a fairly high temperature, and this may provoke either a chemical re-

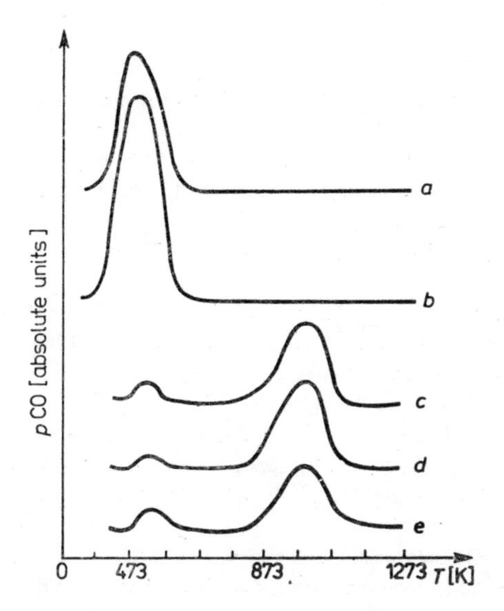

Fig. 6.14 Thermodesorption of carbon monoxide from a rhodium surface (after B. A. Sexton and G. A. Somorjai [210]):

a — pure surface, *b* — rhodium surface after bombardment with argon ions, *c* — surface after heating in streams of CO and H_2, *d* — surface after heating in a stream of CO, *e* — surface after heating in a stream of CO_2.

action between the adsorbate and the solid surface or changes in the adsorbate molecules themselves. The desorption curves are then somewhat difficult to interpret.

Thermodesorption is also widely used to estimate the acidity of a surface.

It has been found recently that metals supported on some supports (TiO_2, V_2O_3, Nb_2O_3, Ta_2O_5) lose the ability to chemisorb hydrogen and carbon monoxide after their reduction with hydrogen above some temperatures. This phenomenon is due to strong interaction between the Group VIII metals and support (SMSI). The nature of this interaction and its effect on chemisorption of gases are not known in detail, and they are a subject of intensive investigations [212].

Very useful methods in the investigations on properties of supported metals are temperature-programmed reduction (TPR) and temperature-programmed oxidation (TPO), which are successfully carried out in chromatographic systems [213].

References

[1] Anderson J. R., *Structure of Metallic Catalysts*, Academic Press, London, New York, San Francisco, 1975.

[2] Gruber H. L., *Anal. Chem.*, **34**, 1828 (1962).

[3] Buyanova N. E., Karnaukhov A. P., Kefeli L. M., Ratner N. D. and Chernyavskaya O. N., *Kinet. Katal.*, **8**, 868 (1967).

[4] Kho Shi-Thoang, Romanovskii B. V. and Topchieva K. V., *Vestnik MGU, ser. Khim.*, **83**, 17 (1967).

[5] Gruber H. L. and Hausen A., *Kolloid. Z. u Z. Polymer*, **214**, 66 (1966).

[6] Dorling T. A. and Moss R. L., *J. Catalysis*, **5**, 111 (1966).

[7] Kral H., *Z. physik. Chem.*, *neue Folge*, **48**, 129 (1966).

[8] Kral H., *Chemiker-Zeit.*, **91**, 41 (1967).

[9] Schlosser E. G., *Chemie-Ing-Techn.*, **39**, 409 (1967).

[10] Brooks C. S. and Kehrer V. I., *Anal. Chem.*, **41**, 108 (1969).

[11] Buyanova N. E., Ibragimova N. B. and Karnaukhov A. P., *Kinet. Katal.*, **10**, 397 (1969).

[12] Buyanova N. E., Kuznecova E. V. and Borisova M. S., *Zavod. Lab.* **35**, 154 (1969).

[13] Levchuk V. S. and Buyanova N. E., *Izv. Akad. Nauk SSSR, ser. Khim.*, 27 (1972).

[14] Paryjczak T., Jóźwiak K. W. and Góralski J., *J. Chromatogr.*, **166**, 65 (1978).

[15] Paryjczak T., Jóźwiak K. W. and Góralski J., *J. Chromatogr.*, **166**, 75 (1978).

[16] Paryjczak T., Jóźwiak K. W. and Góralski J., *J. Chromatogr.*, **155**, 9 (1978); *J. Chromatogr.*, **152**, 375 (1978).

[17] Paryjczak T., Zieliński P. and Jóźwiak K. W., *J. Chromatogr.*, **160**, **247** (1978).

[18] Freel J., *J. Catal.*, **25**, 139 (1972).

[19] Prasad J. and Menon P. G., *J. Catal.*, **44**, 314 (1976).

[20] Prasad J., Murthy K. R. and Menon P. G., *J. Catal.*, **52**, 515 (1978).

[21] Carballo L., Serrano S., Wolf E. E. and Carberry J. J., *J. Catal.*, **52**, 507 (1978).

[22] Buyanova N. E., Zapreeva O. F. and Karnaukhov A. P., *Kinet. Katal.*, **19**, 1196 (1978).

[23] Ivanov A. N., Yagomyagi A. E. and Eyzen O. T., *Kinet. Katal.*, **15**, 1029 (1974).

[24] Fejes P., Nagy F. and Schay G., *Acta Chim. Hung.*, **20**, 451 (1959).

[25] Pitkethly R. and Goble A., *Actes du Deuxieme Congres International de Catalyse*, **3**, 1851, Technip, Paris, 1961.

[26] Hughes R. T., Houston R. J. and Sieg R. P., *Ind. Eng. Chem. Proc. Des. and Dev.*, **1**, 1851 (1962).

[27] Weindenbach G. and Fürst H., *Chem. Techn.*, **15**, 589 (1963).

[28] Mears D. E. and Hausford R. C., *J. Catalysis*, **9**, 125 (1967).

[29] Piringer O. and Tataru E., *J. Gas Chromatogr.*, **2**, 323 (1964).

[30] Yakerson V. N., Lafer A. I. and Rubinstein A. M., *Problemy Kinet. i Kataliza*, Izd. Nauka, **14**, 111 (1970).

[31] Yakerson V. I. and Rozanov V. V., *Izv. Akad. Nauk SSSR, ser. Khim.*, 1461 (1968).
[32] Sokolskii V. D., *Kinet. Katal.*, **11**, 1492 (1970).
[33] Kaźmierczak A., Karski S. and Paryjczak T., *Wiadomości Chem.*, **25**, 791 (1971).
[34] Szymura J. A. and Paryjczak T., The Use of Electron Microscopy in the Investigation of Catalysts, Supports and Adsorbents, *Zeszyty Naukowe PŁ, Chemia*, **37**, 1 (1971).
[35] Kolomiichuk V. N. (Ed.), *Rentgenografiya katalizatorov*, Sib. Otdel. Akad. Nauk SSSR, Novosibirsk, 1977.
[36] Slinkin A. A., *Struktura i katalicheskiye svoystva geterogennykh katalizatorov*, Akad. Nauk SSSR, Moskva, 1971.
[37] Spindler H. and Bagiński K., *Chem. Techn.*, **20**, 548 (1968).
[38] Otto K. and Shelef M., *J. Catal.*, **29**, 138 (1973).
[39] Anderson J. R., *Chemisorption and Reactions on Metallic Films*, Academic Press, London, New York, 1971, Vol. 1, p. 259.
[40] Boreskov G. K. and Karnaukhov A. P., *Zh. Fiz. Khim.*, **26**, 1814 (1952).
[41] Whyte T. E. jr, *Catalysis Rev.*, 117 (1973).
[42] Gruber H. L., *J. Phys. Chem.*, **66**, 48, 204 (1962).
[43] Spenadel L. and Boudart M. J., *J. Phys. Chem.*, **64**, 204 (1960).
[44] Adams C. R., Benesi H. A., Curtis R. M. and Meisenheimer R. G., *J. Catal.*, **1**, 336 (1962).
[45] Benesi H. A., Curtis R. M. and Studer H. P., *J. Catal.*, **10**, 328 (1968).
[46] Adler S. F. and Kearney J. J., *J. Phys. Chem.*, **64**, 208 (1960).
[47] Poltorak O. M. and Boronin V. S., *Zh. Fiz. Khim.*, **39**, 1476 (1965).
[48] Roca F. F., de Mourgues L. and Trambouze Y., *J. Gas Chromatogr.*, **6**, 161 (1968).
[49] Shigehara Y. and Ozaki A., *Nippon Kagaku Zasshi*, **88**, 838 (1967).
[50] Poltorak O. M. and Boronin V. S., *Zh. Fiz. Khim.*, **46**, 467 (1972).
[51] Boronin V. S., Nikulina V. S. and Poltorak O. M., *Zh. Fiz. Khim.*, **46**, 463 (1972).
[52] Boronin V. S., Poltorak O. M. and Tarakulova A. O., *Zh. Fiz. Khim.*, **48**, 258 (1974).
[53] Carballo L., Serrano S., Wolf E. E. and Carberry J. J., *J. Catal.*, **52**, 507 (1978).
[54] Vasilevich A. A., Chesnokova R. V. and Alekseev A. M., *Kinet. Katal.*, **18**, 1311 (1977).
[55] Paryjczak T. and Karski S., *Roczniki Chem.*, **50**, 291 (1976).
[56] Sadek H. and Taylor H. S., *J. Am. Chem. Soc.*, **72**, 1168 (1950).
[57] Rideal E. K. and Trapnell M. B., *Proc. Roy. Soc.*, **A205**, 409 (1951).
[58] Leibowitz L., Low M. J. D. and Taylor H. A., *Phys. Chem.*, **62**, 471 (1958).
[59] Viswanathan N. S. and Yeddanapalli, *Canad. J. Chem.*, **47**, 2933 (1969).
[60] Brooks C. S. and Christopher L. M., *J. Catal.*, **10**, 211 (1968).
[61] Kaźmierczak A. and Paryjczak T., *Roczniki Chem.*, **48**, 51 (1974).
[62] Abeledo C. R. and Selwood P. W., *J. Chem. Phys.*, **37**, 2709 (1962).
[63] Racz G., Szekely G., Huszar K. and Olah K., *Periodica Polytechnica, Technical University, Budapest*, **15**, 111 (1971).
[64] Palczewska W., *Adv. Catal.*, **24**, 245 (1975).
[65] Yates D. J. C., *Trans. Faraday Soc.*, **61**, 2044 (1965).
[66] Paryjczak T. and Jóźwiak K. W., *J. Chromatogr.*, **111**, 443 (1975).

[67] Emmett P. H. and Brunauer S.. *J. Am. Chem. Soc.* **59**, 1553 (1937).
[68] Ozaki A., Kimura T. and Motohashi M., *Nippon Kagaku Zasshi*, **88**, 834 (1967).
[69] Aben P. C., *J. Catal.*, **10**, 224 (1968).
[70] Boronin V. S., Poltorak O. M., Smirnova N. N. and Levitski A., *Vestnik Mosk. Univ., ser. Khim.*, **1**, 13 (1975).
[71] Lanyon M. A. and Trapnell B. M. W., *Proc. Roy. Soc.*, **A227**, 387 (1955).
[72] Ponec V. and Knor Z., *Actes du Deuxieme Congres International de Catalyse*, **1**, 195, Technip, Paris, 1961.
[73] Kubicka H., *React. Catal. Letters*, **5**, 223 (1976).
[74] Ponec V., Knor Z. and Cerny S., *Disc. Faraday Soc.*, **41**, 149 (1966).
[75] Wilson G. E. and Hall W. K., *J. Catal.*, **17**, 190 (1970).
[76] Dorling T. A., Burlace C. J. and Moss R. L., *J. Catal.*, **12**, 207 (1968).
[77] Benson J. E. and Boudart J. M., *J. Catal.*, **4**, 704 (1968).
[78] Flynn P. G. and Wanke S. E., *J. Catal.*, **36**, 244 (1975).
[79] Sermon P. A. and Bond G. C., *Catalysis Rev.*, **8**, (2) 211 (1973).
[80] Dorling T. A. and Moss R. L., *J. Catal.*, **5**, 11 (1966).
[81] Cusimano J. A., Dembinski G. W. and Sinfelt J. H., *J. Catal.*, **5**, 471 (1966).
[82] Boreskov G. K., *Zh. Fiz. Khim.*, **31**, 937 (1958).
[83] Charcosset H., Barthomeuf D., Nicolova R., Revillon A., Tournayan L. and Trambouze Y., *Bull. Soc. chim. France*, **12**, 4555 (1967).
[84] Kanazirev V., Neinska Ya. and Penchev V., *Kinet. Katal.*, **13**, 1246 (1972).
[85] Roberts M. W., *Trans. Faraday Soc.*, **57**, 99 (1961).
[86] Szabo Z. G. and Kallo D. (Eds.), *Contact Catalysis*, Akademiai Kiado, Budapest, 1976.
[87] Paryjczak T. and Gebauer D., *J. Colloid and Inter. Sci.*, **72**, 181 (1979).
[88] Buyanova N. E., Zapreeva O. F., Karnaukhov A. P., Koroleva N. T., Moroz B. M. and Rybak V. T., *Kinet. Katal.*, **18**, 736 (1977).
[89] Paryjczak T. and Zarzycka B., *Roczniki Chem.*, **48**, 1731 (1974).
[90] Paryjczak T. and Szymura J., *Z. anorg. allg. Chem.*, **449**, 105 (1979).
[91] Sermon P. A., *J. Catal.*, **24**, 467 (1972).
[92] Ponec V., Knor Z. and Cerny S., *Collect. Czech. Chem. Comm.*, **30**, 208 (1965).
[93] Klemperer D. F. and Stone F. S., *Proc. Roy. Soc.*, **A243**, 375 (1958).
[94] Bik A., *Sb. Kataliz — voprosy teorii i metody issledovanya*, Izd. Nauka, Moskva, 1955, p. 198.
[95] Zapletal V., Kolomaznok K., Sonkup J. and Ruzicka V., *Chem. Listy*, **62**, 210 (1968).
[96] Suzuki M. and Smi J. M., *J. Catal.*, **21**, 336 (1971).
[97] Brennan D., Hayward D. D., and Trapnell B. M. W., *Proc. Roy. Soc.*, **A256**, 81 (1960).
[98] Buyanova N. E. and Karnaukhov A. P., *Adsorpcya i poristost*, Izd. Nauka, Moskva, 1976, p. 131.
[99] Ponec V. and Cerny S., *Chemisorption and Catalysis by Metals*, Rozprady Ceskoslovenske Akademie, Praha, 1965.
[100] Wanke S. E. and Dougharty N. A., *J. Catal.*, **24**, 367 (1972).
[101] Müller J., *J. Catal.*, **6**, 50 (1966).
[102] Ermakov Yu. I. and Kuznecov B. N., *Dokl. Akad. Nauk SSSR*, **207**, 644 (1972).
[103] Burstein P., Schumilova N. and Tolberg K., *Zh. Fiz. Khim.*, **20**, 789 (1946).

[104] Khasin A. V. and Boreskov T. K., *Izv. Akad. Nauk SSSR, ser. Khim.*, **152,** 1387 (1963).
[105] Walter G., Wurzbacher G. and Kratczyk B., *J. Catal.*, **10**, 336 (1968).
[106] Benson J. E. and Boudart M., *J. Catal.*, **4**, 704 (1965).
[107] Vannice M. A., Benson J. E. and Boudart M., *J. Catal.*, **16**, 348 (1970).
[108] Sandler Y. L. and Durigon D. D., *J. Phys. Chem.*, **72**, 1051 (1968).
[109] Kholyavenko K. M., Rubanik M. Ya. and Chernukhina N. A., *Zh. Fiz. Khim.*, **5**, 505 (1964).
[110] Czanderna A. W., *J. Phys. Chem.*, **68**, 2765 (1964).
[111] Taylor K. C., *J. Catal.*, **38**, 299 (1975).
[112] Dalla Betta R. A., *J. Catal.*, **34**, 57 (1974).
[113] Contour J. P. and Ponnetier G., *Bull. Soc. chim. France*, 3591 (1968).
[114] Ostrovskii V. S., *Usp. Khim.*, **43**, 1931 (1974).
[115] Scholten J., Konvalinka J. and Beekman F., *J. Catal.*, **28**, 209 (1973).
[116] Farauto R. J., *Amer. Ind. Chem. Ing.*, **70**, 9 (1974).
[117] Yanovskii M. I., Roginskii S. Z., Gaziev G. A. and Semenenko E. I., *Sb. Gazovaya khromatografiya*, Izd. Nauka, Moskva, 1965, p. 446.
[118] Karnaukhov A. P. and Buyanova N. E., *International Union of Pure and Applied Chemistry Surface Area Determination*, Butterworths, London, 1969, p. 165.
[119] Barbaux Y., Roger B., Beaufils J. P. and Germain J. E., *J. Chim. Phys. et Phys. Chim. Biol.*, **67**, 1035 (1979).
[120] Jaworska-Galas Z. and Wrzyszcz J., *Chemia stosowana* **A1**, 105 (1966).
[121] Spindler H. and Kraft M., *Z. allg. Chem.*, **391**, 155 (1972).
[122] Menon P. G., Sieders J., Streefkart F. J. and Van Keulen G. J. M., *J. Catal.*, **29**, 188 (1973).
[123] Brooks C. S., *J. Colloid Interface Sci.*, **34**, 419 (1970).
[124] Robell A. J., Ballou E. V. and Boudart M., *J. Phys. Chem.*, **68**, 2748 (1964).
[125] Wentrcek P. and Wise H., *J. Catal.*, **34**, 247 (1975).
[126] Wentrcek P., Kimoto K. and Wise H., *J. Catal.*, **33**, 279 (1974).
[127] Karnaukhov A. P., *Kinet. Katal.*, **12**, 1520 (1971).
[128] Bond G. C., *The IV International Congress on Catalysis* (*Papers*), Izd. Nauka, Moscow, **2**, 250 (1970).
[129] Farrauto R. J., *Amer. Ind. Chem. Ing. Chem. Ind.*, **70**, 9 (1974).
[130] Otto K. and Shelef M., *J. Catalysis*, **14**, 226 (1969).
[131] Otto K. and Shelef M., *J. Catalysis*, **18**, 184 (1970).
[132] Gandhi H. S. and Shelef M., *J. Catalysis*, **24**, 241 (1972).
[133] Gandhi H. S. and Shelef M., *J. Catalysis*, **28**, 1 (1973).
[134] Yao H. and Shelef M., *J. Catalysis*, **31**, 377 (1973).
[135] Bunina R. V. and Sazanova I. S., *React. Kinet. Catal. Lett.*, **3**, 89 (1975).
[136] Vyskocil V. and Tomanova D., *React. Kinet. Catal. Lett.*, **10**, 37 (1979).
[137] Mehandzhiev D. and Dyakova V., *React. Kinet. Catal. Lett.*, **5**, 273 (1976).
[138] Dyakova V. D. and Mehandzhiev D. R., *Comp. Rend. Acad. Bulg. Sci.*, **27**, 1671 (1974).
[139] Lee E. H., *J. Catalysis*, **12**, 314 (1968).
[140] Redhead P. A., Hobson J. P. and Kornelsen E. V., *The Physical Basis of Ultrahigh Vacuum*, Chapman-Hall, London, 1968.
[141] Amenomiya Y. and Cvetanovic R. J., *J. Phys. Chem.*, **67**, 144 (1963).

[142] Amenomiya Y. and Cvetanovic R. J., *J. Phys. Chem.*, **69**, 2046, 2705 (1965).
[143] Cvetanovic R. J. and Amenomiya Y., *Adv. Catalysis*, **17**, 103 (1967).
[144] Amenomiya Y. and Cvetanovic R. J., *J. Catal.*, **15**, 293 (1969).
[145] Cvetanovic R. J. and Amenomiya Y., *Catal. Rev.*, **6**, 21 (1972).
[146] Yakerson V. J., Rozanov V. V. and Rubinstein A. M. *Surface Sci.*, **12**, 221 (1968).
[147] Redhead P. A., *Vacuum*, **12**, 203 (1962).
[148] King D. A., *Surface Sci.*, **47**, 384 (1975).
[149] Popova N. M., Babenkova L. V. and Sokolskii D. V., *Kinet. Katal.*, **10**, 1172 (1969).
[150] Hansen R. S. and Mimeault K. J. in: *Experimental Methods in Catalytic Research*, Ed. Anderson R. B., Academic Press, New York, London, 1968, p. 220.
[151] Lord F. M. and Kittelberger J. S., *Surface Sci.*, **43**, 173 (1974).
[152] Brenner A. and Hucul D. A., *J. Catal.*, **56**, 134 (1979).
[153a] Charlamov V. V., Bogomolov V. I., Mirzabekova I. V. and Pospielov A. V., *Zh. Fiz. Khim.*, **50**, 343 (1976).
[153b] Kollen W. and Czanderna A. W., *J. Colloid and Interface Sci.*, **38**, 152 (1972).
[154] Babenkova L. V., Popova N. M., Blagoveshchenskaya I. N. and Tjuleneva L. V., *Kataliticheskoye gidrirovanye i okislenye*, Izd. Nauka, Alma-Ata, 1975, p. 71.
[155] Evdokimova Z. A. and Yakerson V. J., *Izv. Akad. Nauk. SSSR*, **6**, 1261 (1980).
[156] Konvalinka J. A. and Scholten J. J. F., *J. Catal.*, **48**, 374 (1977).
[157] Rienäcker G., Wölter J. and Engels S., *Z. Chem.*, **10**, 301 (1970).
[158] Franco M. A. and Phillips M. J., *J. Catal.*, **63**, 346 (1980).
[159] Sokolskii D. V., Popova N. M., Babenkova L. V. and Solnyshkova V. K., *Dokl. Akad. Nauk. SSSR*, **210**, 888 (1973).
[160] Aldag A. V. and Schmidt L. D., *J. Catal.*, **22**, 260 (1971).
[161] Popova N. M., Sokolskii D. V. and Sokolova L. A., *Kinet. Katal.*, **13**, 1548 (1972).
[162] Sokolskii D. V., Popova N. M., Babenkova L. V., Blagoveshchenskaya I. N. and Dzhardamalieva K. K., *Izv. Bolg. Akad. Nauk Otd. Khim.*, **6**, 267 (1973).
[163] Savchenko V. J. and Boreskov G. K., *Kinet. Katal.*, **9**, 142 (1968).
[164] Surnov K. N., Bliznakov G. M. and Rishinova M., *Heterogeneous Catalysis*, Proceedings of the Fourth International Symposium, Varna, 1979, Vol. 1, p. 91.
[165] Babenkova L. V., Popova N. M. and Mamashev R. A., *Kataliticheskiye reakcye v zhidkoy faze*, Izd. Nauka, Alma-Ata, 1975, p. 404.
[166] Babenkova L. V., Blagoveshchenskaya I. N., Tyuleneva L. V. and Popova V. M., *Kataliticheskoye gidrirovanye i okislenye*, Izd. Nauka, Alma-Ata, 1974.
[167] Lapuioulade J. and Neil K. S., *Surface Sci.*, **35**, 288 (1973).
[168] Germer G. H. and McRae A. U., *J. Chem. Phys.*, **37**, 1382 (1962).
[169] Yutaka K., Sci Sucke T. and Osamu T., *J. Phys. Chem.*, **68**, 1244 (1964).
[170] Prininger O. and Tataru E., *J. Gas Chromatogr.*, **2**, 323 (1964).
[171] Procop M. and Volter J., *Surface Sci.*, **33**, 69 (1972).
[172] Stephan J. J., Ponec V. and Sachtler W. M., *Surface Sci.*, **47**, 403 (1975).
[173] Tsuchiya S., Amenomiya J. and Cvetanovic R. J., *J. Catal.*, **19**, 245 (1970).
[174] Sokolskii D. V., *Katalizatory gidrogenizatsii*, Izd. Nauka, Alma-Ata, 1975.
[175] Solnyshkova V. K., Babienkova L. V. and Sokolskii D. V. (Eds.) *Katalizatory gidrogenizatsii*, Izd. Nauka, Alma-Ata, 1975.
[176] Farbotko J. M., Ph. D. Thesis, Technical University of Łódź, 1981.

[177] Zakumbaeva G. D. and Sokolskii D. V., *Katalizatory zhidkofaznoy gidrogenizatsyi*, Izd. Nauka, Alma-Ata, 1966.
[178] Balovniev Yu. A. and Tretyakov I. I., *Zh. Fiz. Khim.*, **40**, 1941 (1966).
[179] Sokolskii D. V. and Zakumbaeva G. D., *Adsorbtsya i kataliz na metallakh 8 gruppy v rastvorakh*, Izd. Nauka, Alma-Ata, 1973, p. 58.
[180] Popova N. M., Babenkova L. V., Mamashev R., Omasev C. G. and Sokolskii D. V., *Kataliticheskiye reakcye w zhidkoy faze*, Izd. Nauka, Alma-Ata, 1975, p. 380.
[181] Babenkova L. V., Solnyshkova V. K. and Popova N. M., *Kataliticheskoye gidrirovanye i okislenye*, Izd. Nauka, Alma-Ata, 1974.
[182] Selwood P. W., *J. Catal.*, **42**, 148 (1976).
[183] Zacharov I. I., Pozimentshchikov V. V. and Sutula V. D., *Kinet. Katal.*, **14**, 694. (1973).
[184] Tarina D., Weissmann K. and Barb D., *J. Catal.*, **11**, 348 (1968).
[185] Suhrmann R., Herman A. and Wedler G., *Z. Phys. Chem.*, **35**, 155 (1962).
[186] Omasev C. G., Zakumbaeva G. D. and Sokolskii D. V., *Dokl. Akad. Nauk SSSR*, 234, 1132 (1977).
[187] Delchas T. A. and Tompkins F. C., *Trans. Faraday Soc.*, **64**, 1915 (1968).
[188] Yates D. J. C., Taylor W. F. and Sinfelt J. H., *J. Am. Chem. Soc.*, **86**, 2996 (1964).
[189] Bartholomew C. H. and Boudart M., *J. Catal.*, **25**, 173 (1972).
[190] Richardson J. T. and Dudus R. J., *J. Catal.*, **54**, 207 (1978).
[191] Paryjczak T., Rynkowski J. and Karski S., *J. Chromatogr.*, **188**, 254 (1980).
[192] Karski S. and Paryjczak T., *React. Kinet. Catal. Lett.*, **15**, 419 (1980).
[193] Martin G. A., Ceaphalam N. and Montgolfier P., *J. Chim. Phys.*, **70**, 1422 (1973).
[194] Bartholomew C. H. and Farrauto R. J., *J. Catal.*, **45**, 41 (1976).
[195] Komiyama M., Merrill R. P. and Harnserger H. F., *J. Catal.*, **63**, 35 (1980).
[196] Fleisch T. and Aberman R., *J. Catal.*, **50**, 268 (1977).
[197] Jóźwiak K. W. and Paryjczak T., *J. Catalysis*, **79**, 196 (1983).
[198] Stephan J. J. and Ponec V., *J. Catal.*, **37**, 81 (1975).
[199] Boudart M., Aldag A. V. and Vannice M. A., *J. Catal.*, **18**, 46 (1970).
[200] Brennan D. and Hayes F. H., *Trans. Faraday Soc.* **60**, 589 (1964).
[201] Stephan J. J., Professorial dissertation, Leiden, 1975.
[202] Morgan A. E. and Somorjai G. A., *Surface Sci.*, **12**, 405 (1968).
[203] Winterbottom W. L., *Surface Sci.*, **37**, 195 (1973).
[204] Stephan J. J., Franke P. L. and Ponec V., *J. Catal.*, **44**, 359 (1976).
[205] Madden H. M. and Ertl G., *Surface Sci.*, **35**, 211 (1973).
[206] Madden H. M., Kruppers J. and Ertl G., *J. Vac. Sci. and Technol.* **10**, 26 (1973).
[207] Falconer J. L., Wentreek P. R. and Wise H., *J. Catal.*, **45**, 248 (1976).
[208] Marbrow R. A., Ph. D. Thesis, Univ. of Cambridge, 1977.
[209] Marbrow R. A. and Lambert R. M., *Surface Sci.*, **67**, 489 (1977).
[210] Sexton B. A. and Somorjai G. A., *J. Catal.*, **46**, 167 (1977).
[211] Yates J. T., Williams E. D. and Weinberg W. H., *Surface Sci.*, **91**, 562 (1980).
[212] Maubert A., Martin G. A., Paraliaud H. and Turlier P., *React. Kinet. Catal. Lett.*, **22**, 203 (1983).
[213] Paryjczak T. and Karski S., *React. Kinet. Catal. Lett.*, **15**, 419 (1980).

Chapter 7

Determination of Catalyst Surface Acidity

7.1 Introduction

The catalytic activity of a large group of catalysts used in cracking, hydrocracking, isomerization, polymerization of alkenes, dehydration of alcohols and many other processes is due to the acidity of their surfaces. Knowledge of the number and strength of acidic sites, and also the type of acidity (Brönsted and Lewis) involved, is extremely important as it helps to explain the mechanism of reactions occurring at the surface of these catalysts, and to select the best catalysts for given reactions. The correlation of surface acidity and catalytic activity has not yet been fully explained. It is assumed that in the ionic lattices, the surface cations are Lewis acid sites L whereas the surface anions are Lewis base sites Z. Apart from this, anions containing hydrogen can dissociate with the release of protons — we thus get Brönsted acid sites B.

(Z) (L) O O Me O O (B) H O ⇌ O O Me (−)O O H⁺ O (7.1)

Water coordinately bound to a Lewis site may dissociate and transform it into a Brönsted site [1–3]. It is well known that aquacomplexes are more strongly acidic than pure water.

H H O O O Me O O O ⇌ H⁺ ŌH O O Me O O O (7.2)

The Brönsted acidity can be enhanced by attaching a hydrogen halide to a Lewis site.

$$\text{XH}\text{–}\text{MeO}_5 \rightleftharpoons \text{X}^-\text{–}\text{MeO}_5 \;\; \text{H}^+ \qquad (7.3)$$

where X = F, Cl.

Typical solid acidic catalysts include inorganic oxides of elements with a constant valency, e.g.

in MeO_6 octahedra	in MeO_4 tetrahedra
Me = Al^{3+}, Sc^{4+}, Ti^{4+}, Zr^{4+}	Me = Al^{3+}, B^{+3}, Si^{+4}, P^{+5}

The total charge on the polyhedron is equal to $(v-2c)$e, where v is the oxidation state and c the coordination number. Mixed oxides are much more active catalysts. The presence of acidic sites on the surface of natural aluminosilicates is due largely to the existence of unbalanced negative charges in the crystal lattice. The negative lattice charge is brought about mainly by the isomorphous substitution of tetravalent silicon by trivalent aluminium in SiO_4 tetrahedra [4]. The trivalent aluminium at the surface, needing two electrons to fill up its p orbital, forms Lewis acid sites or, in the presence of water, Brönsted acid sites [5, 6]. The surface acidity of amorphous aluminosilicates is explained in the same way [7, 8]. In synthetic crystalline aluminosilicates, the presence of AlO_4 tetrahedra in the zeolite structure causes negative charges to remain unbalanced and these form ion-exchange sites. If these charges are balanced with protons, we get Brönsted-type activity. If the protons are replaced with multivalent cations, the electrostatic field within the zeolite pores (spherical spaces) is modified and the existence of acidic sites of both types is rendered possible [9].

7.2 Methods of Determining Surface Acidity

Numerous experimental methods of determining the surface acidity of catalysts have been described in detail by Goldstein [10], but they make it difficult to distinguish between Brönsted and Lewis sites. As a matter of fact, only the overall number of acidic sites can be measured regardless of their type; they can only be distinguished by their strength. The concentration of acidic sites on the surface of an aluminosilicate catalyst, depending on the conditions of its preparation and its chemical composition, varies from 10^{12} to 10^{14} sites per cm^2, which corresponds to 0.2–20% of the catalyst's surface area. The energy of acidic sites can be expressed in any units, though usually in the form of the energy released during the reaction of amino-bases with the acidic sites, or in the ability to convert indicators, and is of the order of 50–400 kJ/mol. The surface acidity in aqueous solutions can be estimated by titrating a suspension of the catalyst with a base, by ion-exchange — often used for zeolites [11] — or by poisoning the catalyst surface with alkali metals [12–15]. It is impossible to determine the type of acidity in aqueous solutions since Lewis acid sites can change into Brönsted acid sites. Furthermore, the catalyst poisoning method cannot be applied universally, as a simple relationship between the poisoning of a catalyst and the rate of reaction cannot be found for all cases.

More reliable results of surface acidity determinations are obtained in non-aqueous solutions by differentially titrating *n*-butylamine against adsorption indicators [16–26] (for uncoloured catalysts). Hammett indicators [21] and arylmethanol [23–27] are used as indicators. The Hammett indicators determine the distribution of acidic strength characterized by the so-called "H_0 acid function", which at the same time defines the strength of the Brönsted and Lewis sites. Only Brönsted sites can be estimated with arylmethanol [27]. These indicators change colour when passing from the basic form to the acidic form during the reaction with an acidic site of appropriate strength.

Triphenylchloromethane is a useful reagent for selectively determining Lewis sites

$$(C_6H_5)_3C\cdot Cl + L \rightarrow (C_6H_5)_3C^+ + Cl^- - L . \qquad (7.4)$$

Lewis acid sites can be estimated using Trambouze's method [30, 31]. This is based on the adsorption of ethyl acetate or dioxane, which are typical Lewis bases. The number of Lewis acid sites in aluminosilicate catalysts estimated in this way decreases as the SiO_2 content increases, and is extremely small for pure SiO_2. The surface acidic sites can also be determined by potentiometrically titrating the catalyst with *n*-butylamine in a solution of acetonitrile [32], or calorimetrically, by determining the amount of heat evolved during the reaction of *n*-butylamine with the acidic sites [33–35]. Surface activity is determined spectroscopically using IR [36–41, 71, 78–83], UV, and part of the visible spectrum [42–46, 83–85]. Information on the acidity of a surface is provided by the spectra of hydroxyl groups and molecules adsorbed on the surface, usually ammonia and pyridine. Brönsted and Lewis acid sites can be distinguished spectroscopically.

A basic drawback of the methods used to determine the surface acidity of catalysts in the liquid phase is the fact that the experiments are carried out in conditions different from those in which catalytic reactions normally proceed [47]. At the operating temperature of catalysts, the acidic strength of the sites may change as a result of the removal of water, increases in bond lengths in the crystalline structure of catalysts, etc. That is why methods of determining the surface acidity of catalysts based on adsorption from the gaseous phase, both under static [48–56] and dynamic conditions [35, 47, 57–63, 86–88] are of such significance. Ammonia is the most common adsorbate, although pyridine [55, 64], quinoline [65–67], carbon dioxide [10], alkenes [55, 56], hydrogen sulphide [68], boroethane [69] and boron fluoride [70] are also used. The strength of the acidic sites is generally characterized by the desorption temperature of the chemisorbed bases [49, 50], the heat of adsorption [50] or the activation energy of desorption [53].

7.3 Chromatographic Determination of Surface Acidity

A fundamental problem with the determination of surface acidity by static methods, based on the adsorption of organic bases or ammonia from the gaseous phase, is the difficulty of taking readings at high temperatures — the adsorbate may undergo some chemical change as a result of being in prolonged contact with the catalyst surface. The complexity of the apparatus and the long measurement time also exert an adverse effect. We can obtain conditions very closely approaching those of real catalytic processes if we use chromatography to determine surface acidity. The frontal, elution and elution-frontal techniques are suitable here [55–76].

Ammonia is the adsorbate most often used because of its many advantages, including small molecular size ($\omega_m = 0.16\,nm^2$), great stability at high temperatures, and a suitable dissociation constant enabling surface sites of both high and low acidic strength to be determined; furthermore, it is easily obtained in a highly pure state.

Some workers [36, 74, 75] have criticized the use of ammonia to determine surface acidity because it is a fairly strong base; it is also adsorbed at weak acidic sites which practically do not take part in the catalytic process. Apart from this, there may be some exchange at high temperatures between NH_3 molecules and OH groups with the formation of water molecules and NH_2 groups on the surface. Despite these reservations, the results of acidity estimations using ammonia correlate better with the catalytic activity than do the data obtained from the differential titration of *n*-butylamine against adsorption indicators [73]. The use of different adsorbates for different catalysts, depending on their properties, seems to be a better proposition than trying to look for a universal adsorbate.

Apart from ammonia, one finds that pyridine, benzene, aliphatic amines and quinoline, among others, are used to determine surface acidity by chromatography.

It was Eberly [57] who, for the first time in 1961, estimated the acidity of aluminium oxide, silicon dioxide and aluminosilicate catalysts by frontal chromatography with ammonia as adsorbate. He determined the adsorption of ammonia at high temperatures: 533, 644 and 755 K. A simplified diagram of his apparatus, without the equipment for purifying the carrier gas and adsorbate, is shown in Fig. 7.1.

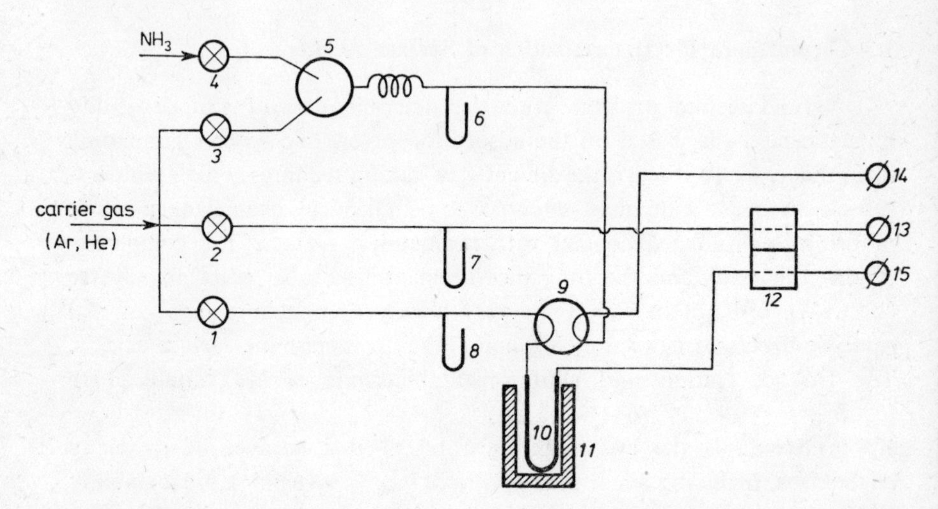

Fig. 7.1 Diagram of the apparatus used to determine surface acidity by frontal chromatography (after P. E. Eberly [57]):

1, 2, 3, 4 — fine control valves, *5* — mixer, *6, 7, 8* — manometers, *9* — four-way tap, *10* — U-tube containing tested adsorbent, *11* — resistance oven, *12* — katharometer, *13, 14, 15* — flow-meters.

The determination of surface acidity by chromatography can be divided into three stages:

(1) initial heating of the sample at 773–873 K in a stream of air or carrier gas (helium, argon) to remove moisture and possible organic compounds;

(2) adsorption and desorption proper of the physically adsorbed ammonia at the temperature of adsorption;

(3) desorption of chemisorbed ammonia during the gradual programmed temperature rise to 773–923 K [60–63].

After having initially heated the sample of catalyst (particle size 0.25–0.5 mm) at 773–873 K in a stream of carrier gas (or, at first, in air), the column is cooled to the measurement temperature, while maintaining a continuous flow of carrier gas at the same time. After reaching the required temperature, ammonia is injected into the carrier gas. The mixture of carrier gas and ammonia flows through the catalyst layer. The moment the surface of the sample becomes saturated with ammonia it begins to flow out of the column, and this fact is recorded on the chromatogram as a front (*AB*, Fig. 7.2).

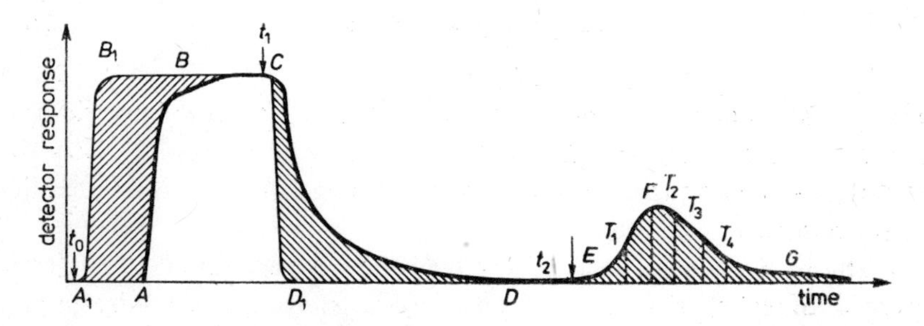

Fig. 7.2 A typical chromatogram of ammonia adsorption. The area A_1AB_1B corresponds to the total amount of sorbed ammonia, the area D_1CD to the quantity of physically sorbed NH_3; the thermodesorption peak *EFG* is the amount of chemisorbed ammonia.

When the height of the chromatogram is constant (plateau), the flow of ammonia is interrupted. The physically-adsorbed ammonia is removed from the surface of the catalyst by a stream of carrier gas until the recorder pen regains the base line. The ammonia chemisorbed on the catalyst's surface is removed by thermodesorption. Depending on the system being tested, the temperature is raised at a constant rate to 773–923 K [61]. The chemisorbed ammonia now removed from the surface of the catalyst is indicated on the chromatogram (Fig. 7.2, curve *EFG*). Figure 7.2 illustrates a typical chromatogram. The curve *AB* represents the adsorption front of ammonia, curve *CD* its desorption. Curves A_1B_1 and CD_1 represent the fronts of the non-adsorbed carrier gas. The total amount of adsorbed ammonia is proportional to the area A_1B_1BA, the amount of physically adsorbed ammonia is proportional to the area CDD_1. The difference between these two areas is proportional to the amount of chemisorbed ammonia and corresponds to the amount of thermally desorbed ammonia given by curve *EFG*. The strength of the acidic sites is characterized by the amount of ammonia chemisorbed at different temperatures. To do this, perpendiculars representing intermediate temperatures can be dropped from the desorption curve *EFG* to the base line, then the area corresponding to a given temperature can be estimated. The amount of ammonia chemisorbed over a given range of temperature can be calculated from these areas, and from them the distribution of acidic sites can be determined.

The quantity of ammonia sorbed by the catalyst is calculated from the equation

$$a_{NH_3} = \frac{kF_c}{mw} S(\mu mol/g), \tag{7.5}$$

where k is the detector constant ($\mu mol/cm^3 cm$), F_c is the volumetric flow rate of the carrier gas (cm^3/min), m is the mass of catalyst (g), w is the recorder tape speed (cm/min), and S is the area AA_1BB_1 (total quantity of ammonia).

The high values of a_{NH_3} at low temperatures correspond to the total number of acidic sites on the surface (including physical adsorption). As the temperature is raised, the weaker acidic sites can no longer hold the chemisorbed ammonia, which remains only at the strong sites. The relationship between the quantity of chemisorbed ammonia and the reciprocal of the temperature is a linear one [61], and can be written as the equation

$$N = A + \frac{B}{T}, \tag{7.6}$$

where N is the number of acidic sites determined from chemisorption data, assuming that one molecule of NH_3 occupies one acidic site, A is a constant depending on the composition of the catalyst, and B is a constant dependent on the nature of the catalyst's surface.

The chromatogram in Fig. 7.3 shows the rapid desorption of ammonia on Al_2O_3 [55]. Increasing the sample outgassing temperature before starting the programmed heating of the column reduces the ammonia peak area and shifts its apex in the direction of the higher temperatures. When ethene was used as adsorbate, two distinct types of acidic site

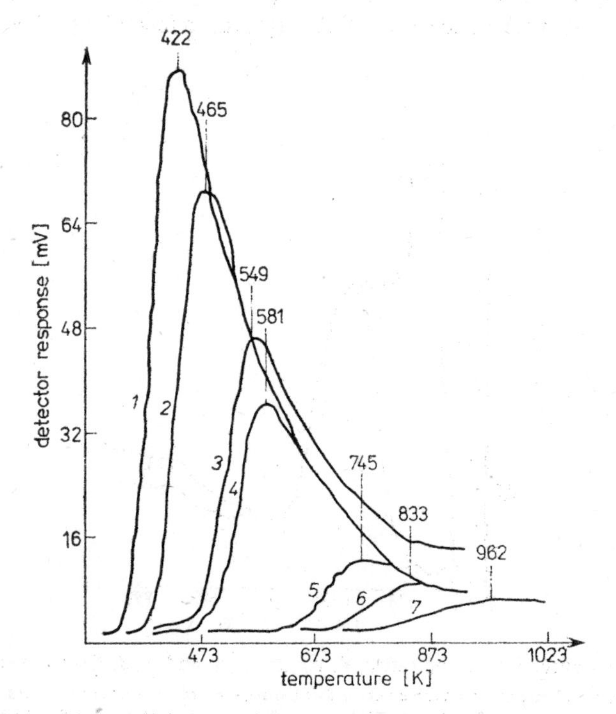

Fig. 7.3 TPD curve for various amounts of adsorbed ammonia; programmed rate of heating β = 15.2°/min (outgassing before heating for 2.5 h at the following temperatures (after Y. Amenomiya *et al.* [55]):
1 — 297 K, *2* — 348 K, *3* — 423 K, *4* — 448 K, *5* — 598 K, *6* — 673 K, *7* — 773 K.

were found [56]. Figure 7.4 shows the chromatogram obtained during the rapid desorption of ethene from an Al_2O_3 surface [56]. There are two ethene peaks on the chromatogram which correspond to two kinds of acidic sites with different energies of adsorption. If before heating the sample is outgassed at 373 K, the first peak disappears, but the other one remains (Fig. 7.4).

If different programmed rates of heating (β) are applied in the experiments, the activation energy of desorption E_d can be determined from the equation

$$2\log T_M - \log\beta = \frac{E_d}{2.3RT_M} + \frac{\log E_d V_m}{Rk_0}, \tag{7.7}$$

where T_M is the peak maximum temperature, E_d is the activation energy of desorption, V_m is the adsorption capacity of the adsorbate, and k_0 is the component part of the rate of desorption, independent of temperature.

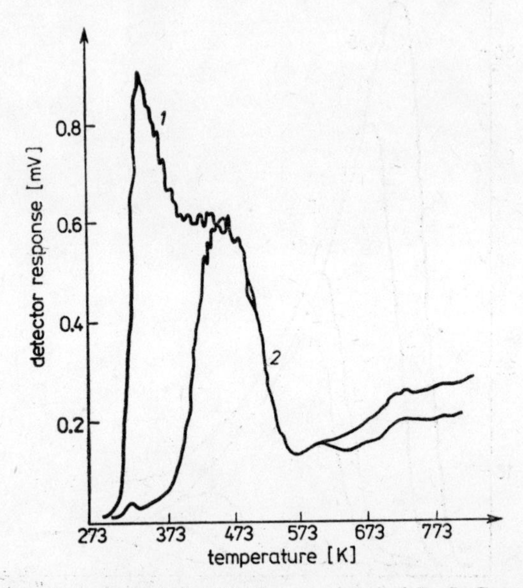

Fig. 7.4 TPD curve for ethene (after Y. Amenomiya and R. J. Cvetanovic [56]):
1 — outgassing for 10 min at room temperature before heating (programmed rate of heating β = 16.03°/min), *2* — outgassing for 6 min at 373 K before heating (programmed rate of heating β = 15.90°/min).

The irreversible chemisorption of ammonia has also been estimated by pulse GC [58, 59, 73]. The reversibly-sorbed ammonia was eluted by the stream of carrier gas, and the irreversibly-sorbed fraction was determined from the difference between the amounts of ammonia introduced and eluted, or by TPD.

Misono *et al.* [35] proposed a method of simultaneously estimating the distribution of acidic sites — their strength and their catalytic activity as studied under catalytic operating conditions. The method is based on the determination of the retention volume and heat of adsorption of benzene (a weak base) on the catalyst, while at the same time covering its surface with pyridine (a strong base), assuming that the pyridine is adsorbed first at the strongest acidic sites, then at successively weaker ones. The experiment was carried out in the following way. At first, very small samples of benzene were injected into the carrier gas stream and its retention times at various temperatures were measured in order to determine the isosteric heat of adsorption at the strongest acidic sites. These strongest sites were then poisoned with pyridine using the frontal technique (initially, the partial pressure of pyridine was 0.4 kPa.) The irreversible adsorption of pyridine was estimated in the same way as for ammonia (Fig. 7.2 — the difference between areas AA_1BB_1 and D_1CD). The isosteric heats of adsorption of benzene were estimated at the strongest unpoisoned acidic sites remaining on the surface. By successively poisoning ever weaker acidic sites with increasing concentrations of pyridine in the carrier gas (up to a partial pressure of 5.65 kPa) and determining the heat of adsorption of benzene, the entire range of surface acidic sites was studied. If instead of benzene some reacting substance is released on to the catalyst, one can, on the basis of the reaction products corresponding to the various degrees of poisoning of the acidic sites with pyridine, investigate the activity and selectivity of the catalyst at different stages of the reaction, depending on its acidity. Kiselev *et al.* [78] used a similar technique when they gradually poisoned the surface of an aluminosilicate catalyst with pulse-wise introduced pyridine to estimate the heats of adsorption of benzene, toluene, xylene and cumene.

The use of chromatography to determine the acidity of catalyst surfaces has enabled further valuable knowledge about acid-base effects in heterogeneous catalysis to be gathered. Since the possibilities of elution chromatography to study surface acidity have not yet been fully implemented, further research in this field may be expected in the near future. The pulse technique is particularly convenient for measuring irreversible adsorption since part of the reversibly sorbed adsorbate is automatically eluted.

References

[1] Pines H. and Haag W. O., *J. Am. Chem. Soc.*, **82**, 2472 (1960).
[2] Pines H. and Ravoise J., *J. Phys. Chem.*, **65**, 1859 (1961).
[3] Kieżel L. and Rutkowski M., *Wiadomości Chem.*, **23**, 721 (1969).
[4] Hansford R. C. in: *Advances in Catalysis and Related Subjects*, Ed. Frankenburg W. G., Academic Press Inc., New York, 1952, Vol. IV.

[5] Tamele M. W., *Disc. Faraday Soc.*, **8**, 270 (1950).
[6] Milliken T. H., Mills G. and Oblad A. G., *Disc. Faraday Soc.*, **8**, 279 (1959).
[7] Thomas C. L., *Ind. Eng. Chem.*, **41**, 2564 (1949).
[8] Fiedorow R. and Dudzik Z., *Wiadomości Chem.*, **32**, 309 (1978).
[9] Hirschler A. E., *J. Catal.*, **2**, 428 (1963).
[10] Goldstein M. S. in: *Experimental Methods in Catalytic Research*, Ed. Anderson, Academic Press, New York, London, 1968, p. 361.
[11] Holm V. C. F., Bailey G. C. and Clark A., *J. Phys. Chem.*, **63**, 129 (1959).
[12] Danforth J. O., *J. Phys. Chem.*, **58**, 1130 (1954).
[13] Stright D. and Danforth J. O., *J. Phys. Chem.*, **57**, 448 (1953).
[14] Topchieva K. V. and Moskovskaya I. E., *Dokl. Akad. Nauk SSSR*, **101**, 517 (1958); **123**, 891 (1958).
[15] Kocarenko L. G. and Dzisko V. A., *Kinet. Katal.*, **9**, 319 (1968).
[16] Benesi H. A., *J. Am. Chem. Soc.*, **78**, 5490 (1956).
[17] Benesi H. A., *J. Phys. Chem.*, **61**, 970 (1957).
[18] Bertolacini R. J., *Anal. Chem.*, **35**, 599 (1963).
[19] Walling C., *J. Am. Chem. Soc.*, **72**, 1164 (1950).
[20] Tamele M. W., *Dis. Faraday Soc.*, **8**, 270 (1950).
[21] Hammett L. P. and Paul M. A., *J. Am. Chem. Soc.*, **56**, 327 (1934).
[22] Hammett L. P. and Deymp A. J., *J. Am. Chem. Soc.*, **54**, 2721 (1932).
[23] Deno N. C., Berkheimer M. E., Evans W. L. and Peterson H. J., *J. Am. Chem. Soc.*, **77**, 3044 (1955); **81**, 2344 (1959).
[24] Deno N. C., Groves P. T. and Saines G., *J. Am. Chem. Soc.*, **81**, 5790 (1959).
[25] Deno N. C. and Houser J. J., *J. Am. Chem. Soc.*, **86**, 1741 (1964).
[26] Deno N. C. and Pittman C. U., *J. Am. Chem. Soc.*, **86**, 1744 (1964).
[27] Hirschler A. E., *J. Catal.*, **2**, 371 (1963).
[28] Leftin H. P. and Hall W. K., *Actes du Deuxieme Congres International de Catalyse*, Technip, Paris, 1961, p. 1353.
[29] Sato M., Aonuma T. and Shiba T., *Proceedings of the 3rd International Congress on Catalysis*, Amsterdam 1965, North-Holland Publishing Company, Amsterdam, 1965, p. 396.
[30] Trambouze Y., *Comp. Rend.*, **237**, 648 (1951).
[31] Trambouze Y., de Mourgues L. and Perrin M., *J. chim. phys.*, **51**, 723 (1954).
[32] Clark R. O., Ballou E. V. and Barth R. T., *Anal. Chim. Acta*, **23**, 189 (1960).
[33] Chessick J. J. and Zettlenmoyer A. C., *Adv. Catal.*, **11**, 263 (1959).
[34] Zettlemoyer A. C. and Chessick J. J., *J. Phys. Chem.*, **64**, 113 (1960).
[35] Misono M., Saito Y. and Yoneda Y., *Proceedings of the 3rd International Congress on Catalysis*, Amsterdam 1964, Wiley, New York, 1964, p. 408.
[36] Parry E. P., *J. Catal.*, **2**, 371 (1963).
[37] Basila M. R., Kantner T. R. and Rhee K. H., *J. Phys. Chem.*, **68**, 3197 (1964).
[38] Szczepańska S. and Malinowski S., *J. Catal.*, **15**, 68 (1969).
[39] Basila M. R. and Kantner T. R., *J. Phys. Chem.*, **70**, 1681 (1966).
[40] Tanaka K. and Ozaki A., *J. Catal.*, **8**, 1 (1967).
[41] Kiselev A. V. and Lygin V. I., *Usp. Khim.*, **31**, 351 (1962).
[42] Dollish F. R. and Hall W. K., *J. Phys. Chem.*, **69**, 4402 (1962).
[43] Hirschler A. E. and Schneider A. J., *J. Chem. Eng. Data*, **6**, 313 (1961).
[44] Leftin H. P. and Hobson M. C., *Adv. Catal.*, **14**, 115 (1963).

[45] Ciecierska-Tworek Z., *Wiadomości Chem.*, **1**, 1 (1972).
[46] Drushel H. V. and Sommers A. L., *Anal. Chem.*, **38**, 1723 (1966).
[47] Paryjczak T., *Wiadomości Chem.*, **22**, 481 (1968).
[48] Clark A., Holm C. F. and Blackburk O. M., *J. Catal.*, **1**, 244 (1962).
[49] Barth R. T. and Ballou E. V., *Anal. Chem.*, **33**, 1080 (1961).
[50] Webb A. W., *Ind. Eng. Chem.*, **47**, 261 (1957).
[51] Richardson R. J. and Benson C. W., *J. Phys. Chem.*, **61**, 406 (1957).
[52] Forni L., *Catalysis Rev.*, **8**, 65 (1973).
[53] Kubokawa Y., *J. Phys. Chem.*, **63**, 546, 550, 555, 739, 747, 936 (1960) **67**, 769 (1963); **69**, 2676 (1965).
[54] Larson J. G., Gerberich H. R. and Hall W. K., *J. Phys. Chem.*, **87**, 1880 (1965).
[55] Amenomiya Y., Chenier J. H. B. and Cvetanovic R. J., *J. Phys. Chem.*, **67**, 54 (1964); **68**, 52 (1964).
[56] Amenomiya Y. and Cvetanovic R. J., *J. Phys. Chem.*, **67**, 144 (1963).
[57] Eberly P. E., *J. Phys. Chem.*, **65**, 68, 1261 (1961).
[58] Pohl K. and Robentisch G., *Z. Chem.*, **5**, 396 (1965).
[59] Hille J., *Chem. Techn.*, **18**, 466 (1966).
[60] Buyanova N. E., Gudkova T. B. and Karnaukhov A. P., *Metody Issled. Katal. Katal. Reakt.*, Izd. Otd. Sibir. Otd. Akad. Nauk SSSR, Novosibirsk, 1965, Vol. 2, p. 55.
[61] Levchuk V. S. and Buyanova N. E., *Izv. Akad. Nauk SSSR, ser. Khim.*, 27, (1972).
[62] Popowicz M., Berak J. M. and Bazarnik A., *Przemysł Chem.*, **51**, 92 (1972).
[63] Witekowa S., Filipiak K. and Jóźwiak K. W., *Przemysł Chem.*, **51**, 807 (1972).
[64] Dovcavadov S. R., Kiselev A. V. and Nikitin I. S., *Kinet. Katal.*, **8**, 238 (1967).
[65] Oblad A. G., Milliken T. H. and Hills G. A. Jr, *Adv. Catal.*, **3**, 199 (1951).
[66] Mills G. A., Boedeker E. R. and Oblad A. G., *J. Am. Chem. Soc.*, **72**, 1554 (1950).
[67] Turkevich J., Nozaki F. and Stamires D., *Proceedings of the 3rd International Congress on Catalysis*, Amsterdam 1964, Wiley, New York, 1965, Vol. 1, p. 586.
[68] De Rossett, J., Finstrom C. G. and Adams C. J., *J. Catal.*, **1**, 235 (1962).
[69] Weiss H. G., Knight J. A. and Shapiro J., *J. Am. Chem. Soc.*, **81**, 1823 (1959).
[70] Schwab C. H. and Krall H., *Proceedings of the 3rd International Congress on Catalysis*, Amsterdam 1964, Wiley, New York 1965, Vol. 1, p. 433.
[71] Tretyakov N. E. and Filimonov V. N., *Kinet. Katal.*, **14**, 803 (1973).
[72] Lobachev V. V., Beznozdrev V. N. and Kazanskii B. A., *Kinet. Katal.*, **14**, 801 (1973).
[73] Filipiak K., Ph. D. Thesis, Technical University of Łódź, 1973.
[74] Peri J. B., *J. Phys. Chem.*, **69**, 231 (1965); **70**, 3168 (1966).
[75] Hirschler A. E., *J. Catal.*, **6**, 1 (1966).
[76] Witekowa S. and Filipiak K., *Zeszyty Naukowe Politechniki Łódzkiej, Chemia*, 34 (1978).
[77] Hall K., Leftin H. P., Cheselke F. J. and O'Reilley D. E., *J. Catal.*, **2**, 506 (1963).
[78] Dzhavadov S. N., Kiselev A. V. and Nikitin J. S., *Zh. Fiz. Khim.*, **42**, 2887 (1968).
[79] Kermarec M., Briend-Faure M. and Delafosse D., *J. Chem. Soc. Faraday Trans.*, 70, 2180 (1974).
[80] Knoezinger H., *Surface*, **40**, 339 (1974).
[81] Kiviet F. E. and Petrahis L., *J. Phys. Chem.*, **77**, 1232 (1973).

[82] Yashima Tatsuaki and Hara Noboyashi, *J. Catal.*, **27**, 329 (1972).
[83] Pickat P., *J. Phys. Chem.*, **78**, 2376 (1974).
[84] Ikemoto Misako, Tsutsumi Kazuo and Takahashi Hiroshi, *Bull. Chem. Soc. Jap.*, **45**, 1330 (1972).
[85] Take Junchiro, Tsuruya Tetsuo, Sato Tetsuo and Yoneda Yukio, *Bull. Chem. Soc. Japan*, **45**, 3409 (1972).
[86] Ai Mamoru and Tsuneo Ikawa, *J. Catal.*, **40**, 203 (1975).
[87] Ai Mamoru, *J. Catal.*, **40**, 318 (1975).
[88] Ai Mamoru, *J. Catal.*, **50**, 291 (1977).

Chapter 8

Determination of the Heat and Other Thermodynamic Functions of Adsorption

8.1 Introduction

Adsorption can be approached not only phenomenologically but also from the energetic point of view; in this way then, we can get an overall view of the process.

The heat of adsorption can be determined in two fundamental ways. One of them is based on the application of the Clausius–Clapeyron equation to adsorption measurements at various temperatures; the other involves direct calorimetric measurements using different types of calorimeter — mostly isothermal and adiabatic [1–6]. Apart from these methods, the heat of adsorption can be estimated from kinetic data [6]. Much useful information can be gained from the relationship of the heat of wetting of solids and the quantity of adsorbate previously adsorbed on their surfaces [4, 7, 8]. The heat exchanged by the system with its surroundings during a given process depends on the nature of that process. If we apply the laws of thermodynamics to experimental data, we may use only those data which correspond to a state of equilibrium. The isosteric heat of adsorption, q_{st}, has recently been estimated by GC from the relationship of the changes of retention times or volumes with temperature, using the Clausius–Clapeyron equation for the calculations; alternatively, virial coefficients can be used (see Chapter 3). Semi-empirical methods for determining the heat of adsorption also exist [9].

Heats of adsorption are the basis for calculating the entropy of adsorption, the free energy change and the chemical potential of an adsorbate during adsorption [10, 11]. In most systems in which physical adsorption takes place, the heats of adsorption for low degrees of coverage considerably exceed the heats of condensation. If the coverage θ is close to a monolayer, these values approach those of the heat of condensation of the adsorbate.

It is reasonable to use the Clausius–Clapeyron equation for calculating the isosteric heat of adsorption from sorption data so long as pressures are low (applicability of Henry's equation) and temperatures fairly close [12, 13, 160].

If the adsorption of a given amount of adsorbate is carried out on a pure, outgassed adsorbent surface, the heat evolved is the so-called integral heat of adsorption ($q_c = \int_0^a q\,\mathrm{d}a$). This heat can be measured directly — isothermally or adiabatically in a calorimeter. It is usually expressed in kJ/mol of adsorbed gas. However, this integral value is only the average heat of adsorption of the injected portion of adsorbate. In adsorption studies, it is important to know the change in the heat of adsorption relative to the degree of coverage of the adsorbent surface, θ. To do this, the gas is introduced in small portions in such a way that each portion covers only a small part of the generally available adsorbent surface. The evolved heats are called the differential heats of adsorption, $q_d(q_d = d_q/\mathrm{d}\theta)$.

The relationship between the differential and isosteric heats of adsorption is given by the equation

$$q_{st} = q_d + RT \;. \tag{8.1}$$

8.2 The Theoretical Basis for Determining the Heat of Adsorption

Adsorption at the surface of a solid is a spontaneous process — it is thus accompanied by a decrease in the standard free energy of the system $\Delta G^\ominus$

$$\Delta G^\ominus = \Delta H^\ominus - T\Delta S^\ominus , \tag{8.2}$$

where $\Delta H^\ominus$ is the change in the standard enthalpy during adsorption, $\Delta S^\ominus$ is the change in standard entropy during adsorption.

The change in the standard free energy $\Delta G^\ominus$ and the equilibrium constant K (Henry's constant) are linked by the following equation:

$$\Delta G^\ominus = -RT \ln K . \tag{8.3}$$

Assuming the rapid attainment of adsorption equilibrium and of the adsorption isotherm within the applicability of Henry's law (a linear section of the isotherm), the specific retention volume V_g is proportional to the partition constant K (of solubility or adsorption)

$$\frac{\mathrm{d}a}{\mathrm{d}c} = K_{a,c} = V_g \,. \tag{8.4}$$

The subscripts to the constant $K_{a,c}$ indicate that the adsorption a has been referred to 1 g of adsorbent and the equilibrium concentration of the gas phase components to unit volume (e.g. mol/l or mmol/l). For a straight-line section of the adsorption isotherm (within the applicability of Henry's law) we get narrow, symmetrical peaks. Over this area of the isotherm, neither the retention volume nor the retention time depends on the size of the injected sample.

If the retention time and retention volume are directly linked to Henry's equilibrium constant K, the thermodynamic characteristics of adsorption can be determined from chromatographic data [14–18].

From equation (8.4) we get

$$K_{a,p} = \frac{a}{p} = \frac{K_{a,c}}{RT} = \frac{V_g}{RT} \,. \tag{8.5}$$

This equation also holds for heterogeneous adsorbent and catalyst surfaces at sufficiently high temperatures and for low degrees of coverage. By substituting expression (8.5) in the Clausius–Clapeyron equation we obtain an expression from which it is easy to determine the isosteric heat of adsorption q_{st} from chromatographic data [19–23], viz.

$$q_{st} = RT^2\left(\frac{\partial \ln p}{\partial T}\right)_a = -R\left(\frac{\partial \ln p}{\partial (1/T)}\right)_a$$

$$= R\frac{\mathrm{d}\ln K_{a,p}}{\mathrm{d}(1/T)} = R\frac{\mathrm{d}\ln \dfrac{V_g}{T}}{\mathrm{d}(1/T)} \,. \tag{8.6}$$

Within the applicability of Henry's law, the isosteric heat of adsorption is independent of a.

If we assume that q_{st} is independent of T, then, since the specific surface area S and the mass of adsorbent m are practically independent of T, we can integrate equation (8.6) and obtain

$$\ln \frac{V_g}{T} = \frac{q_{st}}{RT} + B, \tag{8.7}$$

$$\log \frac{V_g}{T} = \frac{q_{st}}{2.3\ RT} + B, \tag{8.8}$$

where B is a constant of integration.

In order to calculate the isosteric heat of adsorption for narrow, symmetrical peaks, we have to determine the net or adjusted retention

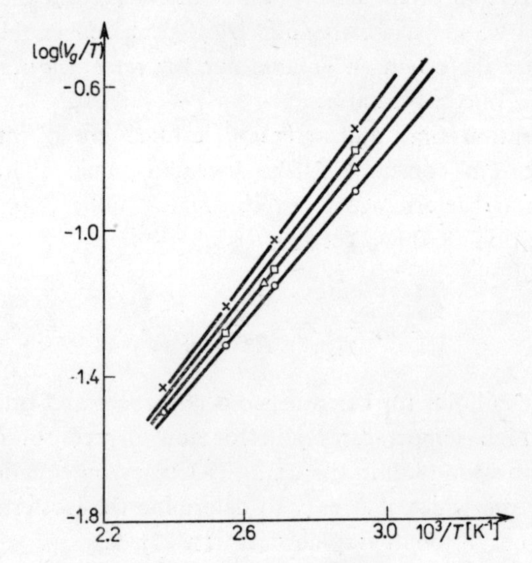

Fig. 8.1 Graph of $\log(V_g/T)$ against $1/T$ for propene on SiO_2 (after R. Grzywna *et al.* [74]):
○ — 5.0; △ — 2.0; □ — 1.5; × — 1.0 cm^3.

volumes for a number of temperatures over the widest possible temperature range, and then construct a graph of $\log(V_g/T)$, $\log(V_R/T)$ or $\log(V_S/T)$ against $1/T$ (Fig. 8.1).

The quantity q_{st} (kJ/mol) is obtained by multiplying the tangent of the angle of inclination of the straight line by 2.303 R. To find q_{st} from the graph of $\log V_g$ (or $\log V_S$, or $\log V_R$) against $1/T$, we must multiply the tangent of the angle of inclination by 2.303 R, then add RT (T is the average temperature of the range studied). If the volumetric flow rate of the carrier gas in the column at different temperatures is kept constant, the isosteric heat of adsorption q_{st} can be estimated directly from

$$\frac{\mathrm{d}\ln t'_R}{\mathrm{d}(1/T)} = \frac{q_{st}}{R}, \tag{8.9}$$

where t'_R is the adjusted retention time. The graph of $\ln t'_R$ against $1/T$ is therefore drawn.

Equation (8.9) holds as long as the adsorption isotherm is linear. In our calculations we have to take into account V_g/T, or the retention volume calculated with respect to a constant temperature, usually 273 K

$$q_{st} = R\frac{\mathrm{d}\ln\dfrac{V_g^{(T)}}{T}}{\mathrm{d}(1/T)} = R\frac{\mathrm{d}\ln V_g^{(273\,\mathrm{K})}}{\mathrm{d}(1/T)} = R\frac{\mathrm{d}\ln t_R}{\mathrm{d}(1/T)}. \tag{8.10}$$

The heat of adsorption can also be calculated from chromatographic data using the Van't Hoff isochore [24]

$$q_{st} = 2.303\,R\,\frac{T_1T_2}{T_2-T_1}\log\frac{V_{g1}}{V_{g2}}, \tag{8.11}$$

where T_1 and T_2 are the absolute temperatures and V_{g1} and V_{g2} are the retention volumes corresponding to them.

For a linear section of the adsorption isotherm we get narrow, symmetrical peaks — the retention volume does not depend on the size of the sample, that is, the heat of adsorption does not depend on the magnitude of a and on the degree of surface coverage θ. In this case retention volumes are calculated from the retention times corresponding to the peak maxima (equation (1.6)).

Where the adsorption isotherm is non-linear and the peaks unsymmetrical, accurate calculation of retention volumes from peak maxima is rather difficult. Further, even if identical amounts of adsorbate are injected, the surface coverage changes with temperature, and thus the basic condition that a = const is violated [25].

For such a case, Carberry [25] proposes that initially the adsorption isotherms be estimated at various temperatures. From them we can find the adsorption isosteres ($\log p$ with respect to $1/T$ at constant a), whose gradient will give the isosteric heat of adsorption

$$q_{st} = -R\left(\frac{\partial\ln p}{\partial(1/T)}\right)_a. \tag{8.12}$$

Beebe and co-workers [26, 27] determined the isosteric heats of adsorption of N_2, Ar, O_2, and CO on various samples of activated charcoal by frontal and pulse GC. Comparison of the values of q_{st} obtained by both these methods with those obtained calorimetrically shows that the pulse technique gives values of q_{st} too low for type II isotherms but too high for type III isotherms. Good results are obtained only for a linear adsorption isotherm. Adsorption isotherms for low degrees of surface coverage at different temperatures were determined by frontal chromatography [28]. The isosteric heat of adsorption was estimated [29] from adsorption isosteres obtained from adsorption isotherms using the Clausius–Clapeyron equation.

The accurate estimation of the heat of adsorption depends on the accuracy of measurement of retention times, gas flow rates and the column temperature; precision is also essential when measuring the size of the adsorbate samples to be injected.

The chief source of error when determining adsorption isotherms chromatographically is the inaccurate measurement of the retention time. As adjusted retention times (the difference between the retention time of a given adsorbate and the gas holdup) are used in calculations, retention times should be made as long as possible in comparison with gas holdups. This can be done by reducing the column temperature — the retention time of the adsorbate is then prolonged without a corresponding extension of the holdup.

In frontal chromatography t'_R is proportional to the quantity of adsorbed adsorbate a. Since the experimental pressure of the adsorbate is constant,

$$\frac{\partial \ln t'_R}{\partial(1/T)} = \left[\frac{\partial \ln a}{\partial(1/T)}\right]_p . \tag{8.13}$$

For a non-linear isotherm [26], having taken q_{st} from equation (8.12) into consideration, we obtain

$$\frac{\partial \ln t'_R}{\partial(1/T)} = -\left(\frac{\partial \ln a}{\ln p}\right)_T \left[\frac{\partial \ln p}{\partial(1/T)}\right]_a = \frac{p}{a}\left[\frac{\partial a}{\partial p}\right]_T \frac{q_{st}}{R} . \tag{8.14}$$

Equation (8.14) differs from equation (8.9) in that we have introduced the additional expression $(p/a)(\partial a/\partial p)_T$. If the adsorption isotherm is linear, this expression is equal to unity. If, however, the adsorption isotherm is non-linear, this factor is greater or smaller than unity, and q_{st}, determined by the pulse technique, is also greater or smaller than the real value.

The heat of adsorption depends on the geometrical and electronic structure of the adsorbate and adsorbent molecules. For n-alkanes the heat of adsorption is a linear function of the number of carbon atoms in the molecule. Wolf and Beyer [30] have even put forward a method of determining the specific surface area of catalysts and adsorbents based on a simple relationship between the heat of adsorption of a homologous series of alkanes and the number of carbon atoms in their molecules n

$$\ln V_g^0 = \frac{\Delta\lambda}{RT} n + \ln(\text{const}\, S), \tag{8.15}$$

where $\Delta\lambda$ is the heat of adsorption per carbon atom in the hydrocarbon molecule, S is the specific surface area, V_g^0 is the specific retention time obtained by extrapolating to $n = 0$ on the graph of $\log V_g$ against n.

It can be seen from Fig. 8.2 that the heats of adsorption estimated chromatographically on graphitized carbon black are somewhat lower

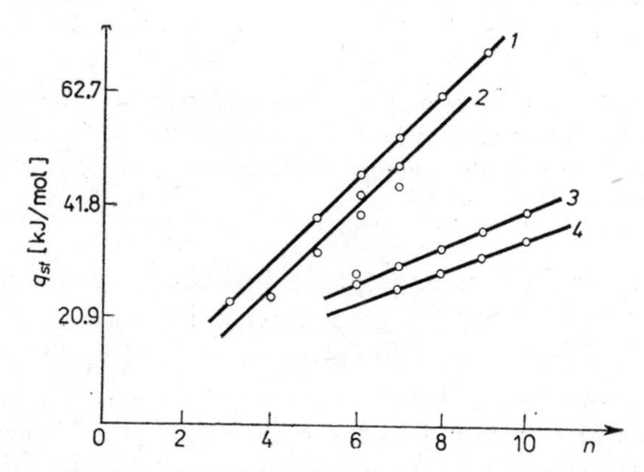

Fig. 8.2 Heats of adsorption of n-alkanes with respect to the number of carbon atoms in the molecule n on graphitized carbon black (*1*, *2*) and silica gels (*3*, *4*) (*1*,*3* — calorimetric data, *2*,*4* — chromatographic data) (after R. S. Petrova *et al.* [24]).

than the values obtained calorimetrically [24]. This difference increases considerably if as adsorbent we use the heterogeneous surface of silica gel instead of the homogeneous surface of graphitized carbon black (Fig. 8.3) [15].

It is evident from Fig. 8.3 that the heats of adsorption estimated chromatographically are much lower than those determined calorimetrically. It must be said that peak symmetry is not sufficient evidence for thermodynamic equilibrium having been attained in the chromatographic column. This was demonstrated, for example, by Keybal *et al.* [31], who described the adsorption of normal hydrocarbons on the non-porous and

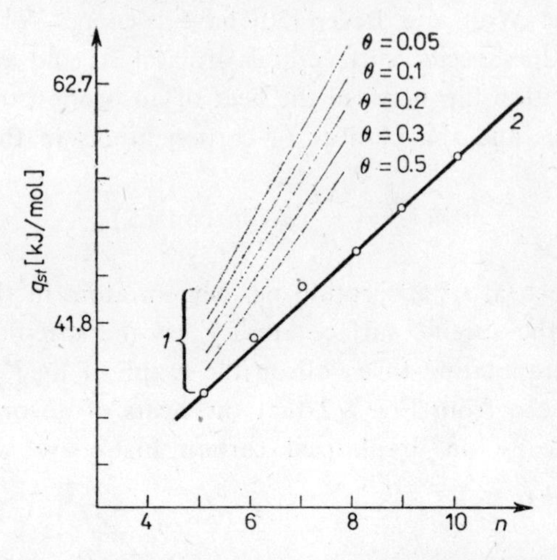

Fig. 8.3 Heats of adsorption of *n*-alkanes on wide-pored silica gels with respect to the number of carbon atoms in the adsorbate molecule (after A. V. Kiselev *et al.* [15]): *1* — heat of adsorption obtained calorimetrically at 293 K for various degrees of surface coverage, *2* — heat of adsorption obtained chromatographically.

thermally uniform surface of graphitized carbon black and in the narrow capillaries of NaX zeolite. We get symmetrical peaks for both adsorbents, but strong peak broadening takes place on the NaX zeolite as the number of carbon atoms in the hydrocarbon increases — it is difficult for the larger molecules to diffuse into the NaX zeolite pores. Despite the symmetrical, though broad, peaks, the processes taking place in the column are far from doing so at equilibrium. Therefore one should expect discrepancies between the thermodynamic values calculated from the maxima of strongly broadened symmetrical peaks and the values obtained under static conditions. This difference becomes greater as the adsorbate molecule size and adsorption energy increase (Fig. 8.4). Proof of this are the heats of adsorption determined for alcohols on zeolites which are one order of magnitude smaller than the real values [75]. The estimation of heats of adsorption using virial coefficients, described in Chapter 3, has many advantages [170].

If we use GC to estimate the heats of adsorption of relatively weakly adsorbing noble gases and lower hydrocarbons on geometrically uniform zeolite crystals, we obtain results which approach those obtained calorimetrically. Particularly good agreement is obtained on a homogeneous, non-porous and non-specific adsorbent such as thermally graphitized carbon black.

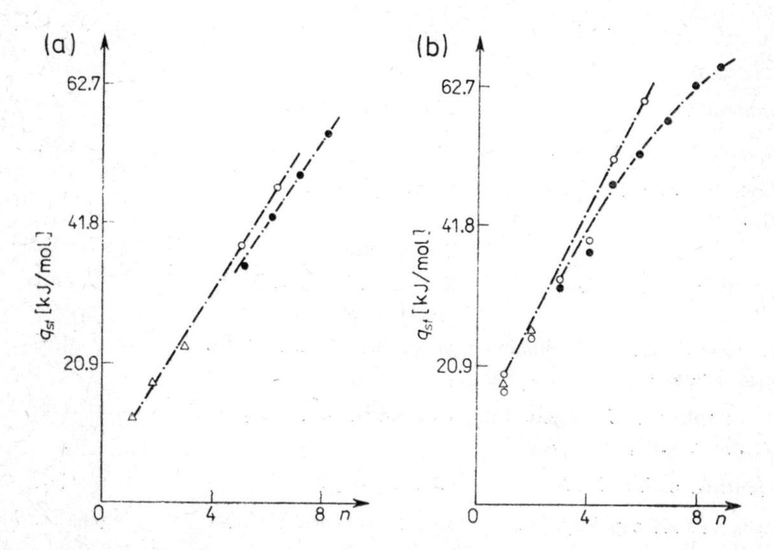

Fig. 8.4 The relationship between q_{st} for n-alkanes at low degrees of surface coverage and the number of carbon atoms n on thermally graphitized carbon black (a) and NaX zeolite (b) (after V. A. Keybal [31]):
○ — calorimetric method, ● — GC method, △ — adsorption method using isosteres.

The fact that we get much lower values for the heat of adsorption with chromatographic methods than with calorimetric methods on heterogeneous surfaces could be explained in the following way. While estimating the heat of adsorption chromatographically it is possible that full thermodynamic equilibrium is not achieved — especially at the most active sites in the narrow pores. Whether or not adsorption equilibrium has in fact been reached in the column can be checked, for example, by estimating the height equivalent to a theoretical plate at a lower temperature; if this then increases, equilibrium has not been attained. That equilibrium in the column has not yet been reached can also be confirmed by an increase in the specific retention volume when the carrier gas flow rate decreases. In the vacuum apparatus (calorimetric

Table 8.1 EXAMPLES OF THE CHROMATOGRAPHIC DETERMINATION OF THE ISOSTERIC HEAT OF ADSORPTION

Adsorbent	*Adsorbate*	*References*
SiO_2, Al_2O_3, 5A zeolite	Ar, O_2, N_2, CO, CH_4, Kr	[19]
SiO_2, activated charcoal	CO, CO_2	[37, 161]
Activated charcoal	hydrocarbons	[38]
Aluminosilicate, MoO_3–Al_2O_3	benzene, heptane	[39]
13X zeolite, SiO_2, Pt/Al_2O_3	benzene	[40]
Various ionic forms of 13X zeolite	benzene, hexane	[41]
Zeolites (various)	hydrocarbons	[42, 171]
Graphitized carbon black	Kr, Xe, $CHCl_3$, CCl_4, hydrocarbons	[20]
Silicon-magnesium and aluminosilicate catalysts	*m*-xylene, *n*-octane, toluene	[43]
Various forms of X zeolite Li^+, Na^+, Mg^{2+}, Ca^{2+}, Ba^{2+}, Ag^+	hydrocarbons, O_2, N_2	[44]
Graphitized carbon black	C_4H_{10}, C_5H_{12}, C_6H_{14}	[45]
SiO_2 in various capillary sizes	alkanes, alkenes, alcohols	[46, 51, 74]
CaA zeolite	hydrocarbons C_1–C_4	[47]
CaX, CaA, NaX	O_2, N_2, CO, hydrocarbons, benzene	[48, 71]
CaA 5A (different moisture contents)	H_2, O_2, N_2, CH_4, CO, Kr, Xe	[49]
CaA 5A, NaX 13X, SiO_2, activated charcoal, Al_2O_3	Ar, O_2, N_2, CO, CO_2, hydrocarbons C_1–C_4	[50]
Macropore SiO_2, graphitized carbon black, NaX and NaA zeolites	*n*-alkanes	[31]
Al_2O_3	hydrocarbons (benzene, cyclohexane, toluene, *n*-heptane)	[52–54]
Graphitized carbon black	various adsorbates	[20, 27, 33, 34, 167, 168]
MgO	*n*-alkanes, benzene, toluene	[35]
TiO_2 with respect to moisture content	hydrocarbons	[36]
Aluminosilicate catalyst	saturated hydrocarbons	[55]

Table 8.1 (continued)

Adsorbent	*Adsorbate*	*References*
Bentonite-34	hexene, cyclohexene, pentane	[56]
Various zeolites of type Y, Na, Mg, Ca, Sr, Ba, Cd, Nd	propene, *n*-hexane, benzene	[57]
Aluminosilicate catalyst	naphthalene, alkylnaphthalenes	[58]
Ag_2O, CuO	CO_2	[59]
Activated charcoal	noble gases, nitrogen, methane	[60]
Cobalt oxide	hydrocarbons C_4-C_6	[61]
Sodium zeolites, Linde Y SK-40 (various Na content)	benzene, toluene, ethylbenzene, xylenes	[62]
Bi_2O_3, MoO_3, SiO_2, Bi-Mo/SiO_2 catalyst	propene, propane, acrolein, CO_2	[63, 169]
Porapak S	Ar, CH_4, CO_2, O_2, N_2	[64]
Porasil C (modified Na_2SO_4), graphitized carbon black	various hydrocarbon halides	[65]
Activated charcoal	oxygen, hydrogen	[66]
Al_2O_3	cyclohexene	[67]
Graphitized carbon black	alkene halides C_1–C_6	[68, 69]
Cu (capillary columns)	hydrocarbons, nonane, diethylbenzene	[70]
Modified glass surface	water, acetone, benzene	[72]
Cr_2O_3	3,3-dimethyl-2-butanol	[162]
γ-Al_2O_3 and CoO(Co_3O_4); MoO_3, Al_2O_3-CoO-MoO_3 catalyst.	thiophene	[163]
α-zirconium phosphate; α-ZrPH, α-ZrPLi α-ZrPNa, α-ZrPK	*n*-hexane, cyclohexane, benzene, 1-hexene	[164]
Pt-Al_2O_3 industrial reforming catalyst	*n*-pentane, *n*-hexane, *n*-heptane, *n*-octane, 2,2-dimethylbutane, 2,3-dimethylbutane, cyclopentane, methylcyclopentane, cyclohexane, benzene, toluene, xylenes	[165]
Carbon molecular sieve	CO_2, H_2S, N_2O, SO_2, CO, NO, N_2, O_2, X_2, Kr	[166]

determinations), the adsorbent surface is thoroughly purified of adsorbed substances. When introducing adsorbent or catalyst into the column for chromatographic determinations, the most active sites on the solid surface may be occupied by molecules of water, ammonia, carbon dioxide or organic substances adsorbed from the air. Trace contaminants in the carrier gas may also be adsorbed, even (although to a small extent only) the carrier gas itself if it is not helium or hydrogen. Chromatographic experiments are carried out at temperatures higher than those which are usual in static (especially calorimetric) experiments. The heat of physical adsorption decreases as the temperature rises. The degree of coverage is usually low during chromatographic experiments; this suggests that only adsorbate–adsorbent interactions occur — at low coverage, adsorbate–adsorbate interactions can be ignored. These latter interactions do, however, exert a considerable influence on the heat of adsorption during calorimetric experiments in which large coverage values are obtained. Adsorbate-adsorbate interactions can also be studied by GC, e.g. when estimating the energy of a hydrogen bond in a monolayer on the surface of a non-specific adsorbent (see Chapter 9) [32–34].

Particularly significant differences in the heats of adsorption estimated by both methods are obtained for specific adsorbents with a small specific surface area. In this case, even a small number of adsorbed or chemisorbed molecules poisons the solid surface to a good extent. This clearly took place on magnesium oxide [35] and titanium dioxide [36]. The heat of adsorption on specific adsorbents of small surface area should be determined at higher temperatures. However, if we use an adsorbent whose specific surface area is small, raising the column temperature may shorten the adjusted retention times overmuch, which in turn will diminish the accuracy of retention volume and heat of adsorption determinations. The chromatographic method of estimating the heat of adsorption is therefore best suited to non-specific adsorbents with a large surface area. The heat of adsorption on adsorbates with a heterogeneous surface decreases especially quickly with temperature rise for low degrees of coverage. The energetic heterogeneity of the surface is particularly great at lower temperatures. This explains why we get much higher values of the heat of adsorption for heterogeneous surfaces when they are determined calorimetrically than with the chromatographic method where higher temperatures are usual. Obviously, the chromatographic determination of the isosteric heat of adsorption does not replace — at least for the present — the more reliable and more accurate calorimetric method. It does, however, allow a quick, simple and reasonably precise estimation of the heat of adsorption, provided that thermodynamic equilibrium has been attained in the column.

By using chromatography, the temperature range for measuring the heat of adsorption can be extended to 573–773 K; the heat of adsorption can also be measured under conditions approaching those of catalytic reactions, which is not possible in ordinary calorimetric and adsorption experiments. Chromatography allows the shortest possible period of contact between adsorbate and adsorbent, so that adsorption processes, including the heat of adsorption, can be studied before a chemical reaction starts. At the same time, because of the high sensitivity of modern detectors, GC offers the possibility of determining the heat of adsorption at such low degrees of coverage θ that interaction between the adsorbed molecules can be ignored even when they are capable of association.

The determination of the isosteric heat of adsorption within the applicability of Henry's law is one of the principal physicochemical applications of GC — the large number of publications dealing with this topic are proof of this [27–72, 159].

Table 8.1 sets out some of the more important papers — types of adsorbate and adsorbent only are quoted.

8.3 Determination of Other Thermodynamic Functions of Adsorption

As we have shown, adsorption is accompanied by a loss of surface free energy and a reduction in the entropy of the gas because the number of degrees of freedom of the molecules has decreased. The net retention volume V_S, the standard change of free energy ΔG^0, the isosteric heat of adsorption q_{st} and the standard change in the entropy of adsorption ΔS^0 are linked by the following equation:

$$\Delta G^{\ominus} = -RT \ln K = -RT \ln V_S = \Delta H^{\ominus} - T\Delta S^{\ominus}, \qquad (8.16)$$

that is

$$\ln V_S = -\frac{\Delta G^{\ominus}}{RT} = -\frac{\Delta H^{\ominus}}{RT} + \frac{\Delta S^{\ominus}}{R} = \frac{q_{st}}{RT} + \frac{\Delta S^{\ominus}}{R} \qquad (8.17)$$

or

$$\log V_S = \frac{\Delta S^{\ominus}}{2.3R} + \frac{q_{st}}{2.3RT}. \qquad (8.18)$$

The change in the standard entropy of the adsorbate during adsorption is also given by this equation

$$\Delta S^{0} = -\frac{1}{T}(q_0 + \Delta\mu^{\ominus}), \tag{8.19}$$

where $\Delta\mu^{\ominus}$ is the standard change in the chemical potential of the adsorbate, and q_0 is the differential heat of adsorption at zero (small) coverage of the adsorbent surface.

$\Delta S^{\ominus}$ is conveniently determined from this equation

$$\Delta S^{\ominus} = R\left(T\frac{\mathrm{d}\ln(V_s/T)}{\mathrm{d}T} - \ln V_s - 1\right). \tag{8.20}$$

Having determined the net retention volume and the isosteric heat of adsorption, it is easy to estimate other thermodynamic functions of adsorption.

Figure 8.5 illustrates the dependence of the logarithm of the net retention volume V_S and the change in standard entropy $\Delta S^{\ominus}$ on the isosteric heat

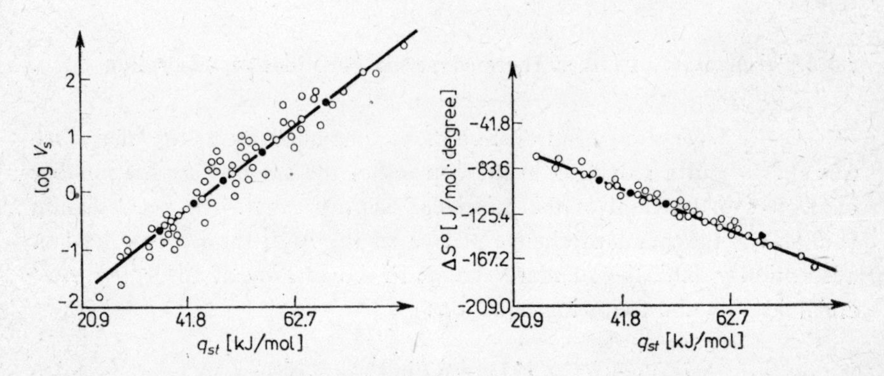

Fig. 8.5 Graphs of log V_S and $\Delta S^{\ominus}$ against q_{st} at 448 K for n-alkanes ● and its derivatives ○ on thermally graphitized carbon black (after L. D. Belyakova *et al.* [17]).

of adsorption q_{st} for n-alkanes and their derivatives on graphitized carbon black. A straight line joins the points representing n-alkanes. The points representing the derivatives of n-alkanes are clustered around the straight lines. The change in entropy is thus only minimally dependent on the adsorbate molecule's structure.

8.4 A More Detailed Discussion of the Chromatographic Determination of the Isosteric Heat of Adsorption

Boucher and Everett [60] determined the isosteric heat of adsorption of Ne, Ar, Kr, Xe, CH_4 and N_2 on activated charcoal. These authors used two columns *A* and *B* whose characteristics are presented in Table 8.2.

Table 8.2 COLUMN CHARACTERISTICS

Column	*Mass of adsorbent* [g]	*Length of packing* [cm]	*Volume of column occupied* [cm³]	*Packing density* [g/cm³]
A	42.50	386.5	80.3	0.530
B	10.06	91.5	18.2	0.552

Column *B* was used for Xe and N_2, column *A* for the remaining adsorbates. Retention values were determined at three temperatures. The carrier gas (H_2) pressure was measured with a mercury manometer at the column inlet and outlet. The columns were made of 6.35 mm copper tubing and were packed with coconut shell coal. Before use, the columns were heated to 578 K and outgassed when already fixed up in the chromatograph. Column *A* was outgassed for 34 hours, column *B* for 24 hours. During intervals in the work, the columns were insulated. Besides the column, the entire flow system was outgassed before starting each series of readings. The experiments were repeated many times; the retention times did not alter even after the column had been in use for a long time. Where the experiments were carried out at temperatures above 273 K, the column was immersed in a water thermostat which could be regulated with an accuracy of ± 0.03. For temperatures below 273 K a cryostat was used; here the temperature could be controlled to within ± 0.015.

The carrier gas flow was controlled within the range 0.8–2.2 cm^3/s in column *A*, and 1.5–5 cm^3/s in column *B*. This flow rate was regulated with an accuracy of $\pm 0.2\%$ during the whole day.

The volumes of samples injected into the carrier gas ranged from 0.02 to 0.3 cm^3. The retention time of the carrier gas was ascertained by introducing a sample of helium into the stream of hydrogen. In all cases the retention times were extrapolated back to a sample of zero size.

The isosteric heats of adsorption determined (except for neon) are about 2.5 to 3.2 times as great as their corresponding enthalpies of condensation.

Strnad *et al.* [63] and Lewicki *et al.* [73] determined the isosteric heats of adsorption of propene, propane, acrolein and CO_2 on bismuth and molybdenum oxides, and on bismuth–molybdenum catalysts, both pure and supported on silica.

Samples of the different adsorbents, with a particle size of 0.3–0.6 mm, were packed into 2.7 mm internal diameter glass columns 1 m long. The carrier gas was nitrogen or helium. The nitrogen was purged of oxygen traces by passing it over reduced copper wire heated to 673 K and then drying it in a freezer containing solid CO_2. The helium wire was purified by passing it over a layer of activated charcoal cooled with liquid nitrogen. The carrier gas flow rate was controlled by means of needle valves. Before taking readings, the adsorbent was heated in a stream of oxygen at 723 K for 1 hour. The catalyst was then cooled to room temperature under a continuing flow of oxygen. Room temperature having been reached, the oxygen was replaced by carrier gas, and the required temperature established in the thermostat. An open U-tube manometer was used to measure the gas pressure at the column outlet. Measurements were made for two different sample sizes, 0.2 and 0.05 cm^3; the samples of acrolein (0.5 cm^3) were injected after saturating the carrier gas with acrolein vapour at room temperature. In most cases, the carrier gas flow rate was 0.0015 m^3/h.

The retention time in these studies was independent of the number of samples; likewise, the heat of adsorption did not depend on the kind of carrier gas used. The gradients of the straight line graphs of $\log t_R$ against $1/T$ were similar for the different volumes of adsorbate (0.2 and 0.05 cm^3), which suggests a constant heat of adsorption within the range of surface coverage studied here. The maximum error in the measurement of retention time was 5% for the Bi–Mo/SiO_2 catalyst, whereas it was somewhat greater for the pure oxide systems as their surface areas were small — the scattering of points on the $\log t_R - 1/T$ graph was greater.

The heats of adsorption of benzene, toluene, ethylbenzene and xylenes were determined on different zeolites at temperatures from 543 to 603 K [62]. The heats of adsorption of these aromatic hydrocarbons were basically independent of the sodium content of the zeolites, but they did rise somewhat when the temperature of zeolite treatment increased (over 823 K). The relationship between the fall in ionization potential of the aromatic hydrocarbons and the increase in the heat of adsorption was found to be linear. For comparison, these authors also studied the behaviour of ethene on the same zeolites. As the temperatures of the initial zeolite treatment increases, the retention volume of ethene falls. If water is introduced into the system, the retention volume of ethylene increases, though reversibly, whereas the retention volume of the aromatic hydrocarbons decreases. It is probable that the aromatic hydrocarbons are primarily adsorbed on sodium and aluminium ions, forming a complex with charge transfer, while the ethylene interacts mainly with hydroxyl ions forming a carbo-cation, or a complex by means of hydrogen bonds.

These studies were performed on a classic chromatographic system equipped for the pulse-wise introduction of samples. The stainless steel column was packed with 0.2 g zeolite (sodium zeolite — Lindc Y SK-40) and placed in a metal block to maintain a constant temperature. The column was thermostatted to within ± 1. The hydrogen carrier gas was purified over a palladium catalyst and 5A molecular sieves. The peak widths and retention volumes of the aromatic hydrocarbons remained independent of the type of carrier gas (He, Ar, N_2), its flow rate and the molecular dimensions of the zeolite.

At the start of each experiment, carrier gas was passed for 2 hours through fresh zeolite at the required temperature. A small quantity of argon, as a non-adsorbing gas, was added to the pulse in order to assess the adjusted retention volume of the hydrocarbons. The authors confirmed the linearity of the isotherm indirectly from the fact that the retention volume was independent of the partial pressure of the adsorbate.

Chromatography has also been successfully used to determine the heat of adsorption of water vapour and benzene on different kinds of leather [76]. The heats of adsorption of water and benzene on natural leathers were determined at temperatures from 323 to 373 K. Of course, these values for the heats of adsorption contain an error due to the simultaneous absorption of water vapour by the leather. Mechanically crushed samples of leather (0.5–0.8 mm) were packed into a 0.8 cm diameter copper column 50 cm in length. The carrier gases used were helium and hydrogen.

The gases were dried completely over silica gel. The carrier gas flow rate, controlled by means of needle valves and a flow-meter, was about 0.0015 m^3/h. Tests were carried out on a traditional chromatograph with pulse-wise introduction of samples.

Before the tests, the leather in the column was heathed in a stream of carrier gas at 343 K for 5 hours. The adsorbates to be tested were introduced 30 minutes after the required temperature was established. Readings were taken for a relatively wide range of adsorbate doses: 1, 2, 3, 4, 5, 6, 9, 12, 15 µl.

While estimating the heat of adsorption of water, the weighed sample of leather was reduced, since it became swollen on absorbing water and this caused a considerable and variable pressure gradient along the column. In order to provide approximately the same conditions of column operation in the various experiments, additional packing was added in the form of 80/100 mesh glass beads. The ratio by weight of glass beads to leather samples was 10 : 1. There was no sorption of water on the glass beads under these experimental conditions. The change in the heat of adsorption of water vapour with respect to sample size is shown in Fig. 8.6. It can

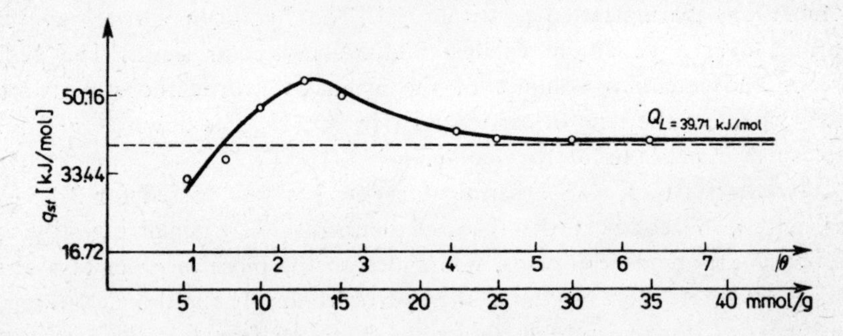

Fig. 8.6 Relationship between the isosteric heat of adsorption of water vapour and the degree of coverage of natural leather (after T. Paryjczak *et al.* [76]).

be seen from this that in the vicinity of the water vapour sample corresponding formally to $\theta = 2$, the heat of adsorption reaches a slight maximum. Adsorbate–adsorbate interaction has to be added to the energy of water-vapour-leather surface interactions. If the sample size is further increased, the values of heats of adsorption and heats of condensation become equal, and the monolayer of water that is formed isolates the surface effect of the leather on the heat effect of water vapour adsorption.

Thermodynamic functions of solutions can be easily determined using GLC [77–171].

References

[1] Anderson A. W., *Physical Chemistry of Surfaces*, 3rd ed., Wiley, New York, 1976.
[2] Young D. M. and Crowell A. D., *Physical Adsorption of Gases*, Butterworths, London, 1962.
[3] Ross S. and Olivier J. P., *On Physical Adsorption*, Wiley-Interscience, New York, 1964.
[4] Flood E. A. (Ed.) *The Solid–Gas Interface*, Edward Arnold Ltd, London, Marcel Dekker Inc., New York, 1967, Vols 1 and 2.
[5] Hayward D. O. and Trapnell B. M. W., *Chemisorption*, Butterworths, London, 1964.
[6] Heinemann H., *Catalysis Reviews*, Marcel Dekker Inc., New York, 1969, Vol. 2.
[7] Zettlemoyer A. C., Young G. J., Chessick J. J. and Healey F. H., *J. Phys. Chem.*, **57**, 649 (1953).
[8] Pierce C., Mooi J. and Harris R. E., *J. Phys. Chem.*, **62**, 655 (1958).
[9] Pabyashkin I. A., *Zh. Fiz. Khim.*, **46**, 431 (1972).
[10] Kington G. L., Beebe R. A., Polley M. H. and Smith W. R., *J. Am. Chem. Soc.*, **72**, 1775 (1950).
[11] Kington G. L. and Smith P. S., *Trans. Faraday Soc.*, **60**, 705 (1964).
[12] Kington G. L. and Smith P. S., *J. Sci. Instr.*, **41**, 145 (1964).
[13] Mooi J., Pierce C. and Smith R. N., *J. Phys. Chem.*, **57**, 657 (1953).
[14] Kiselev A. V., Peskonova E. A., Petrova R. S. and Shcherbakova K. D., *Zh. Fiz. Khim.*, **38**, 161 (1964).
[15] Kiselev A. V., Petrova R. S. and Shcherbakova K. D., *Kinet. Katal.*, **5**, 526 (1964).
[16] Van Deemter J. J., Zuiderweg F. J. and Klinkenberg A., *Chem. Eng. Sci.*, **5**, 271 (1956).
[17] Belyakova L. D., Kiselev A. V. and Kovaleva N. V., *Zh. Fiz. Khim.*, **40**, 1494 (1966).
[18] Amariglio H., *Surface Sci.*, **12**, 62 (1968).
[19] Greene B. A. and Pust H., *J. Phys. Chem.*, **62**, 55 (1958).
[20] Ross S., Saelens J. and Olivier J. P., *J. Phys. Chem.*, **66**, 696 (1962).
[21] Okamura J. P. and Sawyer D. T., *Anal. Chem.*, **43**, 1730 (1971).
[22] Wicarowa O., Novak J. and Janak J., *J. Chromatogr.*, **65**, 241 (1972).
[23] Boucher E. A. and Everett D. H., *Trans. Faraday Soc.*, **67**, 2720 (1971).
[24] Petrova R. S., Zhrapova E. V. and Shcherbakova K. D., *Gazovaya khromatografiya*, Trudy II Vses. Konf. Izd. Nauka, Moskva, 1964, p. 37.
[25] Carberry J. J., *Nature*, **189**, 391 (1961).
[26] Beebe R. A., Evans P. L., Kleinstenber T. C. and Richards L. W., *J. Phys. Chem.*, **70**, 4, 1009 (1966).
[27] Gale R. L. and Beebe R. A., *J. Phys. Chem.*, **68**, 555 (1964).
[28] Gregg S. J. and Stock R., *Gas Chromatography 1962*, Proc. Symp. 2nd., Amsterdam, 1962.
[29] Eberly F. E., *J. Phys. Chem.*, **65**, 1261 (1961).
[30] Wolf F. and Beyer H., *Chem. Techn.*, **11**, 142 (1959).
[31] Keybal V. A., Kiselev A. V., Khudyakov V. L., Shcherbakova K. D. and Yashin Ya. I., *Zh. Fiz. Khim.*, **41**, 2234 (1967).

[32] Belyakova L. D., Kiselev A. V. and Kovaleva N. V., *Anal. Chem.*, **36**, 1517 (1964).
[33] Belyakova L. D., Kiselev A. V. and Kovaleva N. V., *Dokl. Akad. Nauk SSSR*, **157**, 646 (1964).
[34] Kiselev A. V., *Disc. Faraday Soc.*, **40**, 205 (1965).
[35] Kiselev A. V., Nikitin Yu. S. and Petrova R. S., *Kolloid. Zh.*, **27**, 368 (1965).
[36] Kolesnicyna I. V. and Petrova R. S., *Kolloid. Zh.*, **29**, 815 (1967).
[37] Cremer E., *Z. Anal. Chem.*, **170**, 219 (1959).
[38] Habgood A. W. and Hanlan J. F., *Can. J. Chem.*, **37**, 843 (1959).
[39] Eberly P. E. Jr and Kimberlin C. N. Jr, *Trans. Faraday Soc.*, **57**, 1169 (1961).
[40] Eberly P. E. Jr, *J. Phys. Chem.* **64**, 68 (1961).
[41] Eberly P. E. Jr, *J. Phys. Chem.*, **66**, 812 (1962).
[42] Kiselev A. V., Zhrapova E. V. and Shcherbakova K. D., *Neftekhimya*, **2**, 877 (1962).
[43] Moseley R. B. and Archibald R. C., *J. Catalysis*, **2**, 131 (1963).
[44] Habgood H. W., *Can. J. Chem.*, **42**, 2340 (1964).
[45] Chirnside G. C. and Pope G. C., *J. Phys. Chem.*, **68**, 2377 (1964).
[46] Kiselev A. V., Nikitin Yu. S., Petrova R. S., Shcherbakova K. D. and Yashin Ya. I., *Anal. Chem.*, **36**, 1526 (1964).
[47] Petrova R. S., Khrapova E. V. and Shcherbakova K. D., in: *Gas Chromatography 1962*, Ed. Van Swaay, Butterworths, London, 1962, p. 18.
[48] Kiselev A. V., Chernenkova Yu. L. and Yashin Ya. I., *Neftekhimya*, **5**, 589 (1965).
[49] Aubean R., Leroy J. and Champeix L., *J. Chromatogr.*, **19**, 249 (1965).
[50] Arita K., Kuge Y. and Yoshikawa Y., *Bull. Chem. Soc. Japan*, **38**, 632 (1965).
[51] Kiselev A. V. and Yashin Ya. I., *Neftekhimya*, **4**, 634 (1964).
[52] Kubasov A. A., Smirnova I. V. and Topchieva K. V., *Kinet. Katal.*, **5**, 520 (1964).
[53] Oldenkomp R. D. and Houghton G., *J. Phys. Chem.*, **67**, 303 (1963).
[54] Feltl L., Grubner O. and Smolkova E., *Gas Chromatographie 1965*, Academie Verlag, Berlin, 1965, p. 95.
[55] Yakerson V. I., Lafer A. I., Gorskaya L. A. and Rubinstein A. M., *Neftekhimya*, **5**, 264 (1965).
[56] White D. and Cowan C. T., *Trans. Faraday Soc.*, **54**, 557 (1958).
[57] Bogomolov V. I., Minachev Kh. M., Mirzabekova I. V. and Isakov Ya. I., *Izv. Akad. Nauk SSSR, ser. Khim.*, 41, (1968).
[58] Dimitrov Chr., Topalova I. C., Popova Z. I. and Petsev N. D., *Compt. rendus de l'Academie Bulgare des Sciences*, **24**, 875 (1971).
[59] Wydeven T. and Leban M., *J. Chromatogr. Sci.*, **7**, 445 (1969).
[60] Boucher E. A. and Everett D. H., *Trans. Faraday Soc.*, **67**, 2720 (1971).
[61] Yoshikoko Marooka, *Trans. Faraday Soc.*, **67**, 3381 (1971).
[62] Hiroshige Matsumoto, Hideo Futami, Fumiyoshi Kato and Yoshiro Morita, *Bull. Chem. Soc. Japan*, **44**, 3170 (1971).
[63] Strnad J. and Krivanek N., *J. Catal.*, **23**, 253 (1971).
[64] Czubryt J. and Gesser H. D., *J. Chromatogr.*, **59**, 1 (1971).
[65] Okamura J. P. and Sawyer D. T., *Anal. Chem.*, **43**, 13, 1730 (1971).
[66] Ivanova I. T. and Zhukhovitskii A. A., *Zh. Fiz. Khim.*, **43**, 2339 (1969).
[67] Kubasov A. A. and Smirnova I. V., *Zh. Fiz. Khim.*, **46**, 1281 (1972).

[68] Zaprometov A. Yu., Kalashnikova E. V., Kiselev A. V. and Shcherbakova K. D., *Zh. Fiz. Khim.*, **46**, 1230 (1972).
[69] Kiselev A. V., Kuznetsov A. V., Filatova I. Yu. and Shcherbakova K. D., *Zh. Fiz. Khim.*, **44**, 1272 (1970).
[70] Vlobavets M. L. and Ternovskaya L. A., *Zh. Fiz. Khim.*, **46**, 1505 (1972).
[71] Dupont-Pavlovsky N. and Bastick J., *Compt. Rend.*, **269**, 8, 476 (1969).
[72] Fink P. and Wolleschensky E., *Z. Chem.*, **8**, 315 (1968).
[73] Lewicki A., Paryjczak T. and Bereś J., *Roczniki Chem.*, **47**, 981 (1973).
[74] Grzywna R., Kaźmierczak A. and Paryjczak T., *Roczniki Chem.*, **46**, 1585 (1972).
[75] Gryaznova Z. V., Ermilova M. M., Balandin A. A., Tsitsishvili G. V. and Bashin V. I., *Osnovy preshvigeniya kataliticheskogo dejstviya*, Izd. Nauka, Moskva, 1970, Vol. 2, p. 161.
[76] Paryjczak T. and Gebauer A., *Prace Instytutu Skórzanego*, **XVIII**, 131 (1974), **XIX**, 85 (1975).
Paryjczak T., Kaźmierczak A. and Leśniewska E., *Przegląd Skórzany*, **7**, 181 (1981).
[77] Barker P. E. and Lloyd D. L., *J. Inst. Petrol.*, **49**, 73, 471 (1963).
[78] Cruicshank A. J. B., Windsor M. L. and Loung C. L., *Proc. Roy. Soc.*, **A295**, 271 (1968).
[79] Ashworth A. J. and Everett D. H., *Trans. Faraday Soc.*, **56**, 1609 (1960).
[80] Freeguard G. F. and Stock R., *Gas Chromatography*, Butterworths, London, 1962, p. 102.
[81] Giddings J. C., *Anal. Chem.*, **35**, 439 (1963).
[82] Korol A. N., *Sb. Teoriya i primenenye nepodvishnoy fazy v GLCh*, Izd. Znanye, Kiev, 1971, p. 12.
[83] Everett D. H., Gayney B. W. and Young C. L., *Trans. Faraday Soc.*, **64**, 1667 (1968).
[84] Goldup A., Luckhurst G. R. and Swanton W. T., *Nature* **193**, 333 (1962).
[85] Martin R. L., *Anal. Chem.*, **33**, 347 (1961).
[86] Martin R. L., *Anal. Chem.*, **35**, 116 (1963).
[87] Martire D. E., Pecsok R. L. and Purnell J. H., *Nature*, **203**, 1279 (1964).
[88] Berezkin V. G. and Fateeva V. M., *Sb. Teoriya i primenenye nepodvishnoy fazy v GLCh*, Izd. Znanye, Kiev, 1971, p. 60.
[89] Berezkin V. G., Pakhonov V. P., Tatarinskii V. S. and Fateeva V. M., *Dokl. Akad. Nauk SSSR, ser. Khim.*, **180**, 1135 (1968).
[90] Cadogan D. F., Conder J. R., Locke D. C. and Purnell J. H., *J. Phys. Chem.*, **73**, 700, 708, (1969).
[91] Conder J. R., *J. Chromatogr.*, **39**, 273 (1969).
[92] Pecsok R. L. and Gump B. H., *J. Phys. Chem.*, **71**, 2202 (1967).
[93] Berezkin V. G. and Pakhonov V. P., *Zh. Fiz. Khim.*, **42**, 1844 (1968).
[94] Berezkin V. G., Pakhonov V. P., Starovinets V. S. and Berezkina L. G., *Neftekhimiya*, **5**, 438 (1965).
[95] Tatarinskii V. S., Berezkin V. G. and Efremov A. A., *Izv. Akad. Nauk SSSR, ser. Khim.*, 2634 (1968).
[96] Urone P. and Parcher J. F., *Anal. Chem.*, **38**, 270 (1966).
[97] Smith E. D., Johnson L. and Oathout J. M., *Anal. Chem.*, **36**, 1750 (1966).
[98] Cockee N. A. and Tiley P. F., *Chem. a. Ind.*, 1118 (1968).

[99] Korol A. N., *Ukr. Khim. Zh.*, **32**, 329 (1966).
[100] Mon T. R., Forrey R. R. and Teranishi R., *J. Gas Chromatogr.*, **4**, 176 (1966).
[101] Korol A. N., *Nepodvishnaya faza v GLCh*, Izd. Naukovaya Dumka, Kiev, 1969.
[102] Barker P. E. and Hilmi A. K., *J. Gas Chromatogr.*, **5**, 119 (1967).
[103] Everett D. H. and Stoddart C. T., *Trans. Faraday Soc.*, **57**, 746 (1961).
[104] Degeorges J. N. and Vergnard J. M., *Bull. soc. chim. France*, 2295 (1966).
[105] Adlard R., Khan M. A. and Whitham B. T., *Gas Chromatography 1962*, Butterworths, London, 1962, p. 251.
[106] Suprynowicz Z., *Chemia analit.*, **17**, 267 (1972).
[107] Everett D. H., *Trans. Faraday Soc.*, **61**, 1637 (1965).
[108] Windsor M. L. and Young C. L., *J. Chromatogr.*, **27**, 355 (1967).
[109] Cruicshank A. J. B., Windsor M. L. and Young C. L., *Proc. Roy. Soc.*, **A295**, 271 (1966).
[110] Cruicshank A. J. B., Gayney B. W. and Young C. L., *Trans. Faraday Soc.*, **64**, 337 (1968).
[111] Stalkup F. J. and Kobayashi R., *J. Chem. Eng. Data*, **8**, 564 (1963).
[112] Stalkup F. J. and Deans H. A., *Amer. Inst. Chem. Eng. J.*, **9**, 106 (1963).
[113] Van Horn L. D. and Kobayashi R., *J. Chem. Eng. Data*, **12**, 294 (1967).
[114] Koonce K. T., Deans H. A. and Kobayashi R., *Amer. Inst. Chem. Eng. J.*, **11**, 159 (1965).
[115] Koonce K. T. and Kobayashi R., *J. Chem. Eng. Data*, **9**, 494 (1963).
[116] Vigdergauz M. S. and Izmailov R. J., *Primenenie gazovoy khromatografii dlya opredelenya fizikokhimicheskikh svoystv veshchestv*, Izd. Nauka, Moskva, 1970.
[117] Porter P. E., Deal C. H. and Stross F. H., *J. Am. Chem. Soc.*, **78**, 2999 (1956).
[118] Littlewood A. B., *Gas Chromatography — Principles, Techniques and Applications*, Academic Press, New York, 1962.
[119] Purnell J. H., *Gas Chromatography*, Wiley, New York, 1962.
[120] Nogare S. D. and Juvet R. S., *Gas-Liquid Chromatography*, John Wiley, New York, London, 1962.
[121] Littlewood A. B. and Willmot F. W., *Anal. Chem.*, **38**, 1031 (1966).
[122] Kurkchi G. A. and Yogansen A. V., *Zh. Fiz. Khim.*, **40**, 2928 (1966).
[123] Kurkchi G. A. and Yogansen A. V., *Dokl. Akad. Nauk SSSR, ser. Khim.*, **145**, 1085 (1963).
[124] Kwantes A. and Rijnders G. W., *Gas Chromatography*, Butterworths, London, 1958.
[125] Korol A. N., *Neftekhimiya*, **2**, 635 (1963).
[126] Hilmi A., Ellis S. R. M. and Barker P. E., *Brit. Chem. Eng.*, **25**, 1453 (1970).
[127] Korol A. N., *Usp. Khim.*, **41**, 321 (1972).
[128] Desty D. H. and Swanton W. T., *J. Phys. Chem.*, **65**, 766 (1961).
[129] Kurkchi G. A. and Yogansen A. V., *Zh. Fiz. Khim.*, **41**, 158 (1967).
[130] Meyer E. F. and Ross R. A., *J. Phys. Chem.*, **73**, 831 (1971).
[131] James M. R., Giddings J. C. and Keller R. A., *J. Gas Chromatogr.*, 3, 15 (1965).
[132] Genkin A. N. and Boguslavskaya B. I., *Dokl. Akad. Nauk SSSR, ser. Khim.*, **164**, 1089 (1965).
[133] Genkin A. N., *Zh. Fiz. Khim.*, **41**, 1798 (1967).
[134] Evered S. and Pollard F. H., *J. Chromatogr.*, **4**, 451 (1960).
[135] Gainey B. W. and Young C. L., *Trans. Faraday Soc.*, **64**, 349 (1968); Young C. L., *Trans. Faraday Soc.*, **64**, 1537 (1968).

[136] Pease E. C. and Thornburn S., *J. Chromatogr.*, **30**, 344 (1967).
[137] Martire D. E., *4th Int. Symp. Gas Chromatogr.*, Academic Press, New York, 1963.
[138] Tewary Y. B., Sheridan J. P. and Martire D. E., *J. Phys. Chem.*, **74**, 3263 (1970).
[139] Genkin A. N. and Boguslavskaya B. I., *Neftekhimiya*, **6**, 626 (1966).
[140] Gritchina N. D. and Dreving W. P., *Zh. Fiz. Khim.*, **43**, 458 (1969).
[141] Mellado G. L. and Kobayashi R., *Petrol. Ref.*, **39**, 125 (1960).
[142] Smiley M. H., *J. Chem. Eng. Data*, **15**, 413 (1970).
[143] Ogorodnikov S. K., Genkin A. N., Kogan V. B. and Nemtsov M. S., *Sb. Gazovaya khromatografiya*, Izd. Nauka, Moskva, 1964, p. 56.
[144] Turkeltaub N. M., *Zh. Fiz. Khim.*, **31**, 2102 (1957).
[145] Simon J., *Chromatographie*, **4**, 98 (1971).
[146] Anderson J. R., *J. Am. Chem. Soc.*, **78**, 5692 (1956).
[147] Burnett M. G., *Anal. Chem.*, **35**, 1567 (1963).
[148] Bighi C., Betti A., Saglietto G. and Dondi F., *J. Chromatogr.*, **35**, 309 (1968).
[149] Ratkovics F., *Acta Chim. Soc. Hung.*, **49**, 55 (1966).
[150] Vyakhirev D. A. and Kondakova L. V., *Trudy Khim. Khim. Tekhnol. (Gorki)*, **1**, 58 (1966).
[151] Chekalov L. and Porter K. E., *Chem. Eng. Sci.*, **22**, 897 (1967).
[152] Gubbins K. E., Garden S. N. and Walker R. D., *J. Gas Chromatogr.*, **3**, 98, 330 (1965).
[153] Pecsar R. E. and Martin J. J., *Anal. Chem.*, **38**, 1661 (1966).
[154] Petrov A. N., Pankov A. G. and Bogdanov M. I., *Uch. Zap. Yarosl. Tekhnich. In-ta*, **13**, 186 (1970).
[155] Buteyko Kh. F. and Korol A. N., *Neftekhimiya*, **9**, 625 (1969).
[156] Melnikova S. L. and Korol A. N., *T. E. Kh.*, **6**, 377 (1971).
[157] Vyakhirev D. A. and Reshetnikova L. E., *Sb. Gazovaya khromatografiya*, Dzerzhinsk, 1966, p. 286.
[158] Ruban P. P. and Korol A. N., *Zh. Fiz. Khim.*, **44**, 1997 (1970).
[159] Haber J., Najbar J., Pawelek J. and Pawlikowska-Czubak J., *J. Colloid. Interface Sci.*, **45**, (2) 252 (1973).
[160] Kreiner K., Lasoń M. and Żółcińska-Jezierska J., *Roczniki Chem.*, **48**, 95 (1974).
[161] Czajkowski J., Leo J. and Paryjczak T., *Przemysl Chem.*, **53**, 621 (1974).
[162] Nondek L. and Kraus M., *J. Catal.*, **40**, 40 (1975).
[163] Erofeev V. I., Kobal L. M. and Kalechic I. V., *Izv. Akad. Nauk SSSR, ser. Khim.*, 1409 (1977).
[164] Dyer A., Leigh D. and Sharples W. E., *J. Chromatogr.*, **118**, 319 (1976).
[165] Choudhary V. R. and Menon P. G., *J. Chromatogr.*, **116**, 431 (1976).
[166] Doleva I. A., Kiselev A. V. and Yashin Ya. I., *Zh. Fiz. Khim.*, **48**, 1285 (1974).
[167] Vidal-Madjar C., Gonnord M. F. and Guiochon G., *J. Phys. Chem.*, **79**, 732 (1975).
[168] Kalashnikova V., Kiselev A. V., Makogon A. M. and Shcherbakova K. D., *Chromatographia*, **8**, 399 (1975).
[169] Foryś J. and Grzybowska B., *Bull. Acad. Polon. Sci. Sér. Chim.*, **23**, 269 (1975).
[170] Gawdzik J. and Jaroniec M., *J. Chromatogr.*, **131**, 1 (1977).
[171] Keybal V. L. and Shcherbakova K. D., *Vestn. Mosk. Un-ta, Sér. Khim.*, **19**, 258 (1978).

Chapter 9

Interaction of Molecules in the Adsorbent Layer

9.1 Introduction

Physical adsorption is a manifestation of the interaction of intermolecular forces. The interactions between an adsorbate and a solid surface are basically of a quantum mechanical nature — both atomic nuclei and electrons are involved.

A theory of molecular interactions over short distances has yet to be fully worked out. The potential of mutual interaction is usually described as the sum of apparently independent factors, dispersive, electrostatic and chemical interactions.

In physical adsorption there is no transfer or sharing of electrons between atoms of the adsorbate and the surface of the solid; the chemical properties of the substances interacting with each other are not altered, in contradistinction to chemisorption where they are altered, since a new chemical compound is formed at the adsorbent surface. The physical interaction between an adsorbate and a solid surface is the result of attractive or repulsive Van der Waals forces.

If the adsorbate molecule does not have permanent dipole or multipole moments, physical adsorption takes place mainly as a result of dispersive forces. The surface of ionic crystals is surrounded by an external electric field which may induce an electric moment in the adsorbate molecules; additional forces may result therefrom, irrespective of any dispersive interaction. Where permanent moments exist in adsorbate molecules, further interaction with the solid surface may also come into play. The different kinds of adsorption forces have been described in detail in the monographs by Jaycock and Parfitt [1], and by Ościk [2].

Adsorption studies are one of the chief sources of information about molecular interactions. Mutual interaction in the gas–homogeneous solid surface system and the state of molecules adsorbed on a homogeneous surface are easier to formulate theoretically than molecular interaction in the gas–liquid system. On the smooth surface of a solid, molecular interaction is limited to the nearest stationary energy centres on the surface. Where the coverage of the surface with adsorbate is low, adsorbate-adsorbate interaction can be neglected, and attention can be concentrated on adsorbate–adsorbent interaction. GC is eminently suitable for adsorption studies at low pressures. Where the adsorbate coverage on a surface is greater, virial coefficients have to be introduced — they account for the double, triple and other adsorbate–adsorbate interactions in the adsorbent field. The potential energy of adsorption of molecules, at their most easily attained orientation on the surface, is equal to the heat of adsorption at absolute zero. As the heat of adsorption of small coverages on a homogeneous surface is dependent on the temperature to only a small extent, the potential energy of adsorption for a minimum potential curve is close to the value of the isosteric heat of adsorption, which can be determined by chromatography.

The theory of adsorption from the gaseous phase on the homogeneous surfaces of crystals has been worked out from the geometrical and electronic structure of the surfaces of the solid and the adsorbate [3, 4]. The solid is treated as the source of an external potential field whose thermodynamic properties do not change during adsorption. Using the molecular-statistical method, the adsorption isotherm has been calculated for the simplest models (equilibrium constants, retention volumes for zero, small and medium degrees of coverage); so have the heat and entropy of adsorption [5–12]. In order to compare the values calculated theoretically with those obtained experimentally, we must know the value of the heat of adsorption for small degrees of coverage; the calorimetric, adsorptive (isosteres) and, above all, the chromatographic methods used to find this value enable us to do so over a wide range of temperatures.

According to Kiselev [13, 14], Everett [15] and Barrer [16], the molecular interactions taking place during adsorption can be conventionally divided into specific and non-specific, depending on the type of adsorbate molecules and the nature of the adsorbent surface.

Non-specific molecular interaction is largely a dispersive effect, due to the ordered movement of electrons in molecules. This type of interaction commonly occurs between any two molecules.

Specific molecular interaction is due to the uneven distribution of the electron density in the interacting molecules. Only when it takes place over greater distances can specific interaction be treated as classic electrostatic interaction. Hydrogen bonds are a particular manifestation of specific interaction.

9.2 The Classification of Molecules and Adsorbents

9.2.1 The Classification of Molecules

Kiselev [3, 13, 14, 17–19] distinguishes four groups of molecules: A, B, C and D, depending on the local distribution of the electron density in adsorbate molecules.

In group A he classifies molecules with spherically symmetrical electron shells — shells which are like those of the noble gases. The molecules of alkanes are also in this group.

The distribution of the electron density of the molecules in group B is uneven. The negative charge is concentrated at the ends of the bonds, as in alkenes, aromatic hydrocarbons and all molecules having π bonds, or in functional groups having lone pairs of electrons such as amines, esters, ketones, nitriles, etc.

In group C molecules there is a local concentration of positive charge, while the balancing negative charge is spread over the rest of the molecule. Organometallic compounds belong to this group.

Classified in group D are those molecules in which the positive charge is concentrated at one end and the negative charge at the other, for example, in molecules containing OH, NH_2 and =NH bonds such as alcohols, water, primary and secondary amines.

In many cases it is difficult to carry out a strict classification since many molecules having a larger number of functional groups and π bonds can be classified in various groups. Non-specific interaction occurs between all kinds of molecules. Specific interaction occurs only with molecules of groups B, C and D and is supplementary to non-specific interaction.

9.2.2 The Classification of Adsorbents

Bearing in mind the chemical nature of a surface, which is the result of the distribution of electric charges over it, Kiselev [3, 13, 14, 17–19] distinguishes three types of adsorbent.

In type I we find non-specific adsorbents which have no functional groups or exchangeable ions on their surfaces. They interact only non-specifically with molecules belonging to all groups. Included in this group of adsorbents are thermally graphitized carbon black, boron nitride (BN), alkanes and some polymers, e.g. polythene.

Type II adsorbents are those which have positive charges concentrated on their surfaces. Such adsorbents have surface hydroxyl groups which are somewhat acidic, and include the hydroxylated surfaces of acidic oxides — above all, silica gel. The considerable protonization of the hydrogen in the hydroxyl groups at the silica surface can be explained by the fact that the *d* orbital in the silicon atom is unoccupied, which causes a corresponding shift of the electron density. A surface concentration of positive charge is also found where there are acidic centres without protons (Chapter 7) or small radii cations. The negative charge can therefore be spread over a greater volume, e.g. in a large complex anion. Zeolites are adsorbents of this kind. Their surface positive charge, concentrated in exchangeable cations, is compensated by a negative charge spread throughout the large anion (AlO_4^-) which makes up the framework of the zeolite.

Specific adsorbents of type III have surface concentrations of negative charge. Such adsorbents are most often obtained by depositing a layer of B molecules or macromolecules (e.g. polyethylene glycol) on the surface of a non-specific adsorbent (type I). They can also be obtained by chemically modifying another type of adsorbent, for example, by introducing suitable functional groups such as $-C{\equiv}N$.

9.3 Adsorbate–Adsorbent Interactions

Non-specific interaction always occurs between type I adsorbents and any adsorbate molecules. A typical example of a type I adsorbent is graphitized carbon black.

Because of its homogeneous and non-specific surface (usually 6–12 m^2/g), graphitized carbon black is frequently used as an adsorbent in basic research into adsorption phenomena, especially in studies of adsorbate–adsorbent interactions (small degree of coverage) and adsorbate–adsorbate interactions (high degree of coverage). It is a useful model in theoretical considerations based on the molecular theory of adsorption [5, 6, 20–29, 92–97]. This theory enables us to calculate the potential energy of molecular interactions and other thermodynamic properties of an adsorbate–adsorbent system. During the adsorption of simple molecules we take into account the function of the interaction between an adsorbate molecule and the surface carbon atoms of the graphitized carbon black, e.g. φC ... A. In the case of complicated adsorbate molecules such as hydrocarbons and their derivatives, we consider the function of the interaction between one atom and another or between one atom and a group of atoms: φC...C, φC...H, φC...O or φC...CH_3, φC...CH_2, φC...CH, etc. The potential energy of interactions of complicated adsorbate molecules with an adsorbent, $\Phi(z)$, is the sum of all the interactions of their atoms or groups

$$\Phi(z) = \sum_{\mathrm{C}} \sum_{\mathrm{A}} \varphi_{\mathrm{C+A}}, \tag{9.1}$$

where z is the distance from the centre of an adsorbate molecule to the principal plane of the graphite, passing through the centres of the surface carbon atoms, and φC...A is the potential energy of interaction of a lattice C atom with an atom or group of atoms in a molecule.

The function φC...A can be estimated from the Buckingham [30] or Lennard–Jones [31] equation

$$\varphi\mathrm{C...A} = -c_1 r^{-6} - c_2 r^{-10} + B \exp\left(-\frac{r}{p}\right). \tag{9.2}$$

The constants c_1 and c_2 can be determined from the equations given by Kirkwood [32] and Müller [33]. The constant B expresses the distance z_0 of the centres of the atoms or group of atoms from the centre of the surface atoms of graphite at equilibrium. The value of the constant p, as for molecular crystals, is taken to be equal to 0.028 nm.

In the adsorption of dipolar molecules, the inductive energy of attraction of the dipoles for the polarized carbon atoms in the lattice is also included.

The theoretical value of the retention volume can also be calculated, since for small coverages it is equal to Henry's constant for an adsorbate–adsorbent system at equilibrium [5, 6]

$$V_{\mathrm{S}} \approx \frac{1}{8\pi^2 mS} \int \cdots \int \left[\exp\left(-\frac{\Phi}{kT}\right) - 1\right] \sin V \, \mathrm{d}x \, \mathrm{d}y \, \mathrm{d}z \, \mathrm{d}V \, \mathrm{d}\Phi \, \mathrm{d}\Psi, \tag{9.3}$$

where m and S are the mass and specific surface area of the adsorbent, x, y, z are the Cartesian coordinates of the centre of the molecular mass,

V, Φ, Ψ are the normal Euler angles indicating the orientation of the molecule with respect to the surface of the adsorbent, V denoting the angle between the principal axis of the molecule and the axis perpendicular to the surface.

When the adsorbate is a monoatomic molecule, only the Cartesian coordinates, whose origin is at the centre of the molecule, remain. The theoretically calculated values of V_S for noble gases, nitrogen, and even for the relatively complicated molecules of alkanes, on the principal plane of graphite agree very well with the experimental data obtained on graphitized carbon black [5, 6, 34–38] (Fig. 9.1). This proves that non-specific interaction is brought about chiefly by dispersive forces of attraction.

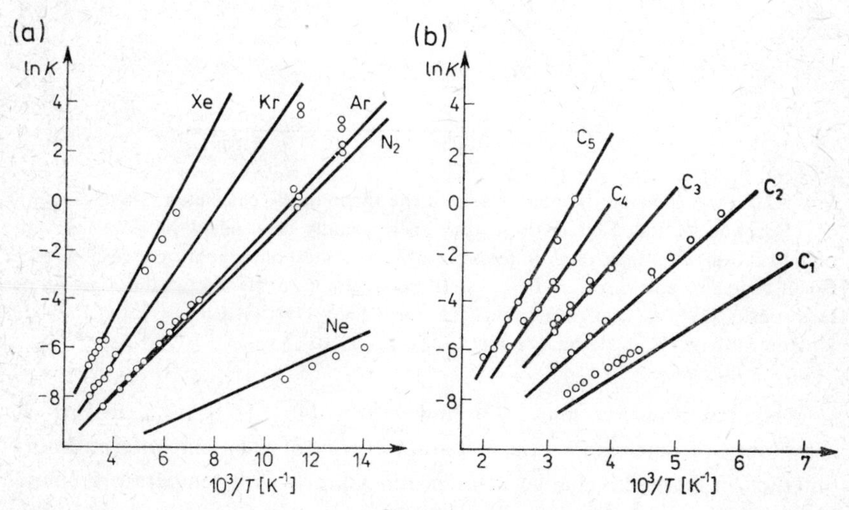

Fig. 9.1 Graph showing the relationship of the calculated (lines) and experimentally obtained (points) values of the logarithm of Henry's constant (retention volume for zero quantity of adsorbate) on the principal plane of graphite (lines) and on the surface of graphitized carbon black (points) to the reciprocal of the temperature for noble gases and nitrogen (a) and *n*-alkanes C_1–C_5 (b) (after A. V. Kiselev *et al.* [34]; A. V. Kiselev [35]; D. P. Poshkus and A. Ya. Afreymovich [36, 37]).

Figure 9.2 shows the relationship of the theoretically calculated values of Φ_0 (filled circles) and the experimentally determined values of the isosteric heat of adsorption (open circles) for zero coverage of graphite to the overall polarizability of adsorbate molecules, α [38–41]. An analogous relationship was obtained on the surface of boron nitride BN [39–40].

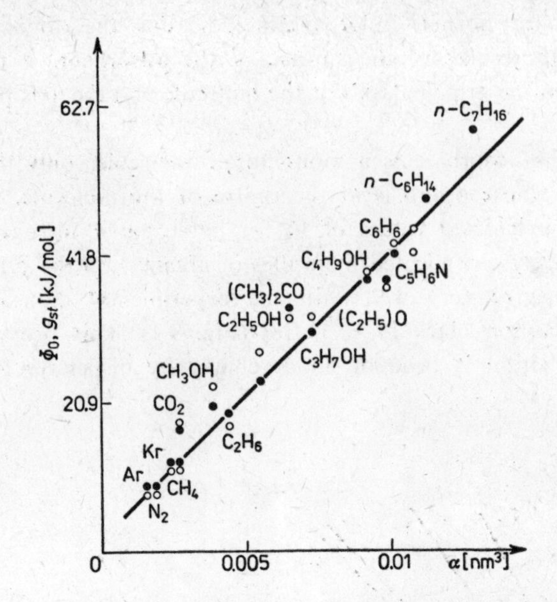

Fig. 9.2 Graph showing the relationship of the theoretically calculated potential energy of adsorption Φ_0 (filled circles) and the experimentally determined values of the heat of adsorption q_{st} (open circles) for various adsorbates on graphitized carbon black (small degree of coverage) to the overall polarizability of the adsorbate (after A. Kitaigorodsky [38]; A. D. Crowell and Chai Ok Chang [39]; G. Curthoys and P. E. Elkington [40]; E. V. Kalashmikova *et al.* [41]).

Hanlan and Freeman [47] and others [48–53] have described the possibility of determining the potential energy of gas–solid intermolecular interaction from the change in retention volume with temperature change

$$\lim_{p\to 0}\left(\frac{N\bar{k}t}{p_r}-V\right)=S\int_0^z\left[\exp\left(-\frac{\Phi(z)}{\bar{k}T}\right)-1\right]\mathrm{d}z\,, \tag{9.4}$$

where N is the number of moles of gas in volume V in contact with S cm^2 of solid surface at an equilibrium pressure of p_r and temperature T, $\Phi(z)$ is the potential energy of the gas–solid interaction, z is the distance from the centre of the molecule to the principal plane of the solid, assuming a flat surface.

The logarithm of the left-hand side of equation (9.4) as a function of $1/T$ gives a straight-line relationship over a wide range of temperatures. Hansen *et al.* [51] have derived a fairly straightforward formula from which the potential energy of molecular interaction can be determined from chromatographic data

$$\ln\left[\lim_{p\to 0} T^{1/2}\left(\frac{N\bar{k}T}{p_r} - V\right)\right] = \ln\left[Sz_0\left(\frac{2\pi}{27T_0}\right)^{1/2}\right] + \frac{T_0}{T} + \frac{175T}{216T_0} + \\ + \frac{109.480}{93.312}\left(\frac{T}{T^0}\right)^2 + \ldots, \quad (9.5)$$

where

$$T_0 = \frac{\Phi(z)}{\bar{k}}. \quad (9.6)$$

Assuming certain approximations we can determine T_0 from a graph of the left-hand side of equation (9.5) against $1/T$, and the potential energy of molecular interaction $\Phi(z)$ from equation (9.6). The energy of molecular interaction for argon, nitrogen, carbon monoxide, methane, propane and propylene with a surface of activated charcoal at temperatures from 300 to 700 K has been determined in this way [51].

Waksmundzki and co-workers [54] determined chromatographically the potential energy of the interaction of CS_2 with the surface of silica gel.

The non-specific dispersive interaction during adsorption on a homogeneous surface of graphitized carbon black is determined by the polarizability and magnetic susceptibility of certain groups of atoms in complicated adsorbate molecules. The geometrical configurations, the orientation of the molecules relative to the adsorbent surface and the Van der Waals radius of those atomic groups in the adsorbate molecule in contact with the graphitized carbon black surface are all very significant [19, 42].

A straight-line relationship exists between the logarithm of the retention volume of adsorbates from various groups on a homogeneous non-specific adsorbent surface (graphitized carbon black, some porous polymers) and their polarizability; the polarizability α of the adsorbate molecules can be derived from this relationship [56–59] (Fig. 9.3).

Since the energy of non-specific molecular interaction depends on the distance between the adsorbent surface and the energetic centres of the atomic groups in the adsorbed molecules (on a flat surface of graphitized carbon black), we can classify molecules which differ only in their geometrical structure, i.e. structural isomers and geometrical stereoisomers [45, 46, 96, 97] (Chromatoscopy). Molecules of n-alkanes are capable only of non-specific interaction with the surface of adsorbents. The homologous series of n-alkanes is therefore used in comparative studies of the non-specific interaction of different adsorbents [55] (Fig. 9.4).

It can be seen from Fig. 9.4 that while the isosteric heats of adsorption q_{st} of n-alkanes on every adsorbent do increase linearly with

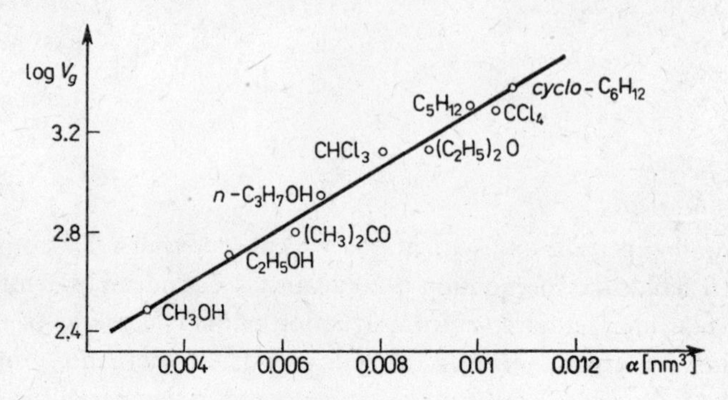

Fig. 9.3 Graph of log V_g on graphitized carbon black at 423 K versus the polarizability of the adsorbate (after A. V. Kiselev *et al.* [56–59]).

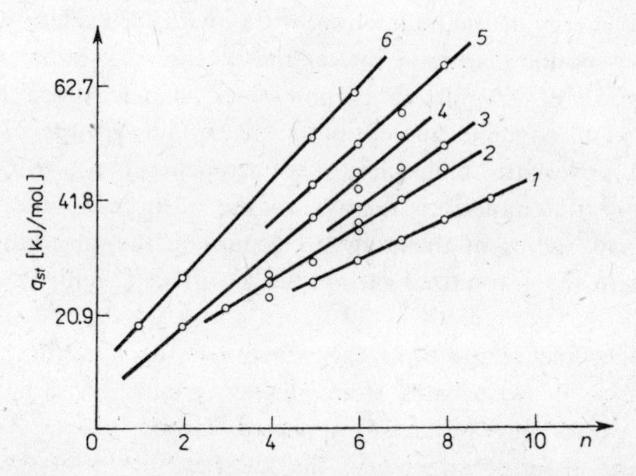

Fig. 9.4 Graphs of q_{st} of n-alkanes for small degrees of coverage on various adsorbents versus the number of carbon atoms n in the molecule (after V. L. Kejbal *et al.*, [55]): *1* — polyethylene glycol (poly(ethane 1,2-diol)) on graphitized carbon black, *2* — wide-pore silica gel, *3* — MgO, *4* — thermally graphitized carbon black, *5* — BN, *6* — NaX zeolite crystals.

the number of carbon atoms in the hydrocarbon molecule, the individual increases differ from one another. Figure 9.4 also shows to what extent the heats of adsorption in the non-specific interaction of n-alkane molecules with various adsorbents can change.

The relationships of $\log V_s$ and q_{st} (for small degrees of coverage of graphitized carbon black surfaces) with the number of carbon atoms in the molecule n are straight lines for homologous series (Fig. 9.5) [43, 44].

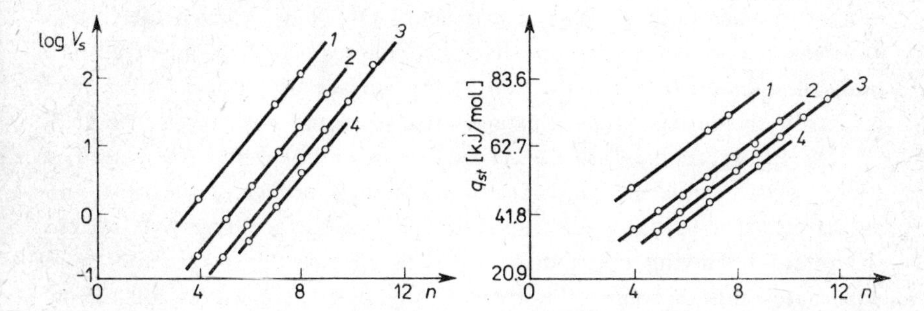

Fig. 9.5 Graphs of $\log V_s$ and q_{st} for various adsorbates on graphitized carbon black at 423 K versus the number of carbon atoms in the molecule (after L. D. Belyakova *et al.* [43]; A. V. Kiselev *et al.* [44]):
1 — *n*-acids, *2* — *n*-alcohols, *3* — *n*-alkenes, *4* — alkylbenzenes.

The heats of adsorption of *n*-alcohol and *n*-fatty acid derivatives for small degrees of coverage of graphitized carbon black surfaces are greater than the heats of adsorption of *n*-alkanes with the same number of carbon atoms in the molecule. For *n*-alcohols, this difference is 6.28 kJ/mol, for *n*-fatty acids 12.15 kJ/mol. On the other hand, the heats of adsorption of *n*-alkylbenzenes are lower by 2.93 kJ/mol than the corresponding values of *n*-alkanes with the same number of carbon atoms. The isosteric heats of adsorption q_{st} of *n*-alkane molecules and their unbranched derivatives are the summed magnitudes of the heats of each group in the molecule. These heats are: q_{CH_3} — 8.8; q_{CH_2} — 6.7; q_{OH} — 8.8; q_{ethers} — 5.45; q_{COOH} — 21.79 kJ/mol [19]. These values enable us to calculate approximate heats of adsorption for straight-chain compounds having the appropriate functional groups.

In practice, type II adsorbents are most often used, having, as they do, concentrated positive charges on their surfaces. The most common of them are silica gels, aluminium oxide and zeolites. The specific adsorption on silica gels is due to the presence of hydroxyl groups on the surface [60–69]. Silica gels with a maximally hydrated surface are particularly suitable for use as specific adsorbents. To activate silica at 423–473 K, most of the adsorbed molecules of water are removed leaving the number of hydroxyl groups on the surface unchanged [70, 71]. At higher temperatures the number of surface OH groups decreases, which leads to a concurrent reduction in the specific adsorption of unsaturated and polar molecules of adsorbate.

The specific adsorption on the surface of γ-Al_2O_3 takes place because of the presence of Al^{3+} ions (Lewis acid), O^{2-} ions, ionized OH groups and electron-acceptor proton defects (Chapter 7). The adsorption of molecules undergoing polarization at the surface of γ-Al_2O_3 takes place primarily on the Al^{3+} ions; this gives rise to strong positive electric fields.

As far as zeolites are concerned, strong non-specific interaction on the adsorbate molecule in the narrow channels occurs at the same time as strong specific interaction on the zeolite surface (positive cations) (Chapter 7). Having taken dispersive and electrostatic forces for simple adsorbates into account, the theoretically calculated values of the adsorption energy Φ_0 on A and X zeolites are in good agreement with the heats of adsorption determined for zero coverage [77–82].

Figure 9.6 shows the significant contribution of the specific interaction energy of the NaX zeolite in the total energy of adsorption of

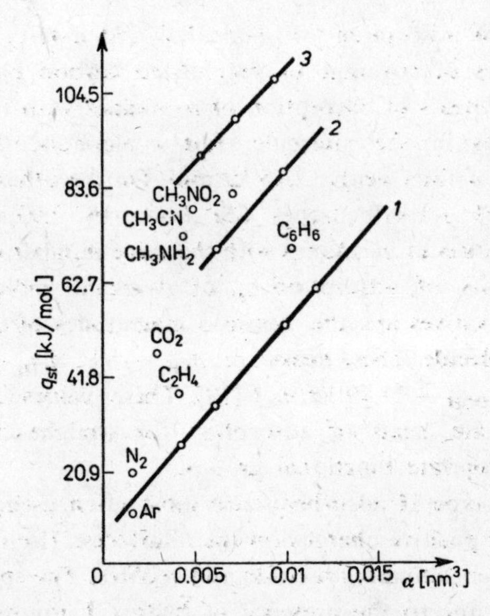

Fig. 9.6 Graphs of the heat of adsorption of molecules from various groups on NaX zeolite for a degree of coverage $\theta = 0.1$ versus the polarizability of these molecules (after V. L. Kejbal [55]; N. N. Avgul *et al.* [73]; A. V. Kiselev *et al.* [74]; A. G. Bezus and A. V. Kiselev [75]; R. M. Barrer and G. C. Bratt [76]:

1 — *n*-alkanes, *2* — ethers, *3* — *n*-alcohols.

molecules belonging to groups B and D. The heats of adsorption of group A, B and C molecules were determined calorimetrically from isosteres ans chromatographically [55, 72–76]. The molecular-statistical expression for Henry's constant (K) for zeolites takes the form [97]

$$K = D \int (e^{-\Phi/RT} - 1) \, dq \, dw \approx D \int e^{-\Phi/RT} \, dq \, dw \,, \qquad (9.7)$$

where Φ is the potential energy of interaction between the molecule and zeolite (total), q is the coordinate of the mass centre of the molecule, w is the Euler angle describing the orientation of the molecule, and D is a coefficient dependent on the symmetry of the molecule and the zeolite crystal.

If polyethylene glycol (poly(ethane 1,2-diol)) is supported on a graphitized carbon black surface, the adsorption of n-alkanes (group A molecules) decreases abruptly while the adsorption of methanol increases (group D molecules) (Fig. 9.7) [83].

Modification of graphitized carbon black by depositing a surface layer of polyethylene glycol on it gives us an adsorbent of type III. By depositing various substances on the surfaces of adsorbents we can gain

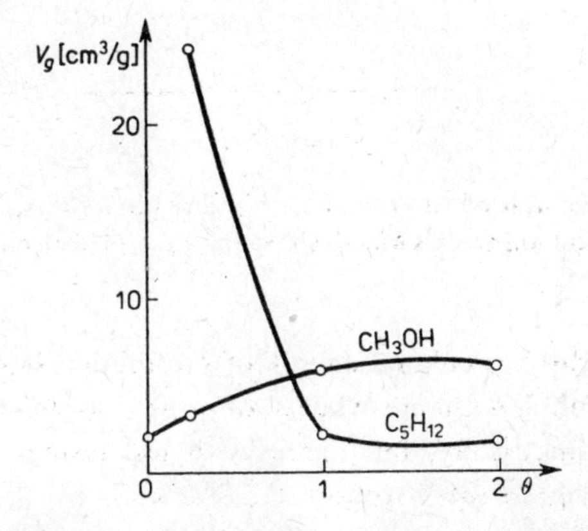

Fig. 9.7 Graphs showing the specific retention volume V_g of n-pentane and methanol on a graphitized carbon black surface modified with polyethylene glycol (poly(ethane 1,2-diol)) versus the degree of coverage of the surface (after L. D. Belyakova *et al.* [83]).

a significant measure of control over the sorptive properties. The homogeneous surface of graphitized carbon black is also a convenient adsorbent in the study of adsorbate-adsorbate interactions in the adsorption layer. This method is especially useful for determining the energy of a hydrogen bond.

9.4 Determination of the Energy of a Hydrogen Bond

The calorimetrically determined heats of adsorption (greater degrees of coverage) of molecules capable of forming hydrogen bonds (alcohols, amines, water, etc.) on the surfaces of type I adsorbents characterize the energy of non-specific interaction with the adsorbent surface, and also the energy of hydrogen bonds between molecules of adsorbate [84–90].

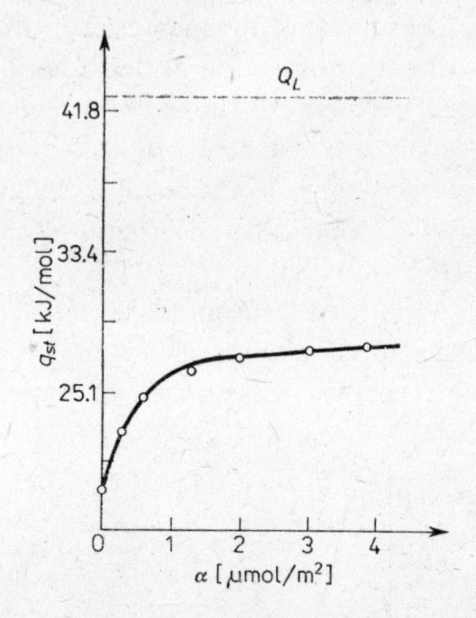

Fig. 9.8 Graph of the heat of adsorption q_{st} of water vapour versus the degree of coverage of a graphitized carbon black surface (Q_L is the heat of condensation) (after L. D. Belyakova *et al.* [86]).

The theoretically calculated energy of the mutual interaction of single molecules of alcohol with adsorbents of type I is less than the values determined calorimetrically, but agrees with the results obtained by GC for very small degrees of coverage θ.

The heats of adsorption of molecules capable of forming hydrogen bonds normally far exceed the values of the heats of condensation. The adsorption of water vapour on graphitized carbon black is an exception; the heats of adsorption in this case are lower than the heats of condensation (Fig 9.8) [86].

The energy of a hydrogen bond in the adsorption layer can be defined by comparing the heats of adsorption (non-specific adsorbent) of molecules capable of forming hydrogen bonds for large and small degrees of coverage θ. For large degrees of coverage, the heat of adsorption is usually estimated calorimetrically. Chromatography is suitable for determining the heats of adsorption for very small degrees of coverage, when adsorbate–adsorbate interaction can be neglected, because the detectors used in this method are extremely sensitive. Apart from this,

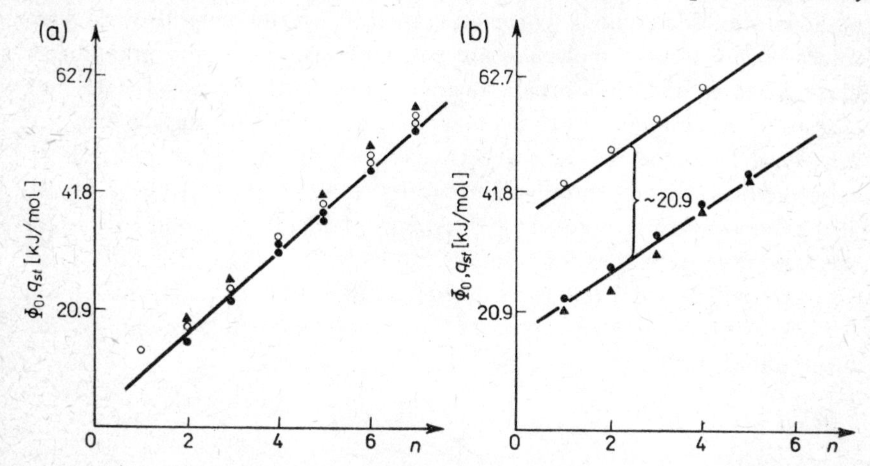

Fig. 9.9 Graph showing the potential energy Φ_0 and isosteric heat of adsorption of *n*-alkanes (a) and *n*-alcohols (b) versus the number of carbon atoms *n* in the molecule (after L. D. Belyakova *et al.* [85]):

○ — calorimetric measurements and determinations from isosteres obtained by the static vacuum method on graphitized carbon black with a coverage $\theta \approx 0.1$; ● — chromatographic data for $\theta \approx 0$; ▲ — theoretically calculated values of the potential energy of interaction of a single molecule with the graphite lattice.

heats of adsorption at higher temperatures not promoting the association of adsorbate molecules on the adsorbent surface can be determined chromatographically.

Figure 9.9 illustrates the relationship between both the heat of adsorption q_{st} and the theoretically calculated potential energy of adsorption Φ_0 of *n*-alkanes and *n*-alcohols with the number of carbon atoms in the molecule for average degrees of coverage (calorimetric and isosteric determinations) and small θ (chromatographic determinations).

For *n*-alkanes (Fig. 9.9a) the heats of adsorption q_{st} determined calorimetrically and isosterically agree with the results obtained from GC and with the theoretically calculated values of the potential energy of adsorption Φ_0.

The lack of specific interactions in *n*-alkanes means that their heats of condensation are not great; they are smaller than the heats of adsorption on graphitized carbon black. As the increase in heats of adsorption of *n*-alkanes during the formation of a monolayer on the graphitized carbon black surface is linear, we can obtain a value of q_0 for zero coverage ($\theta \approx 0$) by extrapolation. The heats of adsorption of n-alcohols obtained chromatographically are about 20.9 kJ/mol lower than those obtained calorimetrically. Such a large discrepancy is due to the fact that the heats of adsorption determined chromatographically relate only to very low values of θ — alcohol molecules are adsorbed separately on a graphitized black surface, and the sorbate interacts only with the adsorbent. The energy of association of n-alcohols on the adsorbent surface can be calculated from the differences between heats of adsorption determined calorimetrically and chromatographically [87]. This energy is about 20.9 kJ/mol, which is, practically, the energy of a hydrogen bond. However, this difference is smaller for isomeric butanols. The reason for this lies in the fact that it is difficult for isomeric alcohols and even impossible for tertiary alcohols to form associated molecules with a large number of other molecules.

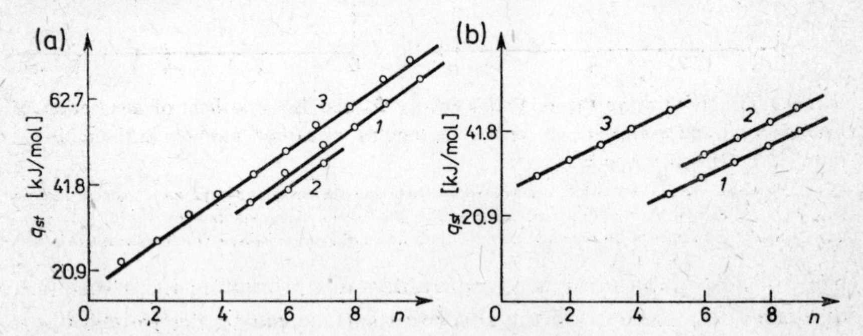

Fig. 9.10 Graph of the heat of adsorption q_{st} of different adsorbates for small degrees of coverage on graphitized carbon black (a) and a layer of polyethylene glycol (poly (ethane 1,2-diol)) deposited on graphitized carbon black (b) versus the number of carbon atoms n in their molecules (after A. V. Kiselev *et al.* [59, 83]):

1 — *n*-alkanes, *2* — aromatic hydrocarbons, *3* — *n*-alcohols.

The energy of a hydrogen bond also be determined chromatographically from the differences between the heats of adsorption of alcohols (or other grup D molecules) and of their corresponding n-alkanes on a monolayer of polyethylene glycol (poly(ethane 1,2-diol)) deposited on an adsorbent-support surface (graphitized carbon black, wide-pore silica gel). The deposited monolayer should be capable of forming hydrogen bonds with molecules of group D adsorbates [59, 83]. Polyethylene glycol is most often used for this monolayer as its surface oxygen atoms are capable of forming hydrogen bonds (Fig. 9.10).

We can see from Fig. 9.10 that on a pure graphitized black surface, incapable of specific interaction, the difference between the heats of adsorption of n-alcohols and n-alkanes with the same number of carbon atoms is about 4.19 kJ/mol. The difference is mainly due to the contribution of the non-specific interaction of oxygen with the carbon black surface. The difference between the heats of adsorption is far greater (about 19.7 kJ/mol) on a polyethylene glycol surface. We can calculate the energy of a hydrogen bond from this difference

$$q_{(H)} = 19.7 - 4.19 \cong 15.5 \text{ kJ/mol}.$$

The energy of the specific interaction of aromatic hydrocarbons with a polyethylene glycol surface was determined in a similar manner [59, 83].

Chulpanova and Yashin [91] determined the energy of a hydrogen bond from the differences between the heats of adsorption of the *ortho*-, *meta*- and *para*-isomers of chlorophenol and nitrophenol. These authors assumed that the *ortho*-isomers were incapable of forming hydrogen bonds with the polyethylene glycol surface because they formed intramolecular hydrogen bonds.

GLC has recently been used with success to determine the energy of hydrogen bonds. The differences between the heats of solution of hydrogen sulphide and acetylene in organic bases and non-polar solvents were used for this purpose [97]. The bond energies of SH...B and CH...B so obtained agreed well with spectrographic results and, above all, with data from thermodynamic calculations (Table 9.1).

Table 9.1 A COMPARISON OF VARIOUS HYDROGEN BOND ENERGIES [kJ/mol] OF HYDROGEN SULPHIDE (SH...B) AND ACETYLENE (CH...B) WITH ORGANIC BASES [97]

Base	I	II	III	I	II	III
	SH ... B			CH ... B		
Dibutyl ether	3.77	5.86	5.02	4.60	3.77	6.70
Cyclohexanone	4.60	5.02	5.02	6.70	3.77	6.70
Tributyl phosphate	5.45	6.70	6.70	7.12	—	8.80
N-methylpyrrolidone	7.96	—	6.28	10.05	7.12	8.38
Hexamethylphosphoramide	8.80	12.99	9.22	10.89	9.63	11.31
Dimethylsulphone	6.28	11.31	7.12	7.12	—	9.22

I — chromatographic data, II — spectral data, III — data from thermodynamic calculations.

References

[1] Jaycock M. J. and Parfitt G. D., *Chemistry of Interfaces*, Ellis Horwood Ltd, John Wiley and Sons, New York, Chichester, Brisbane, Toronto, 1981.
[2] Ościk J., *Adsorption*, Ellis Horwood and PWN, Chichester, Warsaw, 1981.
[3] Kiselev A. V., *Zh. Fiz. Khim.*, **41**, 2647 (1967).
[4] Avgul N. N. and Kiselev A. V., in: *Chemistry and Physics of Carbons*, Ed. Walker P. L., Marcel Dekker, New York, 1970, Vol. 6, p. 1.
[5] Poshkus D. P., *Zh. Fiz. Khim.*, **39**, 2962 (1965).
[6] Poshkus D. P., *Disc. Faraday Soc.*, **40**, 195 (1965).
[7] Barrer R. M., *Proc. Roy. Soc.*, **A161**, 476 (1937).
[8] Avgul N. N., Kiselev A. V., Lygina I. A. and Poshkus D. P., *Izv. Akad. Nauk SSSR, ser. Khim.*, 1196 (1959).
[9] Girifalco L. A. and Lad R. A., *J. Chem. Phys.*, **25**, 693 (1956).
[10] Crowell A. D., *J. Chem. Phys.*, **22**, 1397 (1954).
[11] Crowell A. D., *J. Chem. Phys.*, **26**, 1407 (1957).
[12] Kiselev A. V., Poshkus D. P. and Afreymovich A. Ya., *Zh. Fiz. Khim.*, **39**, 1190 (1965).
[13] Kiselev A. V., *Zh. Fiz. Khim.*, **38**, 2753 (1964).
[14] Kiselev A. V., *Disc. Faraday Soc.*, **40**, 205 (1965).
[15] Everett D. H., in: *Gas Chromatography 1964*, Ed. Goldup A., Butterworths, London, 1965, p. 219.
[16] Barrer R. M., *Colloid. J. Interface Sci.*, **21**, 415 (1966).
[17] Kiselev A. V., *Rev. gen. Caoutch.*, **41**, 377 (1964).
[18] Kiselev A. V., in: *Gas Chromatography 1964*, Ed. Goldup A., Butterworths, London, 1965, p. 238.
[19] Kiselev A. V. and Yashin Ya. I., *Gas Adsorption Chromatography*, Plenum Press, New York, London, 1969.
[20] Avgul N. N., Kiselev A. V. and Lyshna N. A., *Izv. Akad. Nauk SSSR*, 1395 (1961).
[21] Kiselev A. V. and Poshkus D. P., *Zh. Fiz. Khim.*, **13**, 285 (1969).
[22] Sams I. R., *Trans. Faraday Soc.*, **60**, 149 (1964).
[23] Constabaris G., Sams J. B. and Halsey G. D., *J. Phys. Chem.*, **65**, 367 (1961).
[24] Crowell A. D. and Steele W. A., *J. Chem. Phys.*, **34**, 1347 (1961).
[25] Crowell A. D., *J. Chem. Phys.*, **29**, 446 (1958).
[26] Kiselev A. V. and Poshkus D. P., *Trans. Faraday Soc.*, **59**, 176 (1963).
[27] Kiselev A. V. and Poshkus D. P., *Trans. Faraday Soc.*, **59**, 428 (1963).
[28] Avgul N. N., Kiselev A. V. and Lygina I. A., *Trans. Faraday Soc.*, **59**, 2113 (1963).
[29] Sams I. R., Constabaris G. and Halsey G. D., *J. Phys. Chem.*, **64**, 1689 (1960).
[30] Buckingham R. A., *Proc. Roy. Soc.*, **A160**, 94 (1937).
[31] Lennard-Jones J. E., *Trans. Faraday Soc.*, **28**, 333 (1932).
[32] Kirkwood J. C., *Physik. Z.*, **33**, 57 (1932).
[33] Müller A., *Proc. Roy. Soc. (London)*, **A154**, 624 (1936).
[34] Kiselev A. V., Poshkus D. P. and Afreymovich A. Ya., *Zh. Fiz. Khim.*, **42**, 2546 (1968).
[35] Kiselev A. V.. *J. Chromatogr.*, **49**, 84 (1970).

[36] Poshkus D. P. and Afreymovich A. Ya., *J. Chromatogr.*, **58**, 55 (1971).
[37] Poshkus D. P. and Afreymovich A. Ya., *Zh. Fiz. Khim.*, **42**, 1201 (1968).
[38] Kitaigorodsky A., *J. Chim. Phys.*, **63**, 9 (1966).
[39] Crowell A. D. and Chai Ok Chang, *J. Chem. Phys.*, **43**, 4364 (1965).
[40] Curthoys G. and Elkington P. E., *J. Phys. Chem.*, **71**, 1477 (1967).
[41] Kalashnikova E. V., Kiselev A. V., Shcherbakova K. D. and Zamaskaga Z. V., *Chromatographia*, **5**, 278 (1972).
[42] *Fizikokhimicheskie primenenie gazovoy khromatografii*, Izd. Khimya, Moskva, 1973.
[43] Belyakova L. D., Kiselev A. V. and Kovaleva N. V., *Zh. Fiz. Khim.*, **40**, 1949 (1966).
[44] Kiselev A. V., Migunova I. A. and Yashin Ya. I., *Zh. Fiz. Khim.*, **42**, 1235 (1968).
[45] Kiselev A. V. and Yashin Ya. I., *Zh. Fiz. Khim.*, **40**, 429 (1966).
[46] Kiselev A. V. and Yashin Ya. I., in: *Gas Chromatographie 1965*, Eds. Angele H. P., and Struppe H. G., Akademie Verlag, Berlin, 1965, p. 45.
[47] Hanlan J. F. and Freeman M. P., *Can. J. Chem.*, **37**, 1575 (1959).
[48] Barker J. A. and Everett D. H., *Trans. Faraday Soc.*, **58**, 1608 (1962).
[49] Steele W. A. and Halsey G. D. Jr, *J. Chem. Phys.*, **22**, 979 (1954).
[50] Steele W. A. and Halsey G. D. Jr, *J. Phys. Chem.*, **59**, 57 (1955).
[51] Hansen R. S., Murphy J. A. and McGee T. C., *Trans. Faraday Soc.*, **60**, 597 (1964).
[52] Hansen R. S., *J. Phys. Chem.*, **63**, 743 (1959).
[53] Harper J. A., *Diss. Abstr.*, **24** (10), 4008 (1964).
[54] Waksmundzki A., Rudziński W. and Suprynowicz Z., *J. Gas Chromatogr.*, **4**, 93 (1966).
[55] Kejbal V. L., Kiselev A. V., Savinov I. M., Khudyakov V. L., Shcherbakova K. D. and Yashin Ya. I., *Zh. Fiz. Khim.*, **41**, 2234 (1967).
[56] Kiselev A. V., Shcherbakova K. D. and Yashin Ya. I., *Zh. Struktur. Khim.*, **10**, 951 (1969).
[57] Gvozdovich T. N., Kiselev A. V. and Yashin Ya. I., *Neftekhimiya*, **8**, 476 (1968).
[58] Gvozdovich T. N., Kiselev A. V. and Yashin Ya. I., *Chromatographia*, **6**, 3 (1973).
[59] Kiselev A. V., Kovaleva N. Y. and Nikitin Yu. S., *J. Chromatogr.*, **58**, 19 (1971).
[60] Snyder L. R., *J. Chromatogr.*, **25**, 274 (1966).
[61] Snyder L. R., *Separation Sci.*, **1**, 191 (1966).
[62] Snyder L. R. and Ward J. W., *J. Phys. Chem.*, **70**, 3941 (1966).
[63] Peri J. B. and Henseley A. L. Jr, *J. Phys. Chem.*, **8**, 2926 (1968).
[64] Davydov V. Ya., Kiselev A. V. and Zhuravlev L. T., *Trans. Faraday Soc.*, **60**, 2254 (1964).
[65] Zhuravlev L. T. and Kiselev A. V., *Zh. Fiz. Khim.*, **39**, 453 (1965).
[66] Chertov V. M., Dzatbaeva D. B., Plachinda A. S. and Nejmark I. E., *Zh. Fiz. Khim.*, **40**, 520 (1966).
[67] Kiselev A. V. and Lygin V. I., *Usp. Khim.*, **31**, 351 (1962).
[68] Kiselev A. V. and Lygin V. I., *Kolloid. Zh.*, **21**, 581 (1959).
[69] Jegorov M. M., Kvilikhidze V. I., Kiselev A. V. and Krasilnikov G. K., *Kolloid. Z. u. Z. Polymere*, **212**, 126 (1966).
[70] Kiselev A. V., *Structure and Properties of Porous Materials*, Butterworths, New York, London, 1958, p. 195.

[71] Schultze G. R. and Schmidt-Kuster W. J., *Z. anal. Chem.*, **3**, 251 (1964).
[72] Dzhigit O. M., Karpiński K., Kiselev A. V., Melnikova T. A., Mikos K. N. and Muttik T. G., *Zh. Fiz. Khim.*, **42**, 198 (1968).
[73] Avgul N. N., Kiselev A. V., Kurdyukova L. Ya. and Serdobov M. V., *Zh. Fiz. Khim.*, **42**, 188 (1968).
[74] Kiselev A. V., Korenkova Yu. I. and Yashin Ya. I., *Neftekhimiya*, **5**, 589 (1965).
[75] Bezus A. G. and Kiselev A. V., *Zh. Fiz. Khim.*, **40**, 1773 (1966).
[76] Barrer R. M. and Bratt G. C., *Phys. and Chem. Solids*, **12**, 130 (1960).
[77] Avgul N. N., Bezus A. G., Dobrova E. S. and Kiselev A. V., *J. Colloid Interface Sci.*, **42**, 486 (1973).
[78] Kiselev A. V., Lopatkin A. A. and Ryabukhina R. G., *Bull. soc. chim. France*, 1324 (1972).
[79] Kiselev A. V., *Advances in Chemistry Series*, **102**, 37 (1971).
[80] Kiselev A. V. and Lopatkin A. A., in: *Molecular Sieves*, Ed. Soc. Chem. Ind., London, 1968, p. 209.
[81] Brojer P., Kiselev A. V., Lesnik E. A. and Lopatkin A. A., *Zh. Fiz. Khim.*, **42**, 2556 (1968).
[82] Brojer P., Kiselev A. V., Lesnik E. A. and Lopatkin A. A., *Zh. Fiz. Khim.*, **43**, 1579 (1969).
[83] Belyakova L. D., Kiselev A. V., Rozanova L. N. and Khopina V. V., *Zh. Fiz. Khim.*, **42**, 177 (1968).
[84] Belyakova L. D., Kiselev A. V. and Kovaleva N. V., *Dokl. Akad. Nauk. SSSR*, **157**, 646 (1964).
[85] Belyakova L. D., Kiselev A. V. and Kovaleva N. V., *Anal. Chem.*, **36**, 1517 (1964).
[86] Belyakova L. D., Kiselev A. V. and Kovaleva N. V., *Bull. soc. chim. France*, 285 (1967).
[87] Gale R. L. and Beebe R. A., *J. Phys. Chem.*, **68**, 555 (1964).
[88] Avgul N. N., Berezin G. I., Kiselev A. V. and Lygina I. A., *Izv. Akad. Nauk SSSR, ser. Khim.*, 205 (1961).
[89] Avgul N. N., Kiselev A. V. and Lygina I. A., *Koll. Zh.*, **23**, 369 (1961).
[90] Avgul N. N., Kiselev A. V. and Lygina I. A., *Koll. Zh.*, **23**, 513 (1961).
[91] Chulpanova L. V. and Yashin Ya. I., *Zh. Fiz. Khim.*, **44**, 773 (1970).
[92] Avgul N. N., Kiselev A. V. and Poshkus D. P., *Adsorptsya gazov i parov na odnorodnykh poverkhnostyakh*, Izd. Khimya, Moskva, 1975.
[93] Engewald E., Kalashnikova E. V., Kiselev A. V. Petrova R. S., Shilov A. L. and Shcherbakova K. D., *J. Chromatogr.*, **152**, 453 (1978).
[94] Kiselev A. V., Poshkus D. P. and Grumadas A. J., *J. Chem. Soc. Faraday Trans.*, **1**, 75 (1979).
[95] Kiselev A. V. and Poshkus D. P., *J. Chem. Soc. Faraday Trans.*, II, **72**, 950 (1976).
[96] Kiselev A. V., *Chromatographia*, **11**, 691 (1978).
[97] Kiselev A. V., *Fizycheskaya adsorptsiya v mikroporistykh adsorbentakh*, V Konf. po teoret. voprosam adsorptsiy, Izd. Nauka, Moskva, 1979.
[98] Levina O. V., Iogantsev A. V., Kurkchi T. A. and Batsva V. P., *Zh. Fiz. Khim.*, **52**, 153 (1978).

Chapter **10**

The Study of Diffusion Processes

10.1 Introduction

The course taken by adsorption and catalytic processes occurring at the surface of porous adsorbents and catalysts depends to a large extent on the rate of diffusion in the pores of the solid (internal and surface diffusion).

In order to assess the magnitude and influence of diffusion phenomena on the rate of sorption and chemical reaction, we must know the effective coefficient of diffusion D_{ef} which, on a macroscopic scale, characterizes diffusion processes taking place within the pores of a solid. The effective coefficient of diffusion can be determined in a number of ways — they are described in detail in the monograph by Timofeyev [1].

The stationary flow method has found the greatest favour [2–4]. A sample of the solid in the form of a disc is placed in a tube. The gases whose diffusion we are studying are fed to the centres of each side of the disc through thin tubes. Analysis of the outflowing streams enables us to determine D_{ef}. This method has many shortcomings. It cannot be used directly with a granular solid. Only those pores which are linked directly with each other, thus facilitating the flow of gas, affect the value of the effective coefficient of diffusion to be determined. The method does, however, give satisfactory results with isotropic solids.

The effective coefficient of diffusion can be estimated indirectly by measuring the rate of a reaction of known kinetics in the diffusion region. The coefficient determined in this fashion refers only to the active state of the catalyst under reaction conditions. We can also determine the effective coefficient of diffusion by making use of a non-catalytic reaction taking place in the pores of the solid [5].

It is now becoming more frequent for this coefficient to be determined by non-stationary methods [6–8]. In recent years, workers have begun to apply chromatographic techniques to the estimation of D_{ef} [9–59].

The chromatographic method allows the effective coefficient of diffusion to be determined in the particles of a solid without their shape having to be changed; apart from this, such determinations can be carried out over a wide range of temperatures and pressures. Notwithstanding its rapidity and simplicity of execution, the method affords the possibility of determining the effective coefficient of diffusion under conditions approaching those encountered in technological adsorption and catalytic processes. Choudhary [53] provides an exhaustive review of the literature up to 1974 on research into the use of chromatography to study diffusion.

10.2 Determination of the Diffusion Coefficient in the Gaseous Phase

Realizing that the diffusion processes in the band moving along a column packed with granular adsorbent are very complex, Giddings and Seager [11, 12, 56, 57] proposed the determination of the diffusion constant in the gaseous phase on the basis of peak broadening using an empty column. The essence of this method is not therefore directly connected with the chromatographic process. In laminar flow an external exchange of mass takes place only as a result of molecular diffusion. The magnitude of the Reynolds number indicates that at the carrier gas velocities normally used in chromatography we have laminar flow. For laminar flow, the shape of a pulse at the column outlet is described by a Gaussian curve [9, 10]. The width of the Gaussian curve at half height ω (Fig. 1.3) is given by

$$\omega = 4\sqrt{\ln 2 D_g t}\,, \tag{10.1}$$

where D_g is the coefficient of molecular diffusion of the adsorbate in the carrier gas, and t is the elution time of the band.

Giddings and Seager [11, 12] suggest using the formal height of the empty column, equivalent to a theoretical plate H, to estimate the broadening of the chromatographic band

$$H = \frac{2D_g}{u} + \frac{r^2 u}{24 D_g}\,, \tag{10.2}$$

where r is the diameter of the tube.

Figure 10.1 illustrates the relationship of H and u for methane in hydrogen using an empty column [11]. The value of H can be found using equation (1.12).

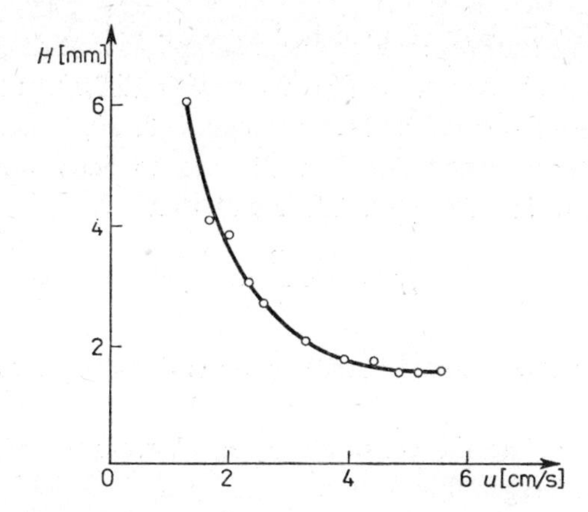

Fig. 10.1 Dependence of H on u for methane in hydrogen using an empty column (300 cm × 4 mm, temp. 298 K) (after J. C. Giddings and S. L. Seager [11]).

We can see from equation (10.2) that the diffusion coefficient D_g can be evaluated from the linear relationship between Hu and u^2 [11, 12]. This method has been used to determine, among others, the coefficient of diffusion of hydrogen in nitrogen [11], methane, ethane, propane and of butane in hydrogen [45]. If the method is to be successful, laminar flow must be maintained throughout the experiment.

Knox and McLaren [16] determined the coefficient of molecular diffusion by introducing a small sample of a non-adsorbing substance into an empty or packed column. After the substance had been introduced, the flow of carrier gas through the column was stopped, allowing the band to diffuse for a given time. The band was then eluted from the column with carrier gas and its width determined. The coefficient of diffusion was estimated from a graph of peak width against the time the substance had been in the column. After having improved this method, Cloete, Smuts and Clerk [46, 47] estimated the diffusion coefficient of C_1–C_5 hydrocarbons, neon, nitrogen and helium in argon, nitrogen and helium at temperatures from 294 to 483 K; Choudhary and Parande [49] did likewise for aniline and nitrobenzene in hydrogen.

10.3 Determination of the Effective Diffusion Coefficient in Porous Solids

The effective diffusion coefficient can be determined chromatographically in a number of ways. D_{ef} can be determined from the rate of desorption into the carrier gas stream of an adsorbate previously adsorbed on the test sample, making the assumption that desorption proper takes place very quickly in comparison with diffusion; the desorption isotherm is linear for small surface coverages [8, 20, 21].

The van Deemter equation can be used to determine the effective coefficient of diffusion D_{ef} [30]. We recall that

$$H = A + \frac{B}{n} + Cu, \tag{10.3}$$

where A, B, C are constants characterizing various kinds of diffusion (see Section 1.3.3).

In order to define the constants A, B, C, we have to determine the effect of the carrier gas flow rate u on the peak broadening. Figure 10.2 shows a typical curve of H against u for a non-porous solid, while in Fig. 10.3 this dependence is illustrated for a porous adsorbent [24].

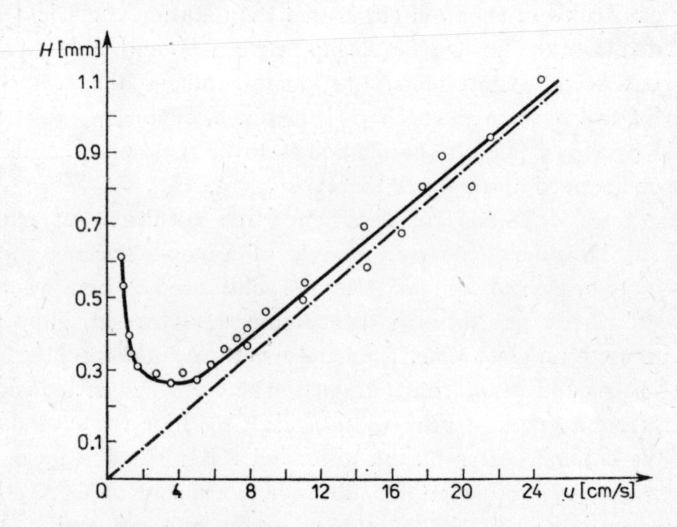

Fig. 10.2 Relationship between H and u for non-porous particles of column packing; particle diameter 0.208 cm, column diameter 5 cm, methane pulse in hydrogen (after B. Davis and D. S. Scott [24]).

If we determine D_{ef} under such conditions that adsorption can be neglected, the constant C (equation (10.3)) for a spherical column packing can be defined by an approximate equation consisting of two parts: the first part takes the internal resistance to mass exchange into account, the second describes the complicated diffusion processes occurring within the pores of a spherical particle [24]

$$C = \frac{\dfrac{E_{\text{pack}}^2 d_p^2}{75(1-E_{\text{pack}})^2 D_g} + \dfrac{E_{\text{pack}} d_p^2}{2\pi^2(1-E_{\text{pack}}) E_p D_{ef}}}{\left[1 + \dfrac{E_{\text{pack}}}{(1-E_{\text{pack}}) E_p}\right]^2}, \tag{10.4}$$

where E_{pack} is the porosity of the packing, d_p is the diameter of the packing particles, E_p is the porosity of the packing particles, D_g is the coefficient of diffusion in the gaseous phase, D_{ef} is the effective diffusion coefficient in the pores. Theoretically, for a non-porous packing, C should be equal to zero.

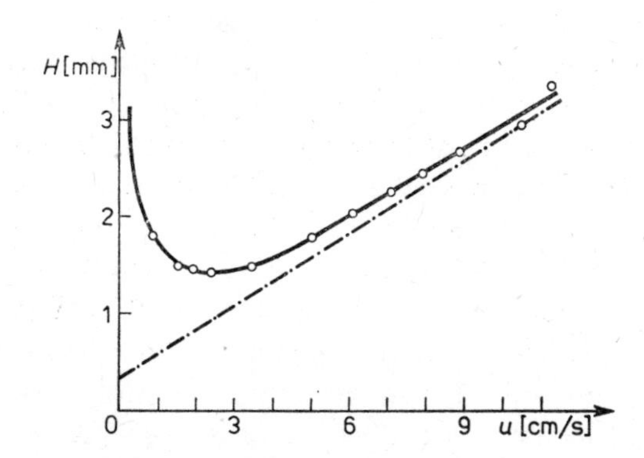

Fig. 10.3 A typical result of pulse broadening for a layer of porous particles; particle diameter 0.597 cm, particle porosity 0.50, column diameter 0.66 cm, pulse of hydrogen in air (after B. Davis and D. S. Scott [24]).

The first part of equation (10.4) takes into consideration the resistance to mass exchange in the gaseous phase during laminar flow. For higher flow rates, mass exchange in the gaseous phase decreases. The effective diffusion coefficient D_{ef} therefore affects the value of C in a fundamental way. It is assumed that radial concentration gradients in a packed layer are slight, and that concentration gradients within the porous particles are linear. The greater the diffusion resistance in the particle, the less reasonable is the assumption of a linear decrease in concentration in the pores, though at the same time the expression representing the effect of particle porosity on the accuracy of determination of D_{ef} increases. Assuming that the first part of equation (10.4) is not usually more than 10% of the value of the second part, even if $D_g = D_{ef}$, we can calculate an approximate value of D_{ef} from the relationship [24]

$$D_{ef} = \frac{E_{pack}}{2C_k(1-E_{pack})E_p}\left[\frac{d_p}{\pi\left(1+\dfrac{E_{pack}}{E_p(1-E_{pack})}\right)}\right]^2, \qquad (10.5)$$

where C_k is the constant C after including the "wall" effect.

Equation (10.3) does not include band broadening due to the wall effect. This effect can be neglected when the ratio of the column diameter to the packing particle diameter is greater than 30; then the gas flow rate at the centre of the column differs very little from that at the walls [31].

Davis and Scott [24] took the wall effect into account when determining C for a non-porous column packing. The van Deemter equation or its various modifications have been used by many workers to determine D_{ef} [22–25, 32]. Habgood and Hanlan [22] determined D_{ef} for nitrogen, methane, ethane, propane and isobutane in the pores of activated charcoal (pore diameter 1.8–2.5 nm) at temperatures from 382 to 585 K. The values of the effective diffusion coefficient obtained were approximately the same, even though the adjusted retention volumes differed by factors of over 100. The authors explain this as being due to two mutually interacting effects: the reduction of Knudsen diffusion because the pore size has become smaller during adsorption, and the increase of surface diffusion which probably plays a big part where a gas is easily adsorbed.

Leffler [23] determined D_{ef} of nitrogen in the pores of aluminium oxide at 195 K, Denisova and Rozental [32] measured D_{ef} for butane in the pores of an aluminium–chromium catalyst at 393 K.

Davis and Scott [24] found that estimating D_{ef} by pulse GC gives satisfactory agreement (4%) with the results obtained by the stationary method for isotropic packing particles only. There was a significant discrepancy between the results obtained by the two methods when an anisotropic catalyst was used.

The determination of the effective diffusion coefficient using the van Deemter equation is an approximate one, because, of course, the equation itself is an approximation.

A more precise approach to the determination of equilibrium constants, rates of adsorption and the corresponding diffusion coefficients under chromatographic conditions was presented by Schneider and Smith [25], who proposed sets of differential equations to describe mass exchange processes in the column. Furthermore, these authors, unlike equation (10.5), took into account diffusion from the gas stream to the surface of the solid and also the concentration change inside the porous particles. They also made the assumption that the adsorption isotherm for small surface coverages was linear, and did not include radial concentration gradients in their calculations.

Schneider and Smith [25] found a relationship between the chromatographic peak moments [33, 34] and equilibrium constants, rates of adsorption and diffusion coefficients

$$u_1' = \frac{\int_0^\infty tc(x,t)\mathrm{d}t}{\int_0^\infty c(x,t)\mathrm{d}t}, \tag{10.6}$$

$$u_2 = \frac{\int_0^\infty (t-u_1')^2 c(x,t)\mathrm{d}t}{\int_0^\infty c(x,t)\mathrm{d}t}, \tag{10.7}$$

where u_1' is the first moment, u_2 is the second central moment, x is the coordinate of the length of the layer measured from the column inlet, c is the concentration of adsorbate in the gaseous phase.

The moments u_1' and u_2 are calculated from the shape of the chromatographic peak with an electronic calculator using the following relationships:

$$\frac{\Delta u_1' - t_0/2}{E_\mathrm{p}(1-E_\mathrm{pack})/E_\mathrm{pack}} = \frac{\varrho_\mathrm{p}}{E_\mathrm{p}} K_\mathrm{A}\left(\frac{x}{u}\right), \tag{10.8}$$

where t_0 is the duration of a pulse of adsorbing gas at concentration c_0, ϱ_p is the apparent density of the particle, and K_A is the adsorption equilibrium constant.

$$\frac{u_2 - t_0^2/12}{2x/u} = \delta_a + \delta_{D_\mathrm{ef}} + \delta_D + \frac{D_\mathrm{g}}{E_\mathrm{pack} u^2}(1+\delta_0)^2, \tag{10.9}$$

where

$$\delta_a = \left(\frac{1-E_\mathrm{pack}}{E_\mathrm{pack}} E_\mathrm{p}\right) \frac{\varrho_\mathrm{p}}{E_\mathrm{p}} \frac{K_\mathrm{A}^2}{k_\mathrm{a}}, \tag{10.10}$$

$$\delta_{D_\mathrm{ef}} = \delta_0 + \frac{(d_\mathrm{p}/2)^2 E_\mathrm{p}}{15 D_\mathrm{ef}} \left(1 + \frac{\varrho_\mathrm{p}}{E_\mathrm{p}} K_\mathrm{A}\right), \tag{10.11}$$

$$\delta_D = \delta_0 + \frac{(d_\mathrm{p}/2)^2 E_\mathrm{p}}{15} \left(1 + \frac{\varrho_\mathrm{p}}{E_\mathrm{p}} K_\mathrm{A}\right)\left(\frac{5}{k_\mathrm{f} d_\mathrm{p}/2}\right), \tag{10.12}$$

where k_a is the adsorption rate constant, and k_f is the coefficient of mass exchange from the gas to the particle surface.

Equations (10.10)–(10.12) define the effect of the adsorption rate constant k_a, the internal diffusion in the pores $\delta_{D_{ef}}$ and the external diffusion from the gaseous phase to the particle δ_D on the value of the second central moment.

The effective coefficient of diffusion D_{ef} can be combined with the coefficient of Knudsen diffusion D_k and surface diffusion D_s in the following equation [35]:

$$D_{ef} = D_k + \frac{\varrho_p}{E_p} K_A D_s . \tag{10.13}$$

Schneider and Smith [25] used these equations just derived to determine the adsorption equilibrium constants of ethane, propane and n-butane on SiO_2 at 323 K. They also calculated the adsorption rate constants and the coefficients of longitudinal, internal and surface diffusion. The experiments were carried out at concentrations of hydrocarbons in the carrier gas not exceeding 1% of those for which the adsorption isotherms were linear. It was found that external diffusion affected transfer processes only to a slight extent; its contribution to the overall transfer process did not exceed 4% for packing particles whose $d_p = 1$ mm. When using the smallest particles ($d_p = 0.22$ mm) the effects of adsorption and external diffusion are evident, although even here the leading part is played by internal diffusion. Surface diffusion was considerable in the overall mass transfer process and decreased when the temperature was raised from 323 to 398 K.

The diffusion of methane, n-hexane and cyclohexane in the pores of an industrial aluminosilicate catalyst has been determined recently using this method [50]. It was found that in the case of strongly adsorbing components such as n-hexane and cyclohexane, surface diffusion was responsible for the transfer of almost 60% of these compounds. Methane, which is only slightly adsorbed, is transported in its entirety in the gaseous phase. The diffusion of 2-methyl-2-butene molecules was studied on A and Y zeolites [54].

One particular advantage of the chromatographic method is that the surface diffusion for very low degrees of coverage (of the order of 10^{-4} monolayer) can be measured.

As there is insufficient experimental material available, it is difficult at the moment to pass a firm judgement on the merits and drawbacks of this method. In order to assess the technique properly, further work on the determination of D_{ef} of different adsorbates for adsorbents and catalysts with different pore structures must be done and the results compared with those obtained by traditional methods. Recently, more and more work has been published on the chromatographic estimation of diffusion coefficients [36–59].

References

[1] Timofeyev D. P., *Kinetika adsorptsii*, Izd. Akad. Nauk. SSSR, Moskva, 1962.
[2] Weisz P. B., *Z. phys. Chemie.*, **11**, 1 (1957).
[3] Scott D. S. and Dullien F. A. L., *Am. Inst. Chem. Eng. J.*, **8**, 113 (1962).
[4] Hoogschagen J., *Ind. Eng. Chem.*, **47**, 906 (1955).
[5] Scott D. S. and Davis B. R., *Ind. Eng. Chem. Fundamentals*, **3**, 20 (1964).
[6] Paryjczak T. and Staszel S., *Przemysł Chem.*, **60** (4), 220 (1981).
[7] Currie J. A., *Brit. J. Appl. Phys.*, **11**, 314 (1960).
[8] Gorring R. L. and de Rosset A. J., *J. Catal.*, **3**, 341 (1964).
[9] Taylor G., *Proc. Roy. Soc.*, **219A**, 186 (1953).
[10] Bournia A. J., Coull J. and Houghton G., *Proc. Roy. Soc.*, **261**, 227 (1961).
[11] Giddings J. C. and Seager S. L., *J. Chem. Phys.*, **33**, 1579 (1960).
[12] Giddings J. C. and Seager S. L., *J. Chem. Phys.*, **35**, 224 (1961).
[13] Fuller E. N. and Giddings J. C., *J. Gas Chromatogr.*, **3**, 222 (1965).
[14] Dacey J. R., *Ind. Eng. Chem.*, **57**, 26 (1965).
[15] Carberry J. J. and Bretton R. H., *J. Chem. Phys.*, **35**, 224 (1961).
[16] Knox J. H. and McLaren L., *Anal. Chem.*, **36**, 1477 (1964).
[17] Littlewood A. B., *Gas Chromatography — Principles, Techniques and Applications*, Academic Press, New York, 1962.
[18] Mackle H., Mayrick R. G. and Rooney J. J., *Trans. Faraday Soc.*, **60**, 817 (1964).
[19] Gianetto A. and Panotti M., *Ann. Chimica*, **50**, 1713 (1960).
[20] Habgood H. W., *Can. J. Chem.*, **36**, 1384 (1958).
[21] Bolt W. A. and Innes J. A., *Fuel*, **38**, 333 (1959).
[22] Habgood H. W. and Hanlan J. F., *Can. J. Chem.*, **37**, 843 (1959).
[23] Leffler A. J., *J. Catal.*, **5**, 22 (1966).
[24] Davis B. and Scott D. S., *The Porous Structure of Catalysis and Transport Processes in Heterogeneous Catalysis*, Izd. Nauka, Siberian Branch, Novosibirsk, 1970, p. 127.
[25] Schneider P. and Smith J. M., *ibid.*, p. 116.
[26] Grubner O., Ralek M. and Kucera E., *Coll. Czechosl. Chem. Comm.*, **31**, 2629 (1966).
[27] Grubner O., Ralek M. and Zikanova A., *ibid.*, **31**, 852 (1966).
[28] Eberly P. E. Jr, *Ind. Eng. Chem. Fundam.*, **8**, 25 (1969).
[29] Davis B. R. and Scott D. S., *Measurement of Effective Diffusivity of Porous Pellets*, Reprint. 48 D. 58th Ann. Meeting A. I. Ch. E., Philadelphia, Pa Dec, 1965.

[30] Van Deemter J. J., Zuiderweg F. J. and Klinkenberg A., *Chem. Eng. Sci.*, **5**, 271 (1956).
[31] Schwartz C. E. and Smith J. M., *Eng. Chem.*, **45**, 1209 (1953).
[32] Denisova T. A. and Rozental A. L., *Kinet. Katal.*, **8**, 441 (1967).
[33] Kubin M., *Coll. Czechosl. Chem. Commun.*, **30**, 2900 (1965).
[34] Kucera E., *J. Chromatogr.*, **19**, 237 (1965).
[35] Masumune S. and Smith J. M., *Am. Inst. Chem. Eng. J.*, **11**, 34 (1965).
[36] Zhukhovitskii A. A., Kim S. N. and Burova O. M., *Zav. Lab.*, **34**, 144 (1968).
[37] Mishchenko A. P. and Gryaznov V. M., *Zh. Fiz. Khim.*, **45**, 953 (1971).
[38] Vatulya N. M., Sukhorukov O. M. and Ventsev M. D., *Zh. Fiz. Khim.*, **45**, 2633 (1971).
[39] Ryzhinskii M. V., Frub A. S. and Prokhorov V. M., *Zh. Fiz. Khim.*, **45**, 2875 (1971).
[40] Nikolaev N. I., *Zh. Fiz. Khim.*, **46**, 1086 (1972).
[41] Vilenchik L. Z., Kolegov V. I. and Belenskii B. G., *Zh. Fiz. Khim.*, **46**, 1109 (1972).
[42] Berezkin V. G., Khoit Yu. and Ogorodnik V. L., *Zh. Fiz. Khim.*, **46**, 1119 (1972).
[43] Huang Young, *J. Chromatogr.*, **70**, 13 (1972).
[44] Ma Yi Hua and Claude M., *Am. Inst. Chem. Eng. J.*, **18**, 1148 (1972).
[45] Chu T. C., Chappelear P. S. and Kobayashi R., *J. Chem. Eng. Data*, **19**, 299 (1974).
[46] Cloete C. E., Smuts T. W. and De Clerk K., *J. Chromatogr.*, **120**, 1 (1976).
[47] Cloete C. E., Smuts T. W. and De Clerk K., *J. Chromatogr.*, **120**, 17 (1976).
[48] De Ligny C. L. and Hammers W. E., *J. Chromatogr.*, **141**, 91 (1977).
[49] Choudhary V. R. and Parande M. G., *J. Chromatogr.*, **132**, 344 (1977).
[50] Rosolovskaya E. N. and Ozhereleva L. T., *Kinet. Katal.*, **19**, 1189 (1978).
[51] Kolk J. F. M., Matulewicz E. R. A. and Moulijn J. A., *J. Chromatogr.*, **160**, 11 (1978).
[52] Veselova I. V. and Tokarev V. K., *Zh. Fiz. Khim.*, **52**, 784 (1978).
[53] Choudhary V. R., *J. Chromatogr.*, **98**, 491 (1974).
[54] Kharlamov V. V., Taranin V. I., Mirzabekova I. V. and Minachev Kh. M., *Izv. Akad. Nauk SSSR, ser. Khim.*, 305 (1977).
[55] Yanovskii M. I. and Berman A. D., *Khromatografiya, Itogi nauki i tekhniki*, Izd. Nauka, Moskva, 1974, Vol. 1, p. 134.
[56] Giddings J. C. and Seager S. L., *Ind. Eng. Chem. Fundam.*, **1**, 277 (1962).
[57] Giddings J. C. and Seager S. L., *J. Chem. Eng. Data*, **8**, 168 (1963).
[58] Schneider P. and Smith J. M., *Am. Inst. Chem. Eng. J.*, **14**, 762 (1968).
[59] Rakshieva N. R., Novak J., Wičars S. and Janak J., *J. Chromatogr.*, **91**, 51 (1974).

Chapter **11**

The Study of Catalytic Reactions

11.1 Introduction

Chemists working on catalysis have shown enormous interest in GC [1–182]. The potential uses of GC to study the kinetics of chemical reactions, including catalytic processes, are far from exhausted.

One of the most important experimental tasks facing researchers in the field of reaction kinetics is the precise specification of the reaction mixture composition. Highly efficient separation (10^3–10^4 theoretical plates), highly sensitive detectors, a short analysis time, and the use of standard apparatus are all responsible for the fact that GC is most often used to analyse the multicomponent mixtures which we normally have to deal with in catalytic reaction kinetics.

Chromatography can be applied in two ways to the study of catalysis.

In the first, the catalyst is placed inside the chromatographic column. Substrates are usually injected pulse-wise into the stream of carrier gas. Packed with catalyst, the column acts as both reactor and separating column. A chemical reaction taking place under so-called chromatographic conditions differs from one occurring normally in that the intermediate and final products are generally separated from the substrates, thus practically preventing any reaction between them. Obviously, the kinetics of catalytic reactions taking place in a chromatographic column differ fundamentally from the kinetics of reactions occurring in flow or flow-circulation apparatus, or in a microreactor. This method is particularly suitable for studying the mechanism of contact processes.

The chromatographic analysis of catalytic processes is described in detail in the exhaustive monograph by Roginskii, Yanovskii and Berman [2]. This chapter will concern itself mainly with the kinetics of catalytic reactions under so-called chromatographic conditions.

In the second method, a microreactor, in which the catalytic reaction is to proceed, is placed immediately before the chromatographic column [1]. The substrates are injected pulse-wise into the carrier gas, passed into the microreactor, and from there into the chromatographic column for post-reaction analysis. This is a very promising and rapid technique, used to analyse such physicochemical properties of catalysts as their activity and selectivity, and catalytic reaction mechanisms.

The microreactor technique is also suitable for analysing the effects of an external electric or magnetic field, and α, β and γ radiation on the adsorptive and catalytic properties of solids.

A number of modifications of this method have been described in the literature [3–13] and all have the following features in common: simplicity and rapidity of measurement, high sensitivity, the capacity to operate with very small quantities of reactants and catalysts, isothermicity — since local overheating is avoided; analysis of the initial periods of operation of a catalyst and its poisoning, finally the coefficients of adsorption of the reactants can be determined, and thus also the surface concentration of the reactants, which enables the real reaction rate constant to be established. However, pulse techniques do not guarantee the stationarity of the process, and data obtained using them do not define the rate of reaction, which is measured in the flow and flow-circulation methods. The technique is, however, excellent for a comparative assessment of catalytic activity.

This lack of stationarity results from the fact that the reactant concentrations vary, as does the state of the catalytically active surface, its chemical composition, degree of oxidation or reduction, etc.

When using the pulse technique to study catalytic processes in the microreactor, it is extremely important to select correctly the input volume of the pulse (V_p) and the volume of the catalyst (V_{cat}). If the ratio $V_p/V_{cat} \gg 1$, the results obtained with this method basically correspond with those from the traditional flow method. This means that the pulse microreactor can be regarded as a flow reactor in which the movement of the pulse takes place under ideal piston displacement conditions.

If the volumetric ratio of the pulse and catalyst is inverted, i.e., when $V_p/V_{cat} \ll 1$, the catalytic reaction will, in a number of cases (e.g. when the sorptive capacity of the catalyst is large), take place under chromatographic conditions. The considerable concentration gradient of the reactants interferes with the working up of the results, nevertheless these are very valuable in analysing the reaction mechanism.

The surface of the catalyst during a reaction proceeding under pulse conditions is constantly renewed by the carrier gas flowing over it at the reaction temperature.

Since very small amounts of reactant are introduced into a microreactor working under chromatographic conditions, we may assume that the results refer to the properties of that section of the catalyst's surface that was not affected by the reaction mixture. On the other hand, if we rapidly introduce one pulse after another, we can assess the change in the catalyst's activity during the chemical reaction.

The catalytic activity of the first pulses is often greater than that estimated under stationary conditions by a few orders of magnitude.

The processes involved in the flow of a pulse of reactant through a layer of catalyst, such as diffusion, adsorption and desorption, exert a significant influence on the reaction kinetics. Chromatographic analysis of catalytic reactions is especially suitable when the equilibrium constant of the reaction is small but the rate of reaction sufficiently fast; it is the separation of products and not the rate of reaction which then limits the extent of the process.

If the volume of reactants adsorbed on the surface of the catalyst is much smaller than the volume of the pulse, their distribution along the layer of catalyst can be neglected. However, as the pulse is broadened by the carrier gas, the results gained are quite different from the piston displacement results. This may be explained by, for example, the reduction of the partial pressures of the reactants as a result of broadening. To calculate the partial pressure of a reactant in the reactor, we have to estimate the extent of pulse broadening [14].

We could also use the so-called method of reacting pulses in our kinetic studies [16]. We do so when a reaction takes place in the reactor column between two pulses of consecutively introduced volatile substances whose rates of migration along the catalyst are different.

Gas chromatography has also been used to study reaction kinetics in liquid–gas and liquid–liquid systems [17]. One reagent is deposited as a thin layer on an inert carrier (GLC). Assuming that peak broadening takes place mainly as a result of mass exchange between the gas and the liquid phase, the kinetic coefficient can be calculated approximately from $\beta = 2u/H$, where u is the linear flow rate of the carrier gas, and H is the height equivalent to a theoretical plate. In practice, $u \approx 2$ cm/s, $H \approx 0.2$ cm and $\beta \approx 40$ s. Thus we can use the chromatographic reactor to study the kinetics of gas–liquid and gas–gas reactions whose rate constant $k \ll s^{-1}$.

The increasing use of the microreactor to study the properties of catalysts and catalytic reactions can be put down to its high sensitivity, simplicity of measurement and the possibility of changing a large number of operating parameters.

11.2 Reversible Reactions

11.2.1 A $\rightleftharpoons$ B Reactions

This type of reversible reaction occurring under chromatographic conditions has been fairly well documented [13, 22, 30–33]. The shape of its chromatogram is highly dependent on its rate at the catalyst surface

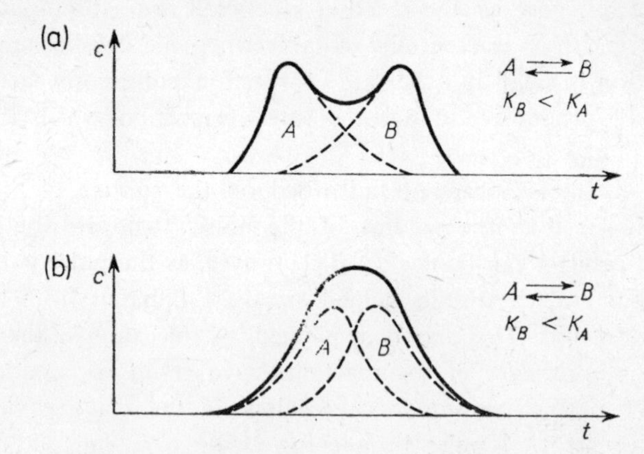

Fig. 11.1 Chromatogram of the reaction **A $\rightleftharpoons$ B**: (a) slow reaction; (b) fast reaction.

(Fig. 11.1). While studying this reaction, Giddings [13, 33] ignored diffusion processes, assuming that reaction equilibrium

$$\mathrm{A} \underset{k_2}{\overset{k_1}{\rightleftharpoons}} \mathrm{B}$$

was established instantaneously under chromatographic conditions. If we inject a mixture of A and B into the reactor, we first get a wide band with two peaks (Fig. 11.1a) corresponding to substances A and B. After some time, the band changes shape and one peak appears, containing A and B at equilibrium concentrations (Fig. 11.1b).

When the adsorption isotherm is linear and the reaction equilibrium is established very quickly, we can write the following equation for the material balance, assuming no diffusion [30]:

$$\left[u\frac{\partial c_A}{\partial x}+E_{pack}\frac{\partial c_A}{\partial t}+(1-E_{pack})\frac{\partial a_A}{\partial t}\right] = k_2 a_B - k_1 a_A$$

$$= \left[u\frac{\partial c_B}{\partial x}+E_{pack}\frac{\partial c_B}{\partial t}+(1-E_{pack})\frac{\partial a_B}{\partial t}\right], \quad (11.1)$$

where c_A, c_B are the concentrations of substances A and B in the gaseous phase, a_A, a_B are the concentrations of A and B at the catalyst surface, E_{pack} is the external porosity of the catalyst surface, and u is the linear flow rate of the carrier gas.

It is evident from both Giddings' statistical theory [13, 33] and Klinkenberg's theory based on the material balance equation [30] that while the mixture of molecules of A and B is being introduced to the layer of catalyst, their peaks disappear as equilibrium is approached, and the width of the band containing molecules A and B in equilibrium concentrations becomes narrower and approaches that of the equilibrium band.

An equilibrium mixture introduced to the catalyst layer is recorded as a single peak during the time

$$t_{AB\,eq} = \frac{x}{u}\,\frac{\dfrac{k_1}{K_B}\,[E_{pack}+(1-E_{pack})K_B]+\dfrac{k_2}{K_A}\,[E_{pack}+(1-E_{pack})K_A]}{\dfrac{k_1}{K_B}+\dfrac{k_2}{K_A}}, \quad (11.2)$$

where K_A, K_B are adsorption equilibrium constants.

Here we come across a certain kind of "chromatographic azeotropy": no matter which values are taken by K_A and K_B, the mixture of A and B at equilibrium cannot be separated. Nevertheless, in this case also, the extent of conversion of substance A, α, under chromatographic conditions is higher than the value of α obtained in a flow reactor. However, the value of α does not exceed that corresponding to a change at equilibrium. The reaction $A \rightleftharpoons B$ can be carried out in one direction if thermochromatographic methods are used (see Section 11.2.4).

11.2.2 $A \rightleftharpoons 2B$ Reactions

Hattori and Murakami [22] found that chromatographic effects influenced the yield of reactions of the type $A \rightleftharpoons 2B$, even though the reaction products could not be separated.

Under chromatographic conditions we get higher yields for such reactions than in a flow reactor (the reaction takes place as on Fig. 11.3). The greater yield under chromatographic conditions can be explained by the different values of the adsorption equilibrium constants K_A and K_B. However, even when $K_A = K_B$, the yield of reaction products is higher under chromatographic conditions than in the classical stationary system [25]. This may be due to diffusion effects. Diffusion above all reduces the rate of a higher order reaction ($n > 1$). In the case of $A \rightleftharpoons 2B$, the rate of a one-way reaction remains unchanged, that of a reversible reaction is reduced. The yield of product B may therefore be greater than under ordinary equilibrium conditions (Fig. 11.3).

11.2.3 $A \rightleftharpoons B + C$ Reactions

Let us consider a reaction of the type $A \rightleftharpoons B + C$ which, under chromatographic conditions, takes place on the surface of a solid with great rapidity. At equilibrium,

$$\begin{array}{ccccc} A_{ads} & \rightleftharpoons & B_{ads} & + & C_{ads}\,. \\ \upharpoonleft\downharpoonright K_A & & \upharpoonleft\downharpoonright K_B & & \upharpoonleft\downharpoonright K_C \\ A_{(g)} & & B_{(g)} & & C_{(g)} \end{array} \qquad (11.3)$$

The theory assumes that adsorption equilibrium is established straight away and that the adsorption isotherm is linear [13, 15]. Diffusion processes are also ignored. The course of reaction (11.3) depends on the sorption equilibrium constants K_A, K_B and K_C [15].

Figure 11.2 shows three examples of how bands A, B, and C in the catalyst layer are distributed depending on the values of the sorption equilibrium constants.

In case (a) (Fig. 11.2) the reverse reaction hardly takes place. The symmetrical band of A cuts off the bands of products B and C, rendering the reverse reaction impossible. In cases (b) and (c) the reverse reaction is inhibited — the more so, the greater the absolute difference $K_B - K_C$ — although the reverse reaction should occur where the bands of B and C overlap. The course of the reverse reaction under chromatographic conditions has been confirmed experimentally [18].

Figure 11.3 illustrates the dependence of the extent of conversion α on the length of the catalyst layer for this type of reaction ($K_A = K_C \neq K_B$) [22]. The figure shows that, under chromatographic conditions, the extent

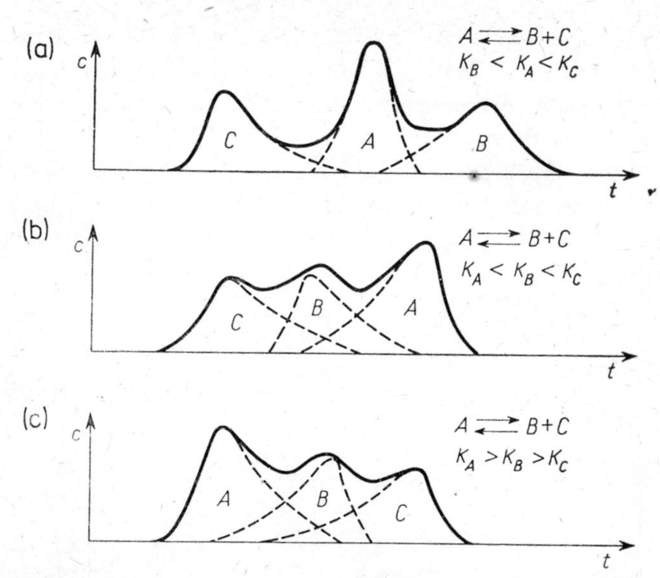

Fig. 11.2 Diagram explaining the course of the reaction A ⇌ B + C under chromatographic conditions.

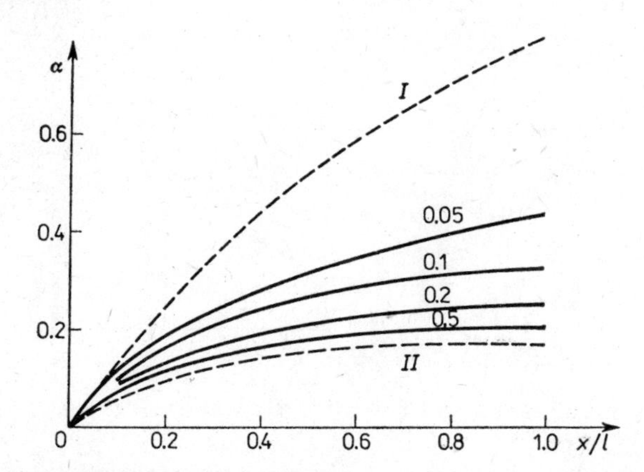

Fig. 11.3 The dependence of the extent of conversion α on the dimensionless length of a catalyst layer for a reaction of the type A ⇌ B + C taking place under chromatographic conditions for different peak widths (number next to continuous curves): *I* — irreversible reaction, *II* — flow reactor.

of conversion α is much higher than that obtained in a flow reactor (*II*) but does not attain the values of the irreversible reaction (*I*).

Roginskii and Rozental [23] repeatedly introduced pulses of reacting substances into the column and confirmed that the various bands in the catalyst layer interact. There is a certain optimum column length which will give a maximum value of α; this is obtained from the dependence of α on the length of the catalyst layer for various pulse sizes and time intervals between them.

The typical apparatus for studying reactions both under chromatographic and ordinary dynamic conditions is illustrated in Fig. 11.4.

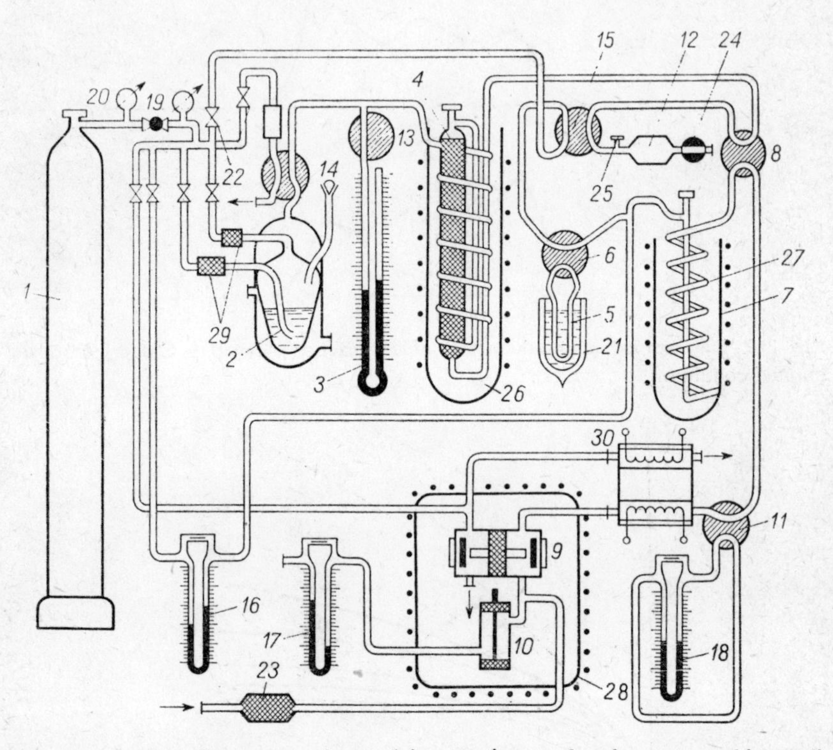

Fig. 11.4 Diagram of apparatus for studying reactions under chromatographic conditions (after S. Z. Roginskii *et al.* [2]):

1 — cylinder containing argon, *2* — saturator, *3* — mercury manometer, *4* — catalytic reactor, *5* — U-tube for freezing, *6, 8, 11, 13-15, 24* — glass taps, *7* — chromatographic column, *9* — ionization detector, *10* — counter, *12* — sampling pipette, *16, 17, 18* — flow meters, *19* — reducer, *20* — manometer, *21* — Dewar vessel, *22* — fine control valve, *23, 29* — dessicators containing $CaCl_2$, *25* — sampling point, *26, 27, 28* — air thermostats, *30* — katharometer.

The dehydrogenation of cyclohexane $C_6H_{12} \rightleftharpoons C_6H_6 + 3\,H_2$ was studied in detail under chromatographic conditions on a Pt/Al_2O_3 catalyst. Figure 11.5 shows the chromatograms obtained for this reaction depending on the number of samples of cyclohexane injected. After introducing the first sample (Fig. 11.5a), we get only one hydrogen peak, which is not recorded by the flame-ionization detector. Benzene and cyclohexane do not appear on the chromatogram as they are irreversibly adsorbed. After injecting the second sample, the benzene peak appcars (Fig. 11.5b)

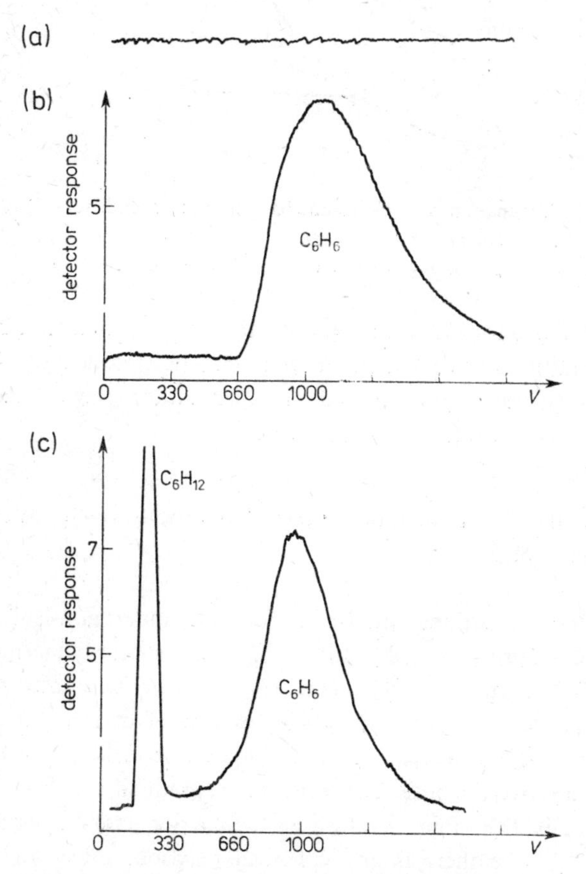

Fig. 11.5 Chromatogram obtained during the dehydrogenation of cyclohexane to benzene on a Pt/Al_2O_3 catalyst: (a) sample 1; (b) sample 2; (c) sample 12 (temperature 408 K, carrier gas flow rate 50 cm^3/min, 0.5 mg cyclohexane per sample) (after S. Z. Roginskii *et al.* [21]).

and we get a narrow cyclohexane peak followed by a large benzene peak for sample 12. There is a distinct separation of the C_6H_{12} and C_6H_6 peaks.

The relationships between the extent of reaction of cyclohexane and $\log(1/c)$ are compared in Fig. 11.6 for the chromatographic system and the

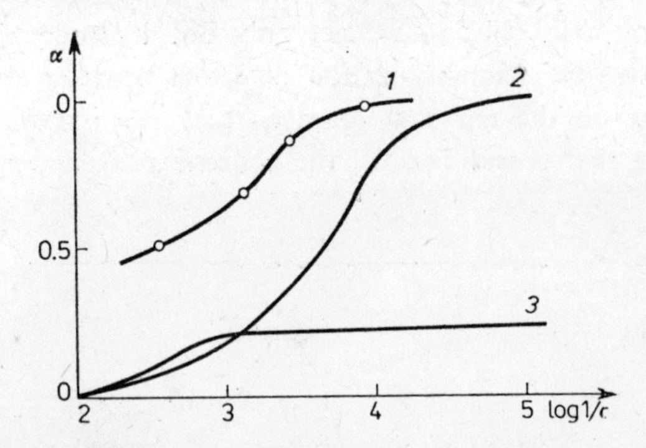

Fig. 11.6 Dehydrogenation of cyclohexane to benzene: dependence of conversion α on log $1/c$ (after S. Z. Roginskii *et al.* [21]):

1 — chromatographic conditions, *2* — equilibrium curve, *3* — flow reactor.

classical flow reactor. It is obvious from the curves that under chromatographic conditions the yield of benzene can be significantly increased as compared with the equilibrium curve. Other authors have obtained similar results for this reaction [11, 18, 24].

11.2.4 $A \rightleftharpoons B + C$ Reactions under Thermochromatographic Conditions

$A \rightleftharpoons B + C$ reactions can be carried out under non-isothermal conditions if we use programmed heating [3, 26] and especially thermochromatography [27–29]. In thermochromatography the band moves along the stationary phase not only because of the flow of carrier gas but because of the simultaneous movement of a temperature field along the column. Normally, an oven whose temperature is gradually rising moves with a velocity u_p in the same direction as the carrier gas. At first, at the low temperature before there is any chemical reaction, substance A migrates along the catalyst layer at a velocity u_A. When $u_p > u_A$, band A gradually enters the higher temperature area and increases its linear velocity u_A because K_A decreases with temperature-increase. At a certain characteristic temperature T_{ch} band A moves along the catalyst layer with a velocity equal to u_p; T_{ch} depends upon the heat of adsorption $q_{st\,A}$ and the linear velocity of the carrier gas, u [27, 29]

$$T_{ch} = \frac{q_{stA}}{R \ln (u_p/u)}\,. \tag{11.4}$$

It may happen that for a given ratio of u_p/u, T_{ch} is small and the reaction $A \rightleftharpoons B + C$ has not yet started, or conversely, the characteristic temperature is higher than the temperature initiating the reaction. In the latter case, the migration of band A is accompanied by the formation of products B and C which move with their own characteristic velocities (they also have characteristic temperatures T_{chB} and T_{chC}).

The reverse reaction $B + C \rightleftharpoons A$ can be completely stopped not only following the spatial distribution of B and C throughout the layer of catalyst, as was the case in the isothermal process (see Section 3.2.3), but also when at least one of the reaction products becomes localized in an area of lower temperature (Fig. 11.7). In such a case, even the reaction $A \rightleftharpoons B$ (see Section 11.2.1) can take place under chromatographic conditions in one direction.

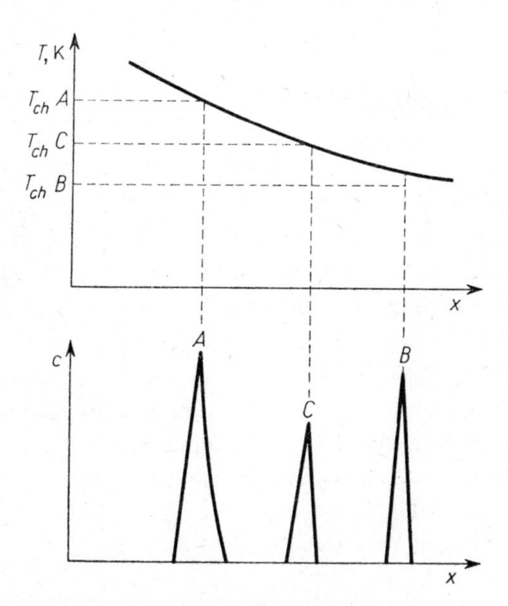

Fig. 11.7 Diagram showing the course of a reaction under thermochromatographic conditions.

In the thermochromatographic process, the band becomes narrow as a result of the negative temperature gradient. The band front is in an area of lower temperature, therefore it moves more slowly than the rear part which is in a warmer layer of catalyst. A narrowing of the band implies a concentration increase in the reaction area. It is probable that reactions whose orders are higher than first take place faster under thermo-chromatographic than isothermal conditions. This method is particularly convenient for studying reactions in which the coefficients of adsorption of the products are smaller than those of the substrates, as, for example, in cracking reactions.

The catalytic process can also be carried out in conditions of temperature displacement without passing a carrier gas [26]. Theoretical analysis indicates that as the oven moves along the reactor, substrates and products are separated in the catalyst layer as discrete bands, arranged in order of decreasing coefficient of adsorption, i.e. the band of the substance most strongly adsorbed is nearest the oven.

In the case of the reaction $A \rightleftharpoons B + C$, for which $K_A > K_B > K_C$, band A is in the reaction area in contact with the oven, while bands B and C migrate to cooler parts of the catalyst.

11.2.5 $A + B \rightleftharpoons AB$ Reactions

This kind of reaction (including $A + B \rightleftharpoons C + D$) cannot usually be carried out by the pulse method under chromatographic conditions if $K_A \neq K_B$ because after, entering the catalyst layer, the substrates become separated. However, this type of reaction can be studied chromatographicaly so long as one of the reactants is the carrier gas itself or is allowed to flow continuously into the carrier gas [45, 46].

This procedure has been applied above all in the study of complexes which form when molecules of the gas phase A interact with the surface of a solid. These reactions are of fundamental importance in catalysis as they are intermediate stages in catalytic processes. The molecules of B capable of forming complexes are usually included in the stationary phase [34–44]. It is assumed that the chemical equilibrium

$$A + B \rightleftharpoons AB \tag{11.5}$$

is reached very rapidly, where AB is the surface complex which is being formed.

The stability constant of the complex K_{AB} is determined from the relationship between the retention time of molecules A and the concentration of substance B, c_B, at the surface of a solid. Henry's constant K is defined from the retention times, then the stability constant of the complex K_{AB} can be found from the angle of inclination of the straight line describing the dependence of K on c_B. The following equation gives this dependence:

$$K = K_0(1+K_{AB}), \tag{11.6}$$

where K_0 is Henry's constant during the adsorption of molecules A at the solid surface in the absence of molecules B, and K is Henry's constant for A in the presence of molecules B at the solid surface.

The formation of complexes by a series of alkenes with iodine deposited on various supports has been studied in great detail [39, 44, 49].

The sequence of processes taking place in the chromatographic column is illustrated by the following diagram:

$$\underbrace{A'_c \underset{k'_{-c}}{\overset{k'_c}{\rightleftharpoons}} A'_s}_{\text{support}} \underset{k'_{-s}}{\overset{k'_s}{\rightleftharpoons}} \underbrace{A}_{\text{gaseous phase}} \underset{k_{-s}}{\overset{k_s}{\rightleftharpoons}} \underbrace{A_s \underset{k_{-c}}{\overset{k_c}{\rightleftharpoons}} A_c}_{\text{solid iodine}}, \tag{11.7}$$

where k with indices indicates the rate constants for each given reaction, A is a hydrocarbon molecule (alkene, alkane), A_s is a molecule adsorbed by the iodine but not forming a complex, A_c is a complex-forming molecule, and A'_s, A'_c are molecules adsorbed forming a complex with the support.

By introducing the appropriate equilibrium constants, we obtain the following relationships:

$$K_s = \frac{[A_s]}{[A]}, \quad K_c = \frac{[A_c]}{[A_s]}, \quad K_a = K_s K_c = \frac{[A_c]}{[A]}, \tag{11.8}$$

or for the support

$$K'_s = \frac{[A'_s]}{[A]}, \quad K'_c = \frac{[A'_c]}{[A_s]}, \quad K'_a = K'_s K'_c = \frac{[A_c]}{[A]}. \tag{11.9}$$

The relative values of K_a and K_c for the case when an alkene molecule does not form a complex with the support surface can be determined from the equations

$$\frac{K_a}{K_a^x} = \frac{t'_{R\,alkene} - t'_{R\,alkane}}{(t'_{R\,alkene} - t'_{R\,alkane})^x}, \tag{11.10}$$

$$\frac{K_c}{K_c^x} = \frac{t'_{R\,rel} - 1}{(t'_{R\,rel} - 1)^x}, \tag{11.11}$$

where $t'_{R\,alkene}$, $t'_{R\,alkane}$ are the retention times of the alkene and alkane having the same number of carbon atoms, the index x refers to the standard substance, and

$$t'_{\mathrm{R\,rel}} = \frac{t'_{\mathrm{R\,alkene}}}{t'_{\mathrm{R\,alkane}}}.$$

When the alkene molecules also form a complex with the surface of the support, equations (11.10) and (11.11) take the forms

$$\frac{K_{\mathrm{c}}}{K_{\mathrm{c}}^{x}} = \frac{t'_{\mathrm{R\,rel}} - t_n}{(t'_{\mathrm{R\,rel}} - t_n)^x}, \tag{11.12}$$

$$\frac{K_{\mathrm{a}}}{K_{\mathrm{a}}^{x}} = \frac{t'_{\mathrm{R\,alkene}} - t_n t'_{\mathrm{R\,alkane}}}{(t'_{\mathrm{R\,alkene}} - t_n t'_{\mathrm{R\,alkane}})^x}, \tag{11.13}$$

where t_n denotes $t_{\mathrm{R\,rel}}$ for a pure support.

Complex formation can be studied not only from the increase in retention time due to the complexing process, but also from the additional broadening of the chromatographic peak [36].

This simple chromatographic method of studying the properties of complexes forming at the surface of a solid may in the future help to determine the mechanisms of many catalytic reactions.

11.3 Irreversible Reactions

11.3.1 A → B Reactions under Ideal Linear Chromatography Conditions

Let us consider the simplest example of a first order reaction A → B for the case in which adsorption of the reactant A takes place quickly in accordance with Henry's linear equation

$$a_{\mathrm{A}} = K_{\mathrm{A}} c_{\mathrm{A}}. \tag{11.14}$$

We shall ignore the effect of diffusion on peak broadening.

The equation for the constant flow of a stream of substance A through an elementary layer of catalyst x takes the form [19]

$$E_{\mathrm{pack}}\frac{\partial c_{\mathrm{A}}}{\partial t} + (1-E_{\mathrm{pack}})\frac{\partial c_{\mathrm{A}}}{\partial t} + u\frac{\partial c_{\mathrm{A}}}{\partial x} + (1-E_{\mathrm{pack}})ka_{\mathrm{A}} = 0 \tag{11.15}$$

(symbols as in equation (11.1)).

From the solution to equation (11.15) we can determine the concentration $c_A(x, t)$ of reactant in any cross-section x of the catalyst layer at time t

$$c_A(x, t) = \Psi(t - t'_R) \exp(-kt'_R), \qquad (11.16)$$

where $\Psi(t)$ is a function describing the type of pulse introduced into the microreactor, t is the time counted from the moment the pulse was injected into the microreactor, k is the rate constant of a heterogeneous first-order catalytic reaction, and t'_R is the adjusted retention time.

It can be seen from equation (11.16) that the pulse of reactant A migrates along the catalyst layer with a constant velocity, while its height gradually becomes smaller although its initial width remains unchanged. As far as a first-order reaction is concerned, the extent of conversion α is independent of the distribution of substance A along the catalyst layer, i.e. of the type of pulse introduced [53, 54].

The rate constant k for this type of reaction is easily obtained from Bassett and Habgood's equation [48], often used in the literature [19, 40–52]

$$kK = \frac{F_c^0}{273Rm} \ln \frac{1}{1-\alpha}, \qquad (11.17)$$

where k, K are the rate constant and Henry's constant, F_c^0 is the volumetric flow rate under normal conditions, m is the mass of the catalyst, α is the extent of conversion, usually defined as the ratio of the area of the peak of substance A at the inlet of the microreactor to its area at the outlet.

The rate constant k (Fig. 11.8) can be calculated from a graph of $\ln(1/(1-\alpha))$ against $1/T$, while a graph of $\ln(kK)$ against $1/T$ gives us the apparent energy of activation.

If both homogeneous and heterogeneous reactions take place in the microreactor simultaneously, the effective rate constant can be evaluated from the equation [55]

$$k_{ef} = \frac{(1-E_{pack})kK_A + E_{pack}k_{hom}}{E_{pack} + (1-E_{pack})K_A}, \qquad (11.18)$$

where k, k_{hom} are the rate constants of the heterogeneous and homogeneous reactions respectively.

The activation energy of the reaction E can be determined from the relationship of k_{ef} with temperature change. If we consider only the heterogeneous reaction, we get

$$E = E_{real} - q_{st} \qquad (11.19)$$

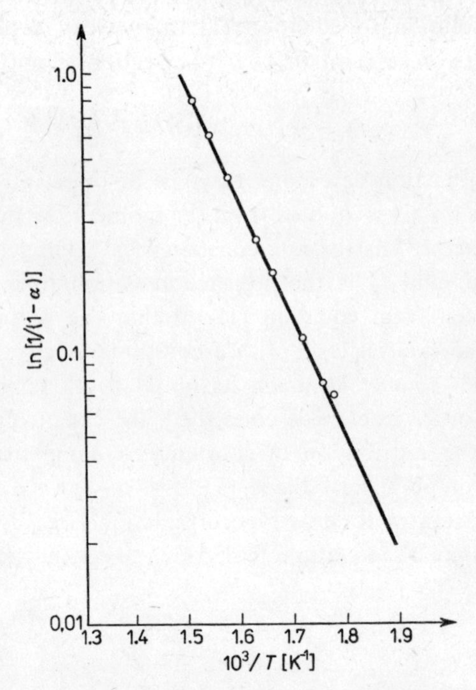

Fig. 11.8 Relationship between catalytic activity and temperature.

and for the homogeneous reaction

$$E = E_{\mathrm{real}} \,. \tag{11.20}$$

We can also obtain information about how the reaction A→B proceeds in the microreactor by analysing the peak of reaction product B [56–58].

The B peak width provides the difference between the Henry constants whereas the shape of the peak depends on the reaction rate constant. The adjusted retention time of product B is given by this equation [58]

$$t'_{\mathrm{R_B}} = t'_{\mathrm{R_A}} + \frac{K_{\mathrm{A}} - K_{\mathrm{B}}}{K_{\mathrm{A}} k} + \frac{t'_{\mathrm{R_A}}}{\alpha}\left(\frac{K_{\mathrm{B}}}{K_{\mathrm{A}}} - 1\right). \tag{11.21}$$

The broadening of the B peak (σ_{B}) is given by

$$\sigma_{\mathrm{B}}^2 = \left(\frac{K_{\mathrm{A}} - K_{\mathrm{B}}}{K_{\mathrm{A}}}\right)^2 \left[\frac{1}{k^2} - \frac{t'_{\mathrm{R_A}}}{\alpha}\left(\frac{1}{\alpha} - 1\right)\right]. \tag{11.22}$$

Equations (11.21) and (11.22) can be used to calculate k and K_{B} from experimental data.

11.3.2 nA → B Reactions under Ideal Gas Chromatography Conditions

For n-th order irreversible reactions proceeding under conditions of ideal gas chromatography the shape of the pulse at the column inlet $\varphi(t)$ is described by the following equation [19]:

$$\varphi(t) = c_A(L, t) = \frac{\Psi(t-t'_{RA})}{\sqrt[n-1]{1+(n-1)kt'_{RA}K_A^{n-1}\Psi^{n-1}(t-t'_{RA})}}, \tag{11.23}$$

where n is the order of reaction, $\Psi(t)$ is a function describing the input pulse, and L is the column length.

It is evident from equation (11.23) that the shape of the reactant pulse at the outlet of the reactor depends on the nature of the input pulse and the reaction kinetics. For reactions of all orders except zero-order, only the height of the output pulse decreases — its width does not change. If we have a zero-order reaction (a triangular pulse), the pulse narrows at the inlet, while for a first-order reaction the extent of conversion α is independent of the type of pulse introduced into the microreactor.

The extent of conversion α is linked to the magnitude and nature of the input pulse by the following relationship:

$$1-\alpha = \frac{\int_{t_{RA}}^{T+t_{RA}} c_A(L, t)\,dt}{\int_0^T \Psi(t)\,dt}, \tag{11.24}$$

where T is the duration of a pulse.

Equations (11.23) and (11.24) give us a further equation from which we can determine the reaction rate constants from experimentally found values of α for rectangular and triangular pulses [19] (Table 11.1). It must be emphasized that rectangular peaks are mathematically identical with the steady-state case, whereas triangular peaks are difficult to obtain experimentally.

Even though α for $n \neq 1$ reactions depends on the shape of the pulse, the difference in α does not exceed 10-15% for various pulses of a uniform average concentration c_{av} [22, 31]. It is thus reasonable to determine the rate of reaction $\bar{w}$ in the microreactor for an average concentration in a pulse and then to correct for the shape of the pulse

$$\bar{w} = \frac{\Delta m_A}{\Delta t V_{cat}} = k_{ef} K^n c_{av}^n, \tag{11.25}$$

Table 11.1 DETERMINATION OF THE BASIC KINETIC CHARACTERISTICS OF REACTIONS OF VARIOUS ORDERS FOR TRIANGULAR AND RECTANGULAR PULSES [19]

Shape of reactant pulse at reactor inlet $\Psi(t)$	*Order of reaction* n	*Expression for the rate constant* k	*Determination of the rate constant* k *from experimental data*	*Determination of the activation energy* E *of a catalytic reaction*
1	2	3	4	5
			m_A; A_0; $1/F_c$	n; B_0; $1/T$
c_0; T	0	$\dfrac{\alpha F_c c_0}{V_{cat}}$	for $m_A = \alpha$ $k = \dfrac{c_0 \tan A_0}{V_{cat}}$	for $n = \ln(1/\alpha)$ $E = R \tan B_0$
$\Psi(t) = \begin{cases} 0; & t<0 \\ c_0 & 0<t<T \\ 0; & t>T \end{cases}$	1	$\dfrac{F_c \ln \dfrac{1}{1-\alpha}}{V_{cat} K}$	for $m_A = \ln \dfrac{1}{1-\alpha}$ $k = \dfrac{\tan A_0}{V_{cat} K}$	for $n = \ln \ln (1-\alpha)$ $E = R \tan B_0$
	2	$\dfrac{F_c}{V_{cat} K^2 c_0} \dfrac{\alpha}{1-\alpha}$	for $m_A = \dfrac{\alpha}{1-\alpha}$ $k = \dfrac{\tan A_0}{V_{cat} K^2 c_0}$	for $n = \ln \dfrac{1-\alpha}{\alpha}$ $E = R \tan B_0$

where $\Delta m_A = m_A \alpha$ is the quantity of reacted substance A, $m_A = V_{sample} c_{av}$ is the quantity of A introduced, t is the time the chromatographic band remained in the catalyst layer, V_{cat} is the volume of catalyst, and k_{ef} is the effective rate constant referred to c_{av}.

Table 11.1 (continued)

1	2	3	4	5
	0	$\dfrac{(1-\sqrt{1-\alpha})F_c c_0}{V_{cat}}$	for $m_A = 1-\sqrt{1-\alpha}$ $k = \dfrac{c_0 \tan A_0}{V_{cat}}$	for $n = \ln \dfrac{1}{1-\sqrt{1-\alpha}}$ $E = R \tan B_0$
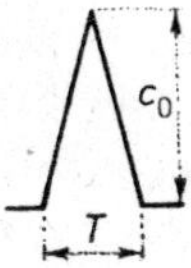	1	$\dfrac{F_c \ln \dfrac{1}{1-\alpha}}{V_{cat} K}$	for $m_A = \ln \dfrac{1}{1-\alpha}$ $k = \dfrac{\tan A_0}{V_{cat} K}$	for $n = \ln \ln (1-\alpha)$ $E = R \tan B_0$
$\Psi(t) = \begin{cases} 0; \; t<0 \\ 2c_0/T \\ 0<t<\dfrac{T}{2} \\ \dfrac{2c_0}{T}(T-t) \\ \dfrac{T}{2}<t<T \\ 0; \; t>T \end{cases}$	2	a* $\dfrac{3}{2}\dfrac{\alpha F_c}{V_{cat} K^2 c_0}$ b** $\dfrac{24 F_c}{V_{cat} K^2 c_0}\dfrac{1}{1-\alpha}$	for $m_A = \alpha$ $k = \dfrac{3}{2}\dfrac{\tan A_0}{V_{cat} K^2 c_0}$ for $m_A = \dfrac{1}{1-\alpha}$ $k = \dfrac{2 \tan A_0}{V_{cat} K^2 c_0}$	for $n = \ln\left(\dfrac{1}{\alpha}\right)$ $E = R \tan B_0$ for $n = \ln (1-\alpha)$ $E = R \tan B_0$

a* — for the case when $\dfrac{c_0 V_{cat} k K^2}{F_c} \ll 1.$

b** — for the case when $\dfrac{c_0 V_{cat} k K^2}{F_c} \gg 1.$

It follows from equation (11.25) that the order of reaction can be calculated from the gradient of the straight line of $\log \bar{w}$ as a function of $\log c_{av}$; the value of k_{ef} is given by the length of the y-axis cut off by this line. Having allowed for the peak shape correction, we can determine the real constant k [19, 22, 31, 60]

$$k = k_{ef} \frac{\left[\frac{1}{T}\int_0^T \Psi(t)\,dt\right]^n}{\frac{1}{T}\left[\int_0^T \Psi^n(t)\,dt\right]}. \tag{11.26}$$

For $n = 1$ and $n = 0$ this correction is equal to unity, i.e. $k = k_{ef}$, regardless of the shape of the pulse. It has also been demonstrated that for rectangular pulses, the correction for any value of n is also unity.

The effect of longitudinal diffusion on the rate of $n\mathrm{A} \rightarrow \mathrm{B}$ type reactions was studied for the case when adsorption equilibrium is established rapidly [25]. It was found that the longitudinal diffusion of a first-order reaction does not usually affect the extent of conversion, but if $n > 1$, the rate of reaction decreases as a result of diffusion in proportion to the order of reaction. This effect increases with a longer layer of catalyst or a reduced carrier gas velocity.

11.3.3 A → B Reactions in which Adsorption Equilibrium is Established Slowly

The equation for the kinetics of sorption, which includes the reaction rate constant k, can be written in the form [62]

$$\frac{\partial a_A}{\partial t} = k_{a_A} c_A - (k + k_{d_A}) a_A, \tag{11.27}$$

where k_{a_A}, k_{d_A} are the rate constants of adsorption and desorption of substance A.

Of course, this equation is applicable only to small degrees of coverage.

When experimentally determining the rate constants k, k_{a_A}, k_{d_A} it is convenient to use equations found using the method of moments and which define the characteristics of peaks, the reactants and products [2]

$$t_{R_A} = \frac{x}{u}\left[E_{pack} + \frac{(1 - E_{pack}) k_{a_A} k_{d_A}}{(k + k_{d_A})^2}\right], \tag{11.28}$$

$$\delta_{\mathrm{A}}^2 = \frac{2x}{u}\frac{(1-E_{\mathrm{pack}})k_{\mathrm{a_A}}k_{\mathrm{d_A}}}{(k+k_{\mathrm{d_A}})^3}, \tag{11.29}$$

$$1-\alpha = \exp\left\{-\frac{x}{u}\left[\frac{(1-E_{\mathrm{pack}})k_{\mathrm{a_A}}k}{k+k_{\mathrm{d_A}}}\right]\right\}, \tag{11.30}$$

where $t_{\mathrm{R_A}}$ is the retention time of component A, δ_{A} is the broadening of the A peak at the reactor outlet, and α is the extent of conversion.

If the reaction proceeds in the kinetic area ($k \ll k_{\mathrm{d_A}}$), equation (11.30) reduces to equation (11.17). The Bassett and Habgood equation holds not only for the case when adsorption equilibrium is established rapidly, but is also more generally applicable. The course of a heterogeneous reaction does not affect the retention time or the band broadening of reactant A for $k \ll k_{\mathrm{d_A}}$ (equations (11.28) and (11.29)). If the values of k and $k_{\mathrm{d_A}}$ are commensurable, the rate at which band A moves along the column increases and its broadening is reduced during the reaction. On the other hand, if migration is restricted by desorption $k \gg k_{\mathrm{d}}$, the adjusted retention time $t'_{\mathrm{R_A}}$ is inversely proportional to k^2, and δ_{A}^2 is inversely proportional to k^3.

The kinetics of a heterogeneous reaction can also be estimated from the shape of the peak due to the reaction product B [58]. It is assumed that the linear equation describing the kinetics of adsorption holds for substances A and B.

The retention time of substance B is

$$t_{\mathrm{R_B}} = t_{\mathrm{R_A}} + \frac{x(1-E_{\mathrm{pack}})}{\alpha u}\,[K_{\mathrm{B}}-K_{\mathrm{A}}^{\mathrm{ef}}] - \frac{k_{\mathrm{a_B}}(k+k_{\mathrm{d_A}})-k_{\mathrm{a_A}}(k+k_{\mathrm{d_B}})}{k k_{\mathrm{d_A}} k_{\mathrm{d_B}}}, \tag{11.31}$$

where $K_{\mathrm{A}}^{\mathrm{ef}} = k_{\mathrm{a_A}}k_{\mathrm{d_A}}/(k+k_{\mathrm{d_A}})^2$ is the effective Henry's constant for the substrate.

Equation (11.31) indicates that the output time of the reaction product should differ from its retention time in ordinary GC [58].

This was confirmed experimentally while studying the cracking of cumene over an aluminosilicate catalyst (Fig. 11.9). Both the peak of the benzene introduced along with the cumene *1* and that of the benzene produced during the cracking of cumene *2* are visible on Fig. 11.9. Equations (11.28)–(11.31) facilitate the estimation of rate constants for the adsorption and desorption of substrates and products during the catalytic process.

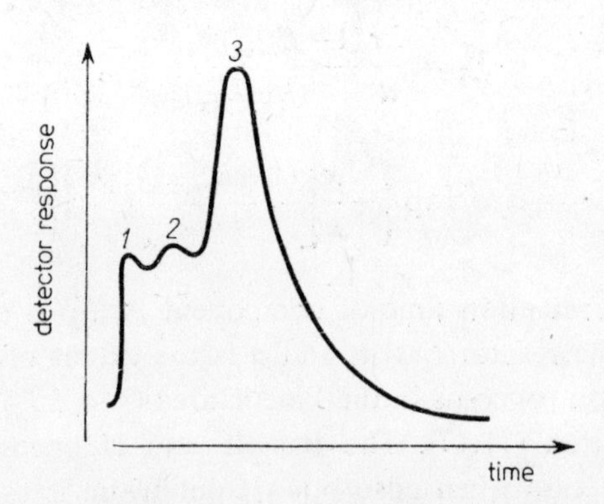

Fig. 11.9 Chromatogram of cumene cracking over an aluminosilicate catalyst; a mixture of benzene and cumene was introduced into the microreactor (after A. D. Berman and M. I. Yanovskii [58]):

1 — benzene introduced into the microreactor, *2* — benzene (cracking product), *3* — cumene.

11.3.4 A → B Reactions with Allowance for Diffusion and the Kinetics of Adsorption

Using the method of moments, Kocirik [63] obtained equations for α and t_{R_A} which allowed for longitudinal diffusion D_{ef} and the kinetics of adsorption

$$\alpha = 1 - \exp\left[\frac{u}{2D_{ef}} - \frac{u}{2D_{ef}}\sqrt{1 + \frac{4D_{ef}(1-E_{pack})kk_{a_A}}{u^2(k+k_{d_A})}}\right], \quad (11.32)$$

$$t_{R_A} = \frac{x}{u}\left[E_{pack} + \frac{(1-E_{pack})k_{a_A}k_{d_A}}{(k+k_{d_A})^2}\right]\frac{1}{r}, \quad (11.33)$$

where r is the expression under the root sign in equation (11.32).

If the coefficient of longitudinal diffusion is small, equation (11.32) becomes equation (11.30).

Where diffusion is involved in a chemical reaction, the migration of molecules A increases. The effect of diffusion is considerable, especially for small u (equation (11.32)). In order to calculate D_{ef} and r, experiments should be carried out at small u, while k_{a_A} and k_{d_A} can be calculated from data obtained with high carrier gas flow rates.

Denisova and Rozental [64] considered the effect of internal diffusion in the pores of the catalyst on a first-order reaction. They also took the kinetics of adsorption inside the catalyst pores into account. When it takes place during a chemical reaction, internal diffusion reduces the output time of the peak. It was found that peak broadening was reduced when diffusion in pores took place during a reaction.

11.3.5 The Application of the Plate Theory to Catalytic Processes Taking Place under Chromatographic Conditions

Kallen and Heilbromer [65] were the first to apply the plate theory to the analysis of catalytic processes taking place in a microreactor. Taking into consideration the course of the reaction A → B on each theoretical plate, these authors derived an equation for the retention volume of substance A under reaction conditions

$$V'_{\mathrm{RA\,react}} = \frac{V'_{\mathrm{RA}}}{1+kV_{\mathrm{A\,eq}}/F_{\mathrm{c}}}, \tag{11.34}$$

where V'_{RA} is the adjusted retention volume of substance A when there is no reaction, $V_{\mathrm{A\,eq}}$ is the volume of carrier gas required for the complete transfer of A from plate N to plate $N+1$.

It is evident from equation (11.34) that reactant A migrates more quickly under reaction conditions than under GC conditions, which is in agreement with what was said in Section 11.3.3 and 11.3.4. The change in retention volume as the reaction proceeds increases as k does. The retention volume also decreases as $V_{\mathrm{A\,eq}}$ increases, i.e. as the time for adsorption equilibrium to be established increases. Moreover, under reaction conditions, the peak width becomes narrower [66].

The value of k can be determined from the equation

$$k = \frac{N(1-\sqrt[N]{1-\alpha})}{V'_{\mathrm{RA\,react}}}F_{\mathrm{c}}, \tag{11.35}$$

where N is the number of theoretical plates (see Section 1.3.2).

Having determined α, V'_{RA} and N, we can evaluate the reaction rate constant k.

11.4 The Kinetics of Reactions at Heterogeneous Surfaces Proceeding in a Microreactor

Roginskii and Rozental [20] considered adsorptive and catalytic processes taking place under chromatographic conditions at heterogeneous surfaces. The equation for adsorption kinetics accounting for the surface reaction holds for those parts of the surface having identical adsorptive and catalytic properties

$$\frac{\partial \theta_A}{\partial t} = k_{a_A} c_A (1-\theta_A) - (k + k_{d_A}) \theta_A, \tag{11.36}$$

where θ_A is the degree of coverage of active sites by molecules of A.

The effective rate constant k_{ef}, which allows for the effect of the heterogeneous surface, for small partial pressures ($\theta_A \ll 1$) and any given partition function $\varrho(k_{a_A}, k_{d_A})$ is given by the expression [67]

$$k_{ef} = N_0 \iint \frac{k k_{a_A}}{k_{d_A} + k} \varrho(k_{a_A}, k_{d_A}) \mathrm{d}k_{a_A} \mathrm{d}k_{d_A}, \tag{11.37}$$

where N_0 is a constant depending on the number of active sites per unit area.

If we know the coefficient of diffusion D_{ef}, estimated independently, we can determine the value of k_{ef} from the amount of unreacted substance $G(L)$. Having been solved, equation (11.37) becomes a straightforward first-order rate equation accounting for the surface heterogencity, assuming that the coefficient of diffusion D_{ef} is small

$$G(L) = G_0 \exp\left(-\frac{k_{ef} L}{u}\right), \tag{11.38}$$

where G_0 is the amount of substance introduced into the reactor, and L is the column length.

11.5 The Radiochromatographically Determined Kinetics of Complex Reactions Taking Place in a Microreactor

Although the quantitative interpretation of the kinetics of processes taking place in a microreactor has so far been applied exclusively to simple reactions, we can none the less obtain valuable information on complex reactions by studying them in a microreactor.

It is not yet clear under what conditions and how precisely it will be possible to determine the courses of all the directions of complex reactions, and to calculate the rate constants of the various directions from data obtained in a system where all these reactions are proceeding simultaneously [68–72]. Among other reactions, the oxidative dehydrogenation of isopentenes to isoprene on an iron-zinc-chromium catalyst has been studied in the microreactor [74]

$$2C_5H_{10}+O_2 \rightarrow 2C_5H_8+2H_2O. \qquad (11.39)$$

A diagram of how the reaction proceeds is presented in Fig. 11.10. It is assumed that:

(1) the reaction is irreversible and proceeds according to a first-order equation with respect to the hydrocarbon and a zero-order equation with respect to the oxygen (present in excess);

(2) under the conditions of measurement, deep oxidation to CO and CO_2 does not take place;

(3) the isomerization of alkenes proceeds according to a first-order equation.

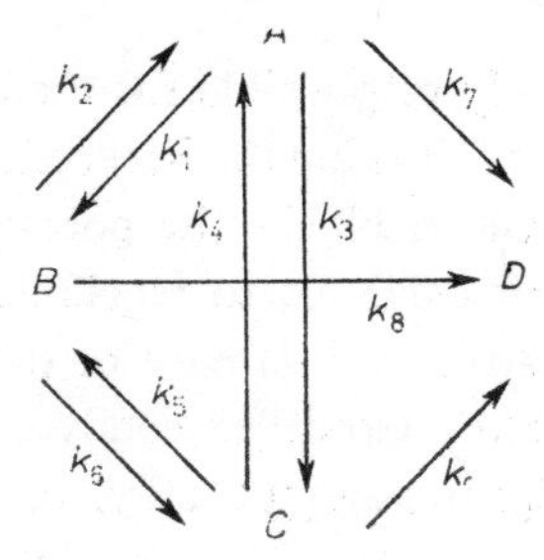

Fig. 11.10 Diagram of the changes taking place during the oxidative dehydrogenation of isopentenes (after R. R. Aliev *et al.* [74]):

A — 3-methyl-1-butene, *B* — 2-methyl-1-butene, *C* — 2-methyl-2-butene, *D* — isoprene.

Initially, the rates of reaction w_A, w_B, w_C and w_D were determined from the initial section of the kinetic curves, obtained independently for a mixture of each pentene isomer and oxygen, and of isoprene and oxygen. From mathematical modelling, the following values of the rate constants were obtained (1/s): $k_5 = 12.8\pm0.4$; $k_6 = 5.5\pm0.2$; $k_7 = 0.7\pm0.2$; $k_8 = 3.7\pm0.2$; $k_9 = 1.1\pm0.1$. These values are in agreement with those obtained by experiment.

The constants k_1, k_2, k_3 and k_4 are very small and are difficult to estimate experimentally. The authors found that $k_3>k_1>k_2>k_4$. The oxidative dehydrogenation of pentenes during which some deep oxidation to CO and CO_2 took place was studied in a similar way [75].

Good results in the study of the kinetics of complex reactions are obtained using radiochromatography [1, 76–88]. The idea of this method is to introduce into the reaction mixture a small amount of one component with a labelled atom. The products of the catalysed reaction are separated and analysed by two detectors such as a katharometer and a radiometric detector (Geiger counter). A comparison of the chromatograms so obtained shows which products can be obtained from the component containing the radioactive isotope.

By introducing into the reaction mixture the probable product of a transition reaction containing a labelled atom, we can study the mechanism and kinetics of the separate stages or the directions of the catalytic reaction.

The microreactor is especially useful here as only very small quantities of labelled substance are needed.

11.6 Gas Chromatography in the Study of Catalyst Poisoning

Three factors are largely responsible for the deactivation of catalysts: the poisoning of active sites following the irreversible adsorption of poisons, the formation of carbon which blocks the pores and reduces the internal surface area of the catalyst available to reactants, and the destruction of active sites as a result of structural damage of the catalyst after long-term operation at high temperature (so-called catalyst sintering). Each of these factors can be studied chromatographically, directly or in combination with other methods.

The activity of a catalyst as a function of the amount of deposited carbon can be easily determined chromatographically by gradually oxidizing the deposited carbon (determination of CO_2) and estimating the catalytic activity for various carbon contents. Deactivation caused by the destruction of active sites (which involved the destruction of the crystal lattice), can also be studied by chromatography (investigation of activity and surface properties) combined with X-ray diffraction. However, catalyst poisoning is very conveniently studied using GC. Usually, a certain amount of poison is injected pulse-wise into a stream of neutral carrier gas before the reactor at the reaction temperature — the poison is adsorbed at the catalyst surface. Following this, the reactants are also introduced pulse-wise and the activity of the poisoned catalyst is defined.

Turkevich *et al.* [120] investigated the relationship between catalytic activity and the quantity of poison which they successively introduced into the reactor as samples. However, if we bear in mind the non-stationary poisoning of a catalyst under pulse conditions, this procedure does not give reliable results [51, 121, 122].

Until recently, there was no theory of catalyst poisoning under pulse conditions. But now, Yanovskii and Berman [123] have worked out such a theory on the basis of the adsorption coefficients of poisons. They assume that there are two kinds of active site on the surface of a catalyst. The chemical reaction takes place on one kind of centre; the other kind merely reversibly adsorbs molecules of poison — heterogeneous catalytic reactions do not occur there either. It is further assumed that poison molecules are adsorbed much more strongly than the reactants and products, and that the adsorption isotherm of the poison is in good agreement with the Langmuir equation.

From these assumptions they have derived an equation defining the change in catalytic activity as a function of the time elapsing from the introduction of the poison. If the poison is adsorbed reversibly, the activity of the catalyst initially falls, but after having reached a minimum value, it gradually regains its original level. The reduction of catalytic activity at the beginning is due to the broadening of the poison band and the distribution of its molecules between the catalytic and adsorption sites. If the poison band reaches the reactor outlet, the activity of the catalyst increases, and attains its former level when the poison molecules have left the microreactor.

The curves illustrating the fall in activity due to catalyst poisoning are very often exponential and can be described by the equation

$$\frac{A_g}{A_0} = y+1-(\sqrt{\mu}+\sqrt{y})^2+\int\limits_{y}^{(\sqrt{\mu}+\sqrt{y})^2} \exp\left[-v_g \frac{\frac{b_g}{b}\left(\sqrt{\frac{z}{y}}-1\right)}{1+\frac{b_g}{b}\left(\sqrt{\frac{z}{y}}-1\right)}\right] dz\,. \quad (11.40)$$

However when the activity curves rise following the desorption of poison from the catalyst, the following equation applies:

$$\frac{A_g}{A_0} = y+\int\limits_{y}^{1} \exp\left[-v_g \frac{\frac{b_g}{b}\left(\sqrt{\frac{z}{y}}-1\right)}{1+\frac{b_g}{b}\left(\sqrt{\frac{z}{y}}-1\right)}\right] dz\,. \quad (11.41)$$

Here $A_0 = \log(1/(1-\alpha_0))$ is the activity of the unpoisoned catalyst; α_0 is the extent of conversion of the reactant for an unpoisoned catalyst; A_g is the activity of the poisoned catalyst; $y = t/t_{max}$ is the dimensionless time; t is the time; t_{max} is the time required for complete catalyst regeneration; $\mu = m_g/a_{m_g}$, where m_g is the amount of poison introduced into the microreactor, and a_{m_g} is the quantity of poison needed to form a monolayer on the surface of the catalyst; b_g is the adsorption coefficient of the poison at active sites, b is the mean coefficient of poison adsorption at adsorptive and catalytic sites; ν_g is the number of poison molecules which can be adsorbed at an active site on the catalyst surface; $z = x/L$, where x is the length of the catalyst layer from the start to a given cross-section. and L is the length of the catalyst layer in the column.

The value of a_{m_g} can be determined from the location of the minimum on the experimental curve representing the dependence of the relative activity on y

$$a_{m_g} = \frac{m_g}{(1-\sqrt{y_{min}})^2}. \tag{11.42}$$

The mean coefficient of poison adsorption, b, can be defined from the time for complete catalyst regeneration

$$b = \frac{F_c t_{max}}{a_{m_g}}. \tag{11.43}$$

We can define the coefficient β, and hence b_g, from the calculated and experimentally obtained data on catalyst poisoning

$$b_g = \beta b. \tag{11.44}$$

The agreement between the theory of poisoning described here and the experimental results is satisfactory [123].

11.7 Examples of Catalytic Reactions Investigated by Chromatographic Methods

Chromatographic methods are widely used today in research into catalytic reactions. This section will deal with just a few examples of such reactions.

It was Kokes, Tobin and Emmett [1] who, in 1955, first used a microreactor (Fig. 12.10) to study cracking. They also indicated the possibilities of radiochromatography for studying the mechanisms of heterogeneous reactions. Dehydrogenation and dehydrocyclization reactions have often been studied using the pulse technique [47, 96, 173, 177, 179–185]. The dehydrogenation of ethane to ethene on cadmium zeolite (4A) catalysts has been studied recently [177]. These catalysts are well-known for their ability to separate alkanes from alkenes at temperatures up to 773 K. During this study, column reactors of internal diameter 6 mm and length varying from 30 to 150 cm were used. The temperature of the column was controlled to within ± 3 by keeping it in a fluid sand bath. Helium or nitrogen was used as carrier gas, and 0.2 to 5 cm^3 pulses of ethane were injected at various intervals of time. Having passed through the reactor, the pulse was analysed in a chromatographic column containing silica

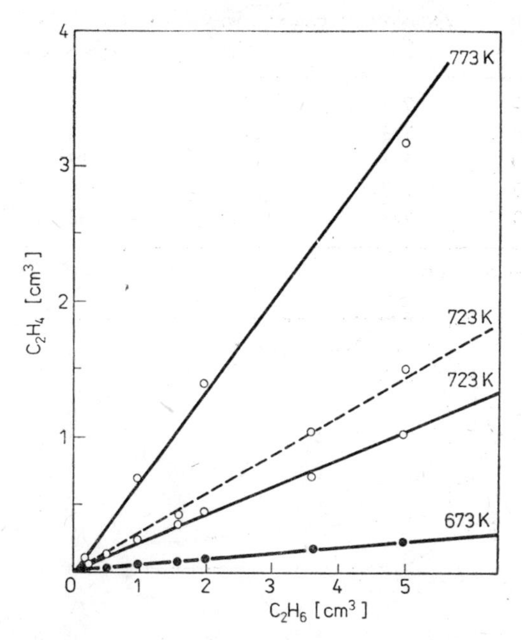

Fig. 11.11 Effect of pulse size of ethane on conversion on Cd-zeolite at various temperatures (after P. Antonucci *et al.* [177]):
(w = 28 g, L = 150 cm, $I.D.$ = 6 mm, F = 25 cm^3 STP/min).

gel. Figure 11.11 shows the effect of sample size on the extent of conversion.

The study was carried out at 673–773 K using a 150-cm-long reactor containing 28 g of 42–65 mesh catalyst. The carrier gas flow rate was 25 cm^3/min. Over the range of pulse sizes used (0.2–5 cm^3), the ethane conversion is approximately constant. Differences do occur, however, when the order of pulse injection is reversed, i.e. when large samples are first injected (dashed line on Fig. 11.11). Bearing in mind the fact that the peaks are symmetrical regardless of the size of the injected pulse, the authors suggest a first-order reaction. The conversion of ethane increases more or less linearly with column length and mass of catalyst; the reactor diameter is identical in every case (Table 11.2).

Considerable changes in the ethane conversion are observed when the first pulses are injected on to the fresh catalyst (Fig. 11.12).

Table 11.2 THE EFFECT OF THE MASS OF CATALYST ON THE CONVERSION OF ETHANE ($F = 25$ cm³/min; size of ethane pulse 0.5 cm³) [177]

Mass [g]	*Temperature* [K]	*Ethane conversion* [%]	*Selectivity to ethene* [%]	t_c [s]
18.7	773	58	95	43
28.0	773	70	94	64
38.0	773	90	87	87
28.0	723	27	100	56
38.0	723	32.5	92	76

t_c — contact time.

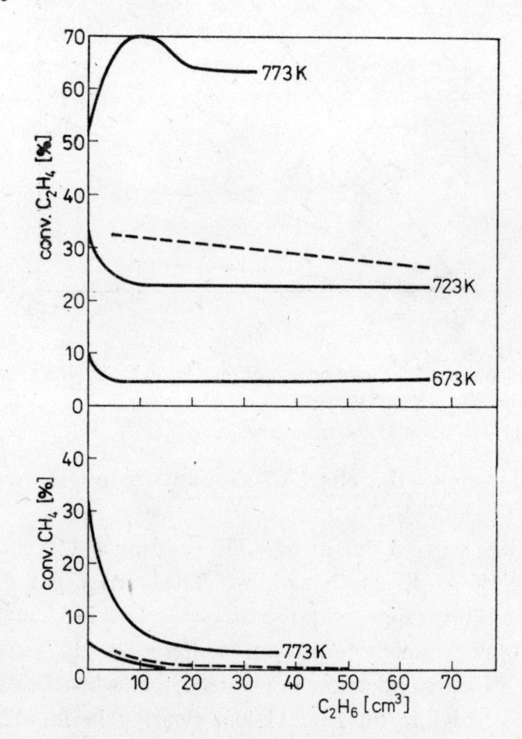

Fig. 11.12 Effect of the number of samples introduced on conversion (pulse volume = 0.5 cm³, other conditions as in Fig. 11.11).

A certain amount of methane is found in the products after the first pulses. After 5–10 pulses have been injected, the catalyst's activity becomes stable and only minimal further changes in the yield of ethene are observed. The Arrhenius activation energy was determined from the stabilized values of ethane conversion to ethene and found equal to 118.15 kJ/mol (Fig. 11.13).

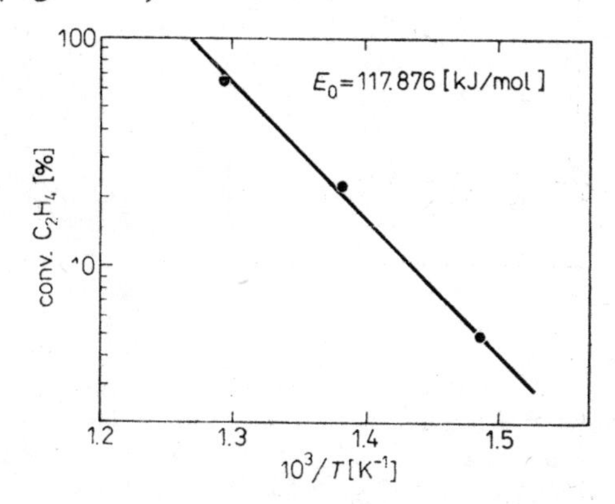

Fig. 11.13 Temperature dependence of conversion to ethene (conditions as in Fig. 11.12).

The effect of the carrier gas flow rate on ethane conversion is given in Table 11.3. Table 11.3 also gives values of Δt defined as the additional time (with respect to the less strongly adsorbed ethane) which the ethene requires to pass through a column packed with cadmium zeolite.

The results in Table 11.3 suggest that kinetic factors, such as adsorption, reaction and desorption, are the deciding influence on the rate of ethane conversion. It may further be noted that the conversion is not limited by the reaction equilibrium.

Table 11.3 THE EFFECT OF THE VOLUMETRIC FLOW RATE OF CARRIER GAS ON ETHANE CONVERSION (length of reactor 150 cm, volume of ethane pulse 0.5 cm³) [177]

F [cm³ STP/min]	*Temperature* [K]	t_c [s]	Δt [s]	*Ethane conversion* [%]
50	723	38	41	17.7
30	723	51	52	21.4
25	723	56	55	22.0
15	723	83	87	28.0
25	773	64	20	64.0

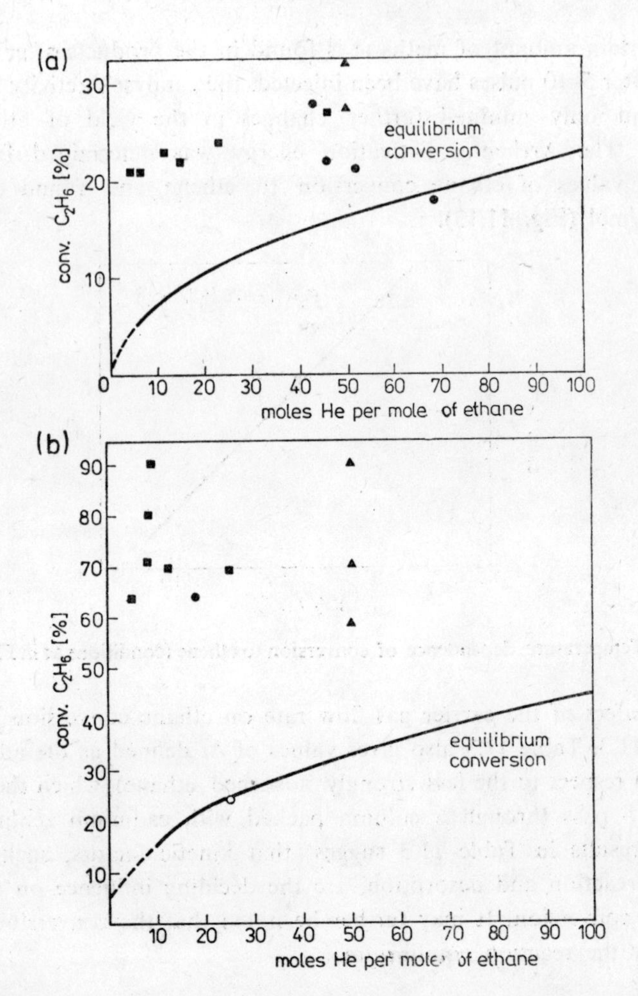

Fig. 11.14 (a) Curve showing the equilibrium conversion of ethane and the results of conversion obtained by the pulse technique at 723 K; (b) Curve showing the equilibrium conversion of ethane and the results of conversion obtained by the pulse technique at 773 K (after P. Antonucci *et al.* [177]):

($K_p/p = 5 \times 10^{-3}$ MPa^{-1}, K_p — ethane dehydrogenation equilibrium constant, p — overall pressure, ▲ — values from Table 11.2, ● — values from Table 11.3, ■ — values from Fig. 11.11).

The authors [177] compare the values of ethane conversion obtained under pulse conditions with thermodynamic equilibrium data calculated for a stream of ethane diluted in helium (Fig. 11.14).

It can be seen from these figures that the ethane conversion obtained under pulse conditions is always higher than the equilibrium conversion, the extent of this difference depending upon the reaction conditions. Greater differences are obtained when the time intervals between the injected pulses of ethane are longer. Factors optimizing the reaction yield are very large pulse sizes, a slow carrier gas flow rate, and a low pulse frequency, necessary in order to avoid undesired interaction between consecutive pulses.

The pulse technique has been used to assess the activity of catalysts in the one-stage dehydrogenation of butane to butadiene [174]. In each

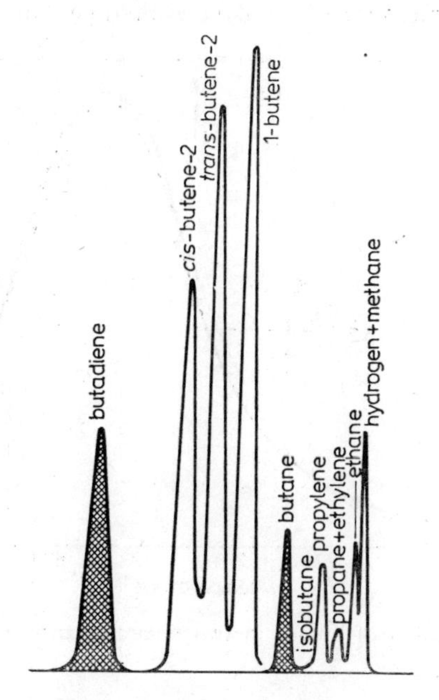

Fig. 11.15 Chromatogram of the dehydrogenation products of butane (peaks at various detector sensitivities) (after R. Potocki *et al.* [174]).

experiment, 1.27 g of aluminium–chromium catalyst was placed in the microreactor and stabilized at 843 K for 3 hours in a stream of helium, after which it was reduced by hydrogen for 30 minutes. The flow rates of both helium and hydrogen were 3.6 dm^3/h. After reduction, the catalyst was cooled in a stream of helium to 673 K, and the experiments were started. At each temperature, 1 cm^3-pulses of butane were injected every 25 minutes. The catalyst operating temperature in the microreactor was varied from 673 to 913 K. Figure 11.15 illustrates a typical chromatogram of the dehydrogenation products.

The initial temperature for the dehydrogenation of butane was taken to be 673 K. Four consecutive pulses of butane were injected at this temperature, reproducible results being obtained after three injections. At successively higher temperatures, one injection was deemed sufficient.

No coke was observed in quantities detectable by derivatographic analysis in the catalysts tested. Deactivation of the catalyst surface due to carbon deposition was minimal, if it took place at all.

Figure 11.16 presents the yield curve of butadiene. Of three experiments using a new measure of catalyst each time, the results of the two

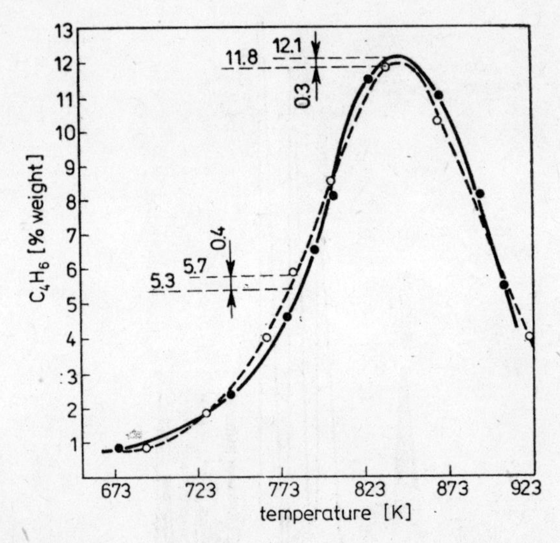

Fig. 11.16 Dehydrogenation of butane in two separate experiments (after R. Potocki *et al.* [174]).

experiments with the most widely differing results are shown graphically. As can be seen, the reproducibility of the results is quite satisfactory.

The dehydrogenation depends significantly on the partial pressure of the butane passed on to the catalyst. In industry the reaction is carried out at a certain negative pressure. The effect of diluting the butane with helium on the yield was investigated. Figure 11.17 illustrates the yields of butadiene for a number of concentrations of butane. The optimum dilution turned out to be one part butane to 5.3 parts helium.

Figure 11.18 shows the dependence between the amounts of butadiene being formed, butenes and unreacted butane on the one hand, and the reaction temperature on the other. The experiment was carried out under confirmed optimal conditions of thermal-gaseous treatment of the catalyst

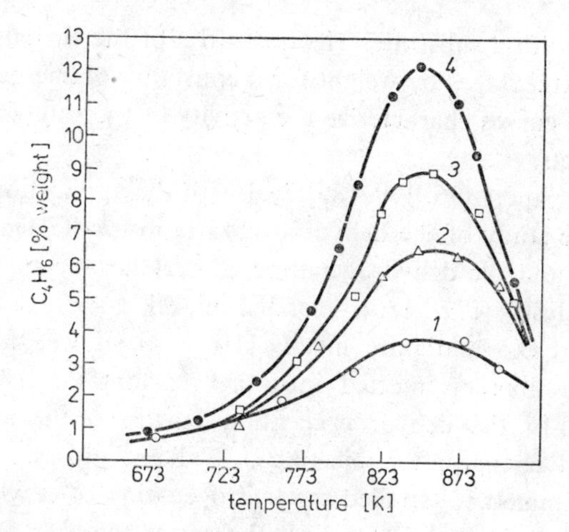

Fig. 11.17 The effect on the butadiene yield of diluting butane with helium (after R. Potocki *et al.* [174]):

1 — pure butane, *2* — 1 : 1 dilution, *3* — 1 : 3 dilution, *4* — 1 : 5.3 dilution.

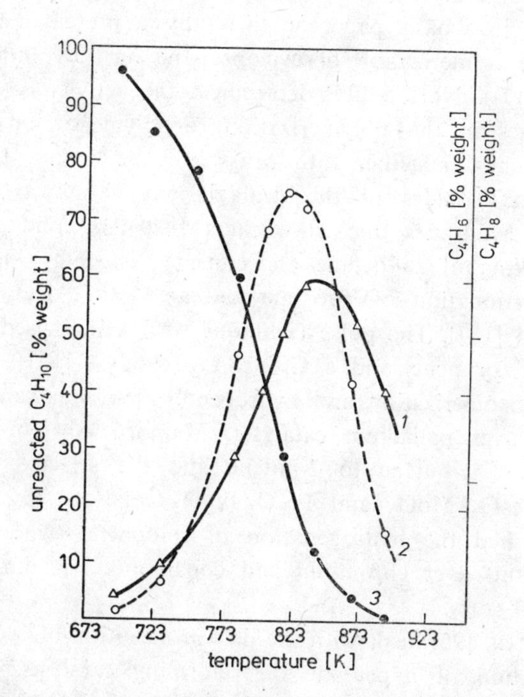

Fig. 11.18 Relationship between the quantity of butadiene *1*, butenes *2* and unreacted butane *3*, and the dehydrogenation temperature (after R. Potocki *et al.* [174]).

and its loading with a substrate. The quantities of the various components were given as percentages by weight for a constant volume pulse of butane of 1 cm^3. These curves characterize the activity of the catalyst with respect to these products.

A series of papers [96, 179–185] deal with the application of the pulse technique to the study of the dehydrocyclization of *n*-heptenes, *n*-hexenes and *n*-alkanes, and the dehydrogenation of cyclohexane over aluminium–chromium catalysts [179, 185], metallic nickel and platinum catalysts deposited on Al_2O_3, and pure metals [180–184]. It was found that the first portions of alkanes injected into the reactors underwent complete cracking [180]. In the dehydrocyclization reactions, the activity of the catalyst did not change after injecting 3–4 alkene pulses.

Hall and Emmett [8] studied the hydrogenation of ethylene on a copper–nickel catalyst. Hall and Hassell [89] assessed the effect of chemisorbed hydrogen on the catalytic activity of a number of metals during hydrogenolysis reactions. The isotopic exchange of H_2–D_2 on Ni/SiO_2 catalysts over a wide range of temperature has been described [155]. Bassett and Habgood [48], in a basic paper on this subject, presented the results of studies on the isomerization of cyclopropane on 13X molecular sieves (equation (11.17)). Norton [90] determined the activity of 5A and 13X molecular sieves in the polymerization, depolymerization and isomerization of alkenes. Together with Moss [91], he defined the selectivity of various metal oxides in the dealkylation of alkylaromatic hydrocarbons. De Mourgues and co-workers [92, 93] conducted research into the cracking of *iso*-octane and cumenes on SiO_2–Al_2O_3 catalysts. The disproportionation of propene on a $MoO_3 \cdot Al_2O_3$ catalyst has been described [159]. The pulse technique was further used to study the interaction of propene and a CrO_3/SiO_2 catalyst [167]. Hartwig [94] described the isomerization and hydrogenolysis of *n*-alkanes at various temperatures over palladium catalysts. Mamoru Ai [162] studied the isomerization of 1-butene to 2-butene and the selective oxidation of alkenes on Fe_2O_3–MoO_3 and Fe_2O_3–V_2O_5 catalysts. Owens and Amberg [95] studied the hydrogenation of thiophene (with simultaneous desulphurization) over chromium and cobalt–molybdenum catalysts deposited on supports.

Barbul *et al.* [96] dealt with the dehydrogenation of cyclohexane and the isomerization of *n*-pentane on reforming catalysts. The catalytic dehydrogenation of *n*-alkanes, the dehydration of alcohols, pyrolysis and hydrogenation reactions under chromatographic conditions are given by

Berezkin *et al.* [170]. Bondar *et al.* [97] synthesized methanol at atmospheric pressure under chromatographic conditions.

Belousov *et al.* [98–101] carried out a chromatographic study of the oxidation of propene on various oxides and metal/support catalysts. They showed that the contact activity when the reaction occurs in the pulse system is 2–3 times greater than the activity under stationary conditions. The papers by Antipina and Yushchenko [102, 103] deal with the cracking of cumene on fluorinated aluminium oxide and zeolites. De Mourgues *et al.* [104] describe the decomposition of *iso*-octane on cracking catalysts. Scott and Philips [156] studied the hydrocracking of *n*-hexane and *n*-decane on a Ni/SiO_2 catalyst. The decomposition of C_6 hydrocarbons (hexane, cyclohexane, 2-methylpentane, 2,2-dimethylbutane and 2-hexene) is described by Pacakova *et al.* [175].

Topchieva *et al.* [105, 106] investigated the kinetics of cumene cracking on crystalline and amorphous SiO_2–Al_2O_3 catalysts and Y-zeolites (Na, Ca, NH_4 forms). The conversion of mono- and dialkylbenzenes on aluminosilicate catalysts has been described [107, 108].

Using a microreactor, the reaction mechanisms of the dehydration of alcohol over aluminium oxide [109] and *X*- and Y-zeolites [110] were studied, as was the decomposition of 2-propanol on oxide catalysts: MgO, CaO and SrO [158].

Dutton and Mounts [111] used radiochromatography to study the mechanism of the hydrogenation of organic acid esters on palladium, platinum and nickel catalysts.

Stein *et al.* [112] established the ease of oxidation of various hydrocarbons in a microreactor on different oxide catalysts in descending order: acetylene (ethyne) > alkenes > cycloalkanes > isoalkanes > aromatic hydrocarbons.

Statsevich *et al.* [113] investigated the activity of vanadium oxide in the oxidation of naphthalene and its derivatives.

In a cycle of papers, Csicsery [114, 115] published the results of his research into the dehydrocyclodimerization of butanes over oxide and platinum catalysts. The catalytic dehydrohalogenation of hydrocarbons on aluminium oxides modified by alkali metal chlorides [157] and the catalytic dehydrohalogenation of 1,1,2-trichloroethane to 1,1-dichloroethylene over Al_2O_3 [161] were also studied using the pulse technique.

Celler and Potocki [116] investigated the hydrogenation of benzene over a Ni/Al_2O_3 catalyst, and together with Berak [117], the oxidation of benzene to maleic anhydride on vanadium catalysts.

Thermochromatography (see Section 11.2.4) can also be applied when studying the effect of the preparation of catalysts on their catalytic properties [118, 119]. The dehydration of trimethylmethanol by the pulse technique is described [153], as is the decomposition of 3-methyl-1-butanol [186] over phosphoric acid supported on quartz.

The papers mentioned above are, of course, only examples of catalytic reactions which can be studied in the microreactor. GC is used very frequently nowadays [120–140]. In fact, it is difficult to imagine modern research into catalysis without the use of GC, at least during some stages.

11.8 General Remarks on the Study of Catalytic Reactions by Chromatography

It is obvious from the material presented above that the pulse technique can be used successfully to solve many problems in catalysis. The range of application of this method will be extended in the future, but this must be accompanied by concurrent developments in theory. The output curve does provide sufficient information about the process taking place in the reactor, but we are not at present in a position to make use of all this data in mathematical modelling.

One must emphasize the difficulties involved in working up the results because of the non-stationarity of the method. The mathematical model used refers only to ideal linear chromatography in which the rates of sorption and diffusion have been ignored. This is obviously reasonable when the rate of reaction is small in comparison with the rate of sorption.

Serious mathematical difficulties are encountered when we assume a non-linear sorption isotherm, or a reaction whose order is greater than 1 — then we have to solve a non-linear system of equations. This problem cannot be solved at the moment, even if we use the elution-frontal method with labelled atoms, because the concentration of substrates continually flowing through the reactor is always changing, and thus measurements for a given surface concentration are impossible. In summary we can say that even though mathematical modelling has gained widespread favour in research into the kinetics of heterogeneous reactions in the microreactor (Roginskii, Yanovskii, Berman), it cannot as yet enable us to make full use of the information we get on the reaction chromatogram. In the future, numerical methods will have to be given greater consideration.

When we carry out a process under chromatographic conditions we obtain higher yields for reversible reactions than we do in the classical flow reactor. It would be useful to carry out some reactions on a technical scale under chromatographic conditions. The main problem with scaling up a chromatographic reactor is that the ability of a chromatographic column to separate decreases quite sharply as its size increases.

The various versions of the chromatographic method differ largely in the shape and nature of the input pulse. This would suggest that a given pulse is especially suitable for studying a given process. Certain attempts have even been made to standardize processes in non-analytical chromatography. Very good results have been obtained, for instance, in the study of the kinetics of heterogeneous reactions by injecting into a small microreactor a "wide" rectangular pulse whose front and rear profiles are as steep as possible [98]. The process occurring in the microreactor is considered to be stationary and microdynamic, and complete adsorption and chemical equilibria are assumed to have been attained. The results obtained can then be worked up in the same way as for ordinary flow reactors. One drawback of the method is the necessity to define the "width" of the pulse which has to be chosen in accordance with the rate at which the adsorption and chemical equilibria are established in the microreactor.

A considerable advance is the recent use of the gradientless pulse technique in a microreactor [141].

The practical application of the microreactor for assessing catalytic activity and studying heterogeneous reactions is outrunning the development of a theory of non-stationary processes taking place under pulse conditions. In catalysis this is nothing new — experimental practice has often been well in advance of theoretical inquiry. However, if applications of the microreactor pulse technique are to develop along the right lines, they must be accompanied by a development of theories of adsorption — chemical processes occurring under pulse conditions. Much intensive work is being done on such theories. The chromatographic pulse technique of studying catalytic processes is a valuable addition to the methods currently being used in this field.

References

[1] Kokes R. J., Tobin H. and Emmett P. H., *J. Am. Chem. Soc.*, 77, 5860 (1955).
[2] Roginskii S. Z., Yanovskii M. I. and Berman A. D., *Osnovy primenenya khromatografii v katalize*, Izd. Nauka, Moskva, 1972.

[3] Leibnitz E. and Struppe H. G., *Handbuch der Gas Chromatographie*, Akad. Verlagsgesellschaft, Leipzig, 1966.
[4] Jamamoto H., O'Hava M. and Kwan T., *Chem. Pharm. Bull.*, **13**, 6724 (1965).
[5] Hofer L. J. E., Geesen P. and Anderson R. B., *J. Catal.*, **3**, 45 (1964).
[6] Stein K. S., Felnak J. J., Thompson G. P., Shultz J. F., Hofer L. J. E. and Anderson R. B., *Ind. Eng. Chem.*, **52**, 671 (1960).
[7] Kubicka H., *J. Catal.*, **12**, 233 (1968).
[8] Hall W. K. and Emmett P. H., *J. Am. Chem. Soc.*, **79**, 2091 (1957).
[9] Ettre L. S. and Brenner N., *J. Chromatogr.*, **3**, 524 (1960).
[10] Keulemans A. T. M. and Voge H. H., *J. Phys. Chem.*, **63**, 476 (1959).
[11] Langer S. H., Yurchak J. Y. and Patton J. E., *Ind. Eng. Chem.*, **61**, 10 (1969).
[12] Phillips C. G. S., Walker M. L., McIlwrick C. R. and Rosser P. A., *J. Chromatogr. Sci.*, **8**, 401 (1970).
[13] Giddings J. C., *J. Chromatogr.*, **3**, 443 (1960).
[14] Guseinov Sh. L., Frolkina I. T., Vasilevich L. A. and Gelbshtein A. I., *Zh. Fiz. Khim.*, **51**, 996 (1977).
[15] Magee E. M., *Ind. Eng. Chem. Fundamentals*, **2**, 32 (1963).
[16] Anders M. W. and Mannering G. J., *Anal. Chem.*, **34**, 730 (1962).
[17] Berezkin V. G., *Usp. Khim.*, **37**, 1348 (1968).
[18] Matsen J. M., Harding J. W. and Magee E. M., *J. Phys. Chem.*, **69**, 522 (1965).
[19] Gaziev G. A., Filipovskii V. Yu. and Yanovskii M. I., *Kinet. Katal.*, **4**, 688 (1963).
[20] Roginskii S. Z. and Rozental A. L., *Kinet. Katal.*, **5**, 104 (1964).
[21] Roginskii S. Z., Yanovskii M. I. and Gaziev G. A., *Gazovaya khromatografiya*, Trudy II Vses. Konf., Izd. Nauka, Moskva, 1964, p. 27.
[22] Hattori T. and Murakarni J., *J. Catal.*, **10**, 114 (1968).
[23] Roginskii S. Z. and Rozental A. L., *Trudy Vses. Konf. po Khim. Reaktoram*, Novosibirsk, 1965, Vol. 1., p. 100.
[24] Liberman A. L., Bragin O. V. and Kazanskii B. A., *Dokl. Akad. Nauk SSSR*, **156**, 1114 (1964).
[25] Berman A. D., Yanovskii M. I. and Roginskii S. Z., *Dokl. Akad. Nauk SSSR*, **190**, 864 (1970).
[26] Yanovskii M. I., Oziraner S. I. and Lu-Pey-Chzhan, *Zh. Fiz. Khim.*, **33**, 1084 (1960).
[27] Zhukhovitskii A. A. and Turkeltaub N. M., *Gazovaya khromatografiya*, Izd. Gostoptekhizdat, Moskva, 1962.
[28] Roginskii S. Z. and Yanovskii M. I., *Gazovaya khromatografiya*, Trudy III Vses. Konf. po gazovoy khromatografii, Dzerzhinsk, 1964, p. 54.
[29] Zhukhovitskii A. A., Zolotareva O. V., Sokolov V. A. and Turkeltaub N. M., *Dokl. Akad. Nauk SSSR*, **77**, 435 (1951).
[30] Klinkenberg A., *Chem. Eng. Sci.*, **15**, 255 (1961).
[31] Hattori T. and Murakami Y., *J. Catal.*, **12**, 166 (1968).
[32] Van Swaay M., *Advances in Chromatography*, **8**, 363 (1969).
[33] Giddings J. C., *J. Chem. Phys.*, **26**, 169 (1957).
[34] Norman R. O. C., *Proc. Chem. Soc.*, 151 (1958).
[35] Gil-Av E., Herling I. and Shabtai J., *J. Chromatogr.*, **1**, 508 (1958); **2**, 406 (1959).
[36] Gil-Av E. and Herling I., *J. Phys. Chem.*, **66**, 1208 (1962).

[37] Shabtai J., Herling I. and Gil-Av E., *J. Chromatogr.*, **11**, 32 (1963).
[38] Muka M. A. and Weiss F. T., *J. Am. Chem. Soc.*, **84**, 4697 (1962).
[39] Cvetanovic R. J., Duncan F. J., Falconer W. E. and Sunder W. A., *J. Am. Chem. Soc.*, **88**, 1602 (1966).
[40] Genkin A. N., Ogorodnikov S. K. and Nemcov M. S., *Neftekhimiya*, **2**, 837 (1962).
[41] Genkin A. N. and Boguslavskaya B. I., *Neftekhimiya*, **5**, 897 (1965).
[42] Genkin A. N. and Boguslavskaya B. I., *Neftekhimiya*, **6**, 626 (1966).
[43] Cvetanovic R. J., Duncan F. J., Irwin W. E. and Irwin R. S., *J. Am. Chem. Soc.*, **87**, 1827 (1965).
[44] Falconer W. E. and Cvetanovic R. J., *J. Chromatogr.*, **27**, 20 (1967).
[45] Zimin R. A., Roginskii S. Z. and Yanowskii M. I., *Sb. Metody issled. katal. katal. reakt.*, Izd. Otd. Sibir., Otd. Akad. Nauk SSSR, Novosibirsk, 1965, Vol. 3, p. 279.
[46] Zizin V. T., Sokolova V. I., Masagutov R. M. and Georg G. A., *Khim. Tekhnol. Topliv i Masel*, **4**, 59 (1965).
[47] Rozenbrat M. I., Mortikov E. S. and Kazanskii A., *Dokl. Akad. Nauk SSSR*, **166**, 619 (1966).
[48] Bassett D. W. and Habgood H. W., *J. Phys. Chem.*, **64**, 769 (1960).
[49] Yushchenko V. V. and Antipina T. V., *Zh. Fiz. Khim.*, **45**, 445 (1971).
[50] Topchieva K. V., Rosolovskaya E. N. and Shakhnovskaya O. L., *Vestnik Mosk. Univ., ser. Khim.*, **4**, 39 (1968).
[51] Kho-Shi-Thoang, Romanovskii B. V. and Topchieva K. V., *Kinet. Katal.*, **7**, 122 (1966).
[52] Spozhakina A. A., Moskovskaya I. F. and Topchieva K. V., *Vestnik Mosk. Univ., ser. Khim.*, **3**, 13 (1967).
[53] Berezkin V. G., Kruglikova V. S. and Belikova N. A., *Dokl. Akad. Nauk SSSR*, **158**, 182 (1964).
[54] Berezkin V. G., Kruglikova V. S. and Segreeva V. E., *Kinet. Katal.*, **6**, 758 (1965).
[55] Roginskii S. Z. and Rozental A. L., *Dokl. Akad. Nauk SSSR*, **146**, 152 (1962).
[56] Filipovskii V. Yu., Gaziev G. A. and Yanovskii M. I., *Sb. Metody issled. katal. katal. reakt.*, Izd. Otd. Sibir., Otd. Akad. Nauk SSSR, Novosibirsk, 1965, Vol. 3, p. 313.
[57] Filipovskii M. I., Gaziev G. A. and Yanovskii M. I., *Dokl. Akad. Nauk SSSR*, **167**, 143 (1966).
[58] Berman A. D. and Yanovskii M. I., *Dokl. Akad. Nauk SSSR*, **197**, 369 (1971).
[59] Roginskii S. Z., Aliev R. R., Berman A. D., Lokteva N. K., Smenenko Z. I. and Yanovskii M. I., *Dokl. Akad. Nauk SSSR*, **176**, 1114 (1967).
[60] Germain J. E., *Compt. rend.*, **263**, 27 (1966).
[61] Aliev R. R., Berman A. D., Lokteva N. K., Roginskii S. Z. and Yanovskii M. I., *Kinet. Katal.*, **9**, 610 (1968).
[62] Roginskii S. Z. and Rozental A. L., *Dokl. Akad. Nauk SSSR*, **146**, 152 (1962).
[63] Kocirik M., *J. Chromatogr.*, **30**, 459 (1967).
[64] Denisova T. A. and Rozental A. L., *Kinet. Katal.*, **8**, 2 (1967).
[65] Kallen J. and Heilbromer E., *Helv. Chim. Acta.*, **43**, 489 (1960).
[66] Nakaraki M. and Nishino M., *Yakugaka Zasshi*, **85**, 305 (1965).

[67] Roginskii S. Z., *Adsorptsiya i kataliz na neodnorodnykh poverkhnostyakh*, Izd. AN SSSR, Moskva, 1948.
[68] Kittel I. K., Meraki P. and Watson C. C., *Ind. Eng. Chem.*, **57**, 12 (1965).
[69] Kittel I. K., Hunter W. G. and Watson C. C., *Am. Instr. Chem. Eng. J.*, **11**, 1051 (1965).
[70] Jones G. D., MacWilliams D. C. and Braxtor N. A., *J. Org. Chem.*, **30**, 1994 (1965).
[71] Higgings J., Investigations of rates and mechanisms of reactions, in: *Technique of Organic Chemistry*, Ed. Weissberger A., Interscience, New York, 1963, Vol. VIII, 2nd ed.
[72] Emanuel N. M. and Knoppe D. G., *Kurs khimicheskoy kinetiki*, Izd. Visshaya shkola, Moskva, 1962.
[73] Fuks I. S. and Joffe I. I., *IV International Congress on Catalysis, Symposium II*, Izd. Nauka, Moscow, 1968.
[74] Aliev R. R., Gagarin S. G., Kholodyakov N. I. and Yanovskii M. I., *Neftekhimiya*, **8**, 687 (1968).
[75] Aliev R. R., Gagarin S. G., Yanovskii M. I. and Zhomov M. I., *Neftekhimiya*, **7**, 851 (1967).
[76] Roginskii S. Z., Semenko E. I. and Yanovskii M. I., *Dokl. Akad. Nauk SSSR*, **153**, 383 (1963).
[77] Semenenko E. I., Roginskii S. Z. and Yanovskii M. I., *Kinet. Katal.*, **5**, 486 (1964).
[78] Semenneko E. I., Roginskii S. Z. and Yanovskii M. I., *Gazovaya khromatografiya*, Trudy III Vses. Konf. po gazovoy khromatografii, Izd. Nauka, Moskva, 1966, p. 433.
[79] Semenenko E. I., Roginskii S. Z. and Yanovskii M. I., *Kinet. Katal.*, **6**, 320 (1965).
[80] Semenenko E. I., Yanovskii M. I. and Roginskii S. Z., *Sb. Metody issled. katal. katal. reakt.*, Izd. Otd. Sibir., Otd. Akad. Nauk SSSR, Novosibirsk, 1965, Vol. 2, p. 290.
[81] Yanovski M. I., Kapustin D. S. and Nogotkov–Ryutin V. A., *Sb. Problemy kinet. katal.*, Izd. Akad. Nauk SSSR, Moskva, 1957, p. 391.
[82] Yanovskii M. I., Gaziev G. A., Kornyakov S. V., Gavrilova V. I. and Titova N. Ya., *Khromatografiya, teoriya i primenenie*, Izd. Akad. Nauk SSSR, Moskva, 1960, p. 309.
[83] Yanovskii M. I. and Gaziev G. A., *Vestnik Akad. Nauk SSSR*, **5**, 27 (1960).
[84] Hightower J. W., Gerberlich H. R. and Hall W. K., *J. Catal.*, **7**, 57 (1967).
[85] Aleksandrov A. Yu. and Yanovskii M. I., *Kinet. Katal.*, **2**, 794 (1961).
[86] Neiman M. B., *Intern. J. Appl. Isot.*, **3**, 20 (1958).
[87] Neiman M. B. and Gal. D., *Primenenie radioaktivnykh izotopov v khimicheskoy kinetike*, Izd. Nauka, Moskva, 1970.
[88] Collins C. G. and Deans H. W., *Am. Inst. Chem. Eng. J.*, **14**, 25 (1968).
[89] Hall W. K. and Hassell J. A., *J. Phys. Chem.*, **67**, 636 (1963).
[90] Norton C. J., *Chem. Ind.* (*London*), 258 (1962).
[91] Norton C. J. and Moss T. E., *Ing. Eng. Chem. Prod. Res. Develop.*, **3**, 23 (1964).
[92] De Mourgues L., Fichet M. and Chassaing G., *Bull. soc. chim. France*, 1918 (1962).
[93] De Mourgues L. and Capony J., *Chim. anal.* (*Paris*), **45**, 103 (1963).
[94] Hartwig M., *Brennst. Chem.*, **45**, 234 (1964).

[95] Owens P. J. and Amberg C. H., *Adv. Chem. Ser.*, **33**, 182 (1961).
[96] Barbul M., Serban Gh., Ghejan I. and Filotti T., *Petrol Gaze*, **19**, 181 (1968).
[97] Bondar P. G., Leleka V. E., Sushchaya L. and Gernet D. V., *Kinet. Katal.*, **9**, 1178 (1968).
[98] Belousov V. M., Rubanik M. Ya. and Gershingorina A. V., *Ukr. Khim. Zh.*, **31**, 444 (1965).
[99] Belousov V. M. and Gershingorina A. V., IV International Congress on Catalysis, Izd. Nauka, Moscow, 1970, Vol. 1, p. 260.
[100] Gershingorina A. V., Belousov V. M. and Rubanik M. Ya., *Kataliz i katalizatory*, Izd. Naukovaya Dumka, Kiev, 1966, p. 41.
[101] Belousov V. M., Gershingorina A. V., Rubanik M. Ya. and Verlyan Z. F., *Kinet. Katal.*, **7**, 850 (1966).
[102] Yuschenko V. V. and Antipina T. V., *Neftekhimiya*, **8**, 870 (1968).
[103] Yuschenko V. V. and Antipina T. V., *Kinet. Katal.*, **11**, 134 (1970).
[104] De Mourgues L., Fichet M. and Chassaing G., *Bull. soc. chim. France*, 1918 (1962),
[105] Spozhanina A. A., Moskovskaya I. F. and Topchieva K. V., *Kinet. Katal.*, **8**. 614 (1967).
[106] Valid-Berge E., Romanovskii B. V., Topchieva K. V. and Kho-Shi Thoang, *Kinet. Katal.*, **9**, 931 (1968).
[107] Matsumoto H., Take J. I. and Yoneda Y., *J. Catal.*, **11**, 211 (1968).
[108] Mochida I. and Yoneda Y., *J. Catal.*, **7**, 386 (1967).
[109] Isagulants G. V., Derbencev I. I., Klabunovskii E. I. and Balandin A. A., *Izv. Akad. Nauk SSSR, ser. Khim.*, 985 (1964).
[110] Graznova Z. V., Ermilova M. M., Tsitsishvili G. V., Andrónikashvili T. G. and Krupennikova A. Yu., *Kinet. Katal.*, **10**, 1336 (1969).
[111] Dutton H. J. and Mounts T. L., *J. Catal.*, **3**, 363 (1964).
[112] Stein K. S., Freenau J. J., Thompson G. P., Shultz J. F., Hofer L. J. E. and Anderson R. B., *Ind. Eng. Chem.*, **52**, 671 (1960).
[113] Statsevich V. P., Korneichuk G. P., Skorbilina T. G. and Shaprinskaya T. M., *Kinet. Katal.*, **10**, 1917 (1969).
[114] Csicsery S. M., *J. Catal.*, **17**, 207, 216, 315, 323 (1970).
[115] Csicsery S. M., *J. Catal.*, **18**, 30 (1970).
[116] Celler W. and Potocki R., *Przemysł Chem.*, **49**, 147 (1970).
[117] Celler W., Potocki R. and Berak J. M., *Przemysł Chem.*, **49**, 230 (1970).
[118] Golosman E. Z., Yakerson V. I. and Ilicheva A. M., *Izv. Akad. Nauk SSSR, ser. Khim.*, 844 (1969).
[119] Golosman E. Z., Yakerson V. I., Alekseev A. M. and Ilicheva A. M., *Izv. Akad. Nauk SSSR, ser. Khim.*, 837 (1969).
[120] Turkevich J., Nozaki F. and Stamiers D., *Proc. III Intern. Congress on Catalysis*, Amsterdam, 1965, p. 586.
[121] Kho-Shi Thoang, Romanovskii B. V. and Topchieva K. V., *Vestnik Moskv. Univ., ser. Khim.*, **8** (3), 17 (1967).
[122] Romanovskii B. V., *Kinet. Katal.*, **7**, 129 (1966).
[123] Yanovskii M. I. and Berman A. D., I Vses. Konf. po kinetike kataliticheskikh reaktsii, NIFKhI im. L. Ya. Karpova, Moskva, 1971.
[124] Dinwiddie J. A. and Morgan W. A., U. S. Pat., 2 976 132 (1961).

[125] Bitner E. D., Davison V. L. and Dutton J. H., *J. Amer. Oil. Chem. Soc.*, **46**, 113 (1969).
[126] Magee E. M., Canad. Pat., 631 882 (1961).
[127] Roginskii S. Z., Yanovskii M. I. and Gaziev G. A., *Dokl. Akad. Nauk SSSR*, 140, 1125 (1961).
[128] Phillips C. S. G., Davis A. J. H., Saul R. G. L. and Wormald J., *J. Gas Chromatogr.*, **5**, 424 (1967).
[129] Langer S. H., Yurchak I. Y. and Patton J. E., *Ind. Eng. Chem.*, **61** (4), 11 (1969).
[130] Phillips C. S. G., Walker M L., McIlwrick C. R. and Rosser P. A., *J. Chromatogr. Sci.*, **8**, 401 (1970).
[131] Curtin D. Y., Kampmeier J. A. and O'Connor B. R., *J. Am. Chem. Soc.*, **87**, 863 (1965).
[132] Sergio C. and Lucio J., *Ind. Eng. Chem. Prod. Res. Develop.*, **2**, 281 (1965).
[133] Yanovskii M. I. and Berman A. D., *J. Chromatogr.*, **69**, 3 (1972).
[134] Schulz W. R. and Roy D. L., *Can. J. Chem.*, **42**, 2480 (1964).
[135] Wallace T. J. and Makon J. J., *J. Am. Chem. Soc.*, **86**, 4099 (1964).
[136] Bufalini J. J. and Altshuller A. P., *Can. J. Chem.*, **43**, 2243 (1965).
[137] Hugueny C. de M., Trambouze L. Y. and Prettre M., *Bull. soc. chim. France*, 497 (1965).
[138] McInnes A. G., *Can. J. Chem.*, **43**, 1998 (1965).
[139] Wichterlova B. and Jiru P., *Chem. Listy*, **59**, 1451 (1965).
[140] Langer S. H., Yurchak J. Y. and Shanghessy C. M., *Anal. Chem.*, **40**, 1747 (1968).
[141] Shukin V. P. and Velyaminov S. A., *Kinet. Katal.*, **12**, 533 (1971).
[142] Burenkova L. N., Subbotina L. B., Kho-Shi-Thoang and Topchieva K. V., *Vestnik Moskv. Univ., ser. Khim.*, **14**, 27 (1973).
[143] Tuong Van Dao, Kubasov A. A. and Topchieva K. V., *Vestnik Moskv. Univ., ser. Khim.*, **14**, 146 (1973).
[144] Topchieva K. V., Romanovskii B. V., Ivanova T. M., Kho-Shi-Thoang and Vishnevskii L. V., *Vestnik Moskv. Univ., ser. Khim.*, **14**, 223 (1973).
[145] Kubasov A. A., Ratov A. N. and Topchieva K. V., *Vestnik Moskv. Univ., ser. Khim.*, **14**, 285 (1973).
[146] Topchieva K. V., Kho-Shi-Thoang and Monyakin A. P., *Vestnik Moskv. Univ., ser. Khim.*, **14**, 282 (1973).
[147] Burenkov L. N., Trusova V. I., Kho-Shi-Thoang and Topchieva K. V., *Vestnik Moskv. Univ., ser. Khim.*, **14**, 291 (1973).
[148] Topchieva K. V. and Kho-Shi-Thoang, *Vestnik Moskv. Univ., ser. Khim.*, **14**, 363 (1973).
[149] Bodrina D. E. and Rudenko A. P., *Vestnik Moskv. Univ., ser. Khim.*, **14**, 250 (1973).
[150] Sosnina I. E. and Lysenko S. V., *Vestnik Moskv. Univ., ser. Khim.*, **14**, 354 (1973).
[151] Saha N. C. and Mathur D. S., *J. Chromatogr.*, **81**, 207 (1973).
[152] Valitov N. Kh., Ibragimov F. Kh. and Lysikov V. M., *Kinet. Katal.*, **19**, 103 (1978).
[153] Vinnik M. I. and Obraztsov P. A., *Kinet. Katal.*, **19**, 239 (1978).
[154] Zhitomirskii B. M., Agafonov A. V., Berman A. D., Yanovskii M. I. and Zhomov A. K., *Zh. Fiz. Khim.*, **51**, 908 (1977).

[155] Scott K. F. and Phillips C. S. G., *J. Catal.*, **51**, 131 (1978).
[156] Scott K. F. and Phillips C. S. G., *J. Chromatogr.*, **112**, 61 (1975).
[157] Lycourghiotis A., Katsanos N. A. and Hadzistelios I., *J. Catal.*, **36**, 385 (1975).
[158] Szabo Z. G., Jover B. and Ohmacht R., *J. Catal.*, **39**, 225 (1975).
[159] Giordano N., Padovan M., Vaghi A., Bart J. C. J. and Castellan A., *J. Catal.*, **38**, 1 (1975).
[160] Schultz P., *Anal. Chem.*, **47**, 1979 (1975).
[161] Michida I., Uchino A., Fujitsu H. and Takeshita K., *J. Catal.*, **51**, 72 (1978).
[162] Ai Mamoru, *J. Catal.*, **52**, 16 (1978).
[163] Perot G., Guisnet M. and Maurel R., *J. Catal.*, **41**, 14 (1976).
[164] Yermakov Yu. I., Kuznetsov B. N. and Ryndin Yu., *J. Catal.*, **42**, 73 (1976).
[165] Kraitr M., Komers R. and Cuta F., *Anal. Chem.*, **48**, 974 (1974).
[166] O'Brien M. J. and Grob R. L., *J. Chromatogr.*, **155**, 129 (1978).
[167] Sawerysyn J. P., Sochet L. R., Carlier M. and Lucquin M., *Bull. soc. chim. France*, **3–4**, 199 (1977).
[168] Langer H. S., Melton H. R. and Griffith T. D., *J. Chromatogr.*, **122**, 487 (1976).
[169] Novak J. and Reznicek J., *J. Chromatogr.*, **91**, 757 (1974).
[170] Berezkin V. G., Sojak L. and Uhdeova J., *J. Chromatogr.*, **98**, 157 (1974).
[171] Rao T. S. and Gandhe B. R., *J. Chromatogr.*, **88**, 407 (1974).
[172] Berezkin V. G., *J. Chromatogr.*, **91**, 559 (1974).
[173] Mathur D. S., Chanbey U. D. and Sinha A., *J. Chromatogr.*, **99**, 281 (1974).
[174] Potocki R., Berak J. M. and Wojtaszek T., *Przemysł Chem.*, **53**, 551 (1974).
[175] Pacakova V. and Kozlik V., *Chromatographia*, **11**, 266 (1978).
[176] Maggiore R., Giordano N., Crisafulli C., Castelli F., Solarino L. and Bart J. C. J., *J. Catal.*, **60**, 193 (1979).
[177] Antonucci P., Giordano N. and Bart J. C. J., *J. Chromatogr.*, **150**, 309 (1978).
[178] Anders M. W. and Mannering G. J., *Anal. Chem.*, **34**, 730 (1962).
[179] Mortikov E. S., Rozengart M. I. and Kazanskii B. A., *Izv. Akad. Nauk SSSR, ser. Khim.*, 103 (1968).
[180] Paal Z. and Rozengart M. I., *Acta Chim. Acad. Sci. Hung.*, **49**, 395 (1966).
[181] Paal Z. and Tetenyi P., *Acta Chim. Acad. Sci. Hung.*, **53**, 193 (1967).
[182] Paal Z. and Tetenyi P., *Acta Chim. Acad. Sci. Hung.*, **54**, 273 (1968).
[183] Paal Z. and Tetenyi P., *Acta Chim. Acad. Sci. Hung.*, **58**, 105 (1968).
[184] Paal Z. and Rozengart M. I., *Acta Chim. Acad. Sci. Hung.*, **54**, 287 (1967).
[185] Bragin O. V. Liberman A. L., Preobrazhenskii A. V. and Kazanskii B. A., *Izv. Akad. Nauk SSSR, ser. Khim.*, 2260 (1967).
[186] Obraztsov P. A. and Vinnik M. I., *Kinet. Katal.*, **18**, 103 (1977).

Chapter **12**

Microreactor Techniques

12.1 Introduction

In chromatography it is often the practice to combine chromatographic separation with a chemical reaction. This reaction may take place in the chromatographic column itself or, more commonly, in a microreactor connected to the chromatographic apparatus [1–38]. This kind of chromatography is called reaction gas chromatography [1].

Reaction chromatography is used in order to:

(1) study the course of a chemical reaction (also in the gas–liquid system) [2, 28, 32] or the properties of a catalyst (microreactor chromatography);

(2) analyse non-volatile compounds which cannot normally be analysed chromatographically (thermal decomposition to give volatile products) [3] — pyrolytic chromatography;

(3) carry out a quantitative identification of those gaseous components of a mixture which must be converted by means of a chemical reaction to other compounds so that separation can be effected;

(4) increase the sensitivity of the detector.

This chapter will deal with the first application of reaction GC mentioned above, and the different types of microreactor and methods of connecting them to chromatographic systems will be discussed.

Pulse techniques for studying reaction kinetics vary according to the volatility of the reactants and the type of reaction involved [32]. Some of the basic variants for reactions of the type $A + B + ... \rightarrow C + D$ are set out in Table 12.1.

Various sets of apparatus are used in studying reaction kinetics [32]. Some basic block diagrams of apparatus are illustrated in Table 12.2. Four fundamental types of system are shown — the position of the reactor with respect to the chromatographic column differs in each case.

Table 12.1 VARIANTS OF THE PULSE TECHNIQUES USED IN REACTION KINETICS [32]

Initial reactants — volatile	*One initial reactant volatile, the other non-volatile*	*Initial reactants — non-volatile*
1. Both volatile reactants are injected into the column reactor. Method used to study kinetics of catalytic reactions (Chapter 11). 2. One reactant is injected pulse-wise into the column reactor while the other is passed continuously into the reactor in the carrier gas stream (Chapter 11). 3. One reactant is first injected pulse-wise into the column reactor, then, after some time, the second. The reaction takes place during the time the second component is "catching the first one up" in the column (so-called chromatographic conditions).	4. The volatile reactant is injected pulse-wise, the non-volatile reactant is either in the liquid phase (usually deposited on a support) or is the surface of a solid (chemisorptive processes, e.g. on metals) (Chapter 6). 5. The volatile reactant is passed continuously into the column, the non-volatile one is in the liquid phase or is the surface of a solid (Chapters 6 and 7).	6. The initial reactants are used as the non-volatile phase in the column-reactor. A mixture of standard non-reacting components is injected pulse-wise into the column; changes in their retention times provide information about changes in the composition of the stationary phase in the column (usually the liquid phase) [39].

Diagram 1 shows the straightforward chromatographic system in which the column is also the reactor. In diagrams 2.1, 2.2, 2.3, and 2.4 the column is placed before the reactor in order to obtain pulses of pure reactant. The temperatures of the column and reactor may vary.

The layouts in 3.1 and 3.2 are most often used in catalysis research. The separation of reaction products is effected in the column placed after the reactor.

The system shown in diagram 4 is the most versatile. Pure substances can be obtained before entry into the reactor and analysed after having passed through it.

Table 12.2 BLOCK DIAGRAMS OF APPARATUS FOR STUDYING THE KINETICS OF CHEMICAL REACTIONS [32]

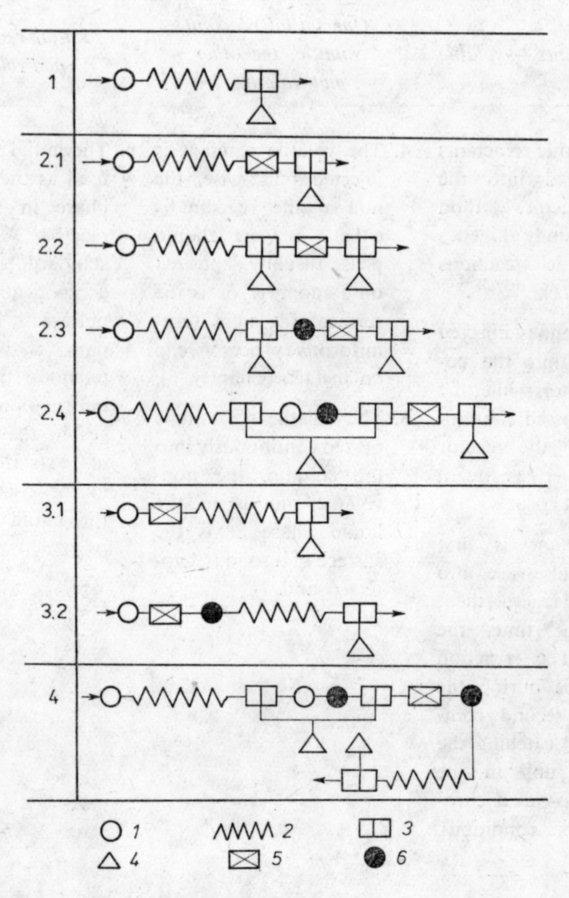

1 — injection port, *2* — chromatographic column, *3* — detector, 4 — recording device, *5* — reactor, *6*— freezer.

While constructing such chromatographic apparatus, the full possibilities of the method should be borne in mind:

(1) a pure initial substrate can be obtained ("preparative" chromatography in analytical columns);

(2) the two reactants are mixed well;

(3) the reaction mixture can be introduced as a "sharp" pulse, i.e. rapidly, or as a "rectangular" pulse, i.e. over a certain period, or else one or more substrates can be passed continuously into the reactor;

(4) the reaction products can be separated chromatographically, and their concentrations can be estimated before and after the reaction;

(5) the reaction conditions can be stabilized (temperature, carrier gas flow rate, etc.).

One important advantage of the direct pulse technique is that contaminated initial reactants can be used as they will be purified chromatographically before the reaction takes place. The versatility and reliability of the method are thus increased. To paraphrase Ostwald's well-known statement: GC allows us to obtain precise kinetic information even if we use impure starting substances.

12.2 Microreactors

A typical catalytic pulse microreactor is illustrated in Fig. 12.1 [5]. A carrier gas is passed through the system — it may be a neutral gas or one of the reactants. A small pulse of reactant is injected as a gas or liquid before the reactor. In most cases, the microreactor is a quartz or

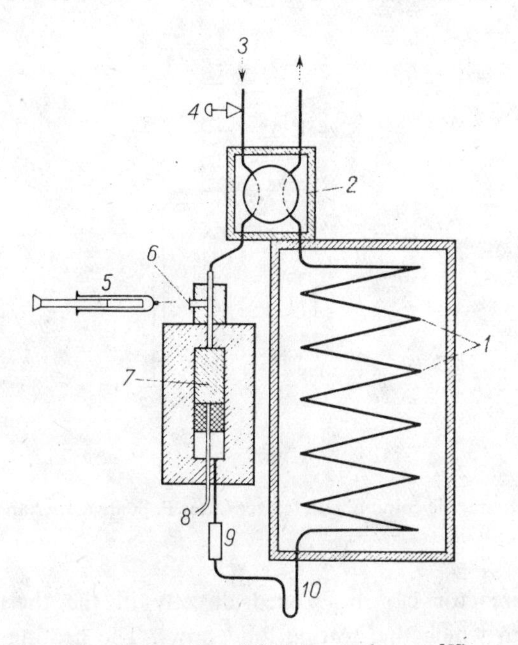

Fig. 12.1 Catalytic pulse microreactor (after R. Anderson [5]):
1 — chromatographic column, 2 — detector, 3 — carrier gas inlet, 4 — needle valve, 5 — microsyringe, 6 — injection port, 7 — reactor, 8 — thermocouple, 9 — dessicator, 10 — freezer.

glass tube about 1 cm in diameter and about 10 cm long. It is heated electrically. The carrier gas flows from the microreactor through a dessicator and freezer to the chromatographic column and to the detector — usually a katharometer. The column packing depends on the mixture emerging from the microreactor.

In the tube about 1 m long connecting the injection port with the microreactor, the concentration profile of the injected pulse is often broadened, sufficiently so for any further broadening taking place in the microreactor to be of no consequence. This undesirable effect should be eliminated as far as possible. If the carrier gas is one of the reactants, the injected pulse should be mixed well with the carrier gas before entry to the microreactor. Additional detectors are sometimes inserted before and after the microreactor in order to estimate concentration profiles [6].

Water is removed before the column on 3A or 4A molecular sieves (Fig 12.1). If desorption of reaction products from the catalyst proceeds slowly (a very broad peak), they are condensed in the freezer *10* cooled with liquid nitrogen (Fig. 12.2). The condensed reaction products can be rapidly passed into the column by substituting hot water for liquid nitrogen.

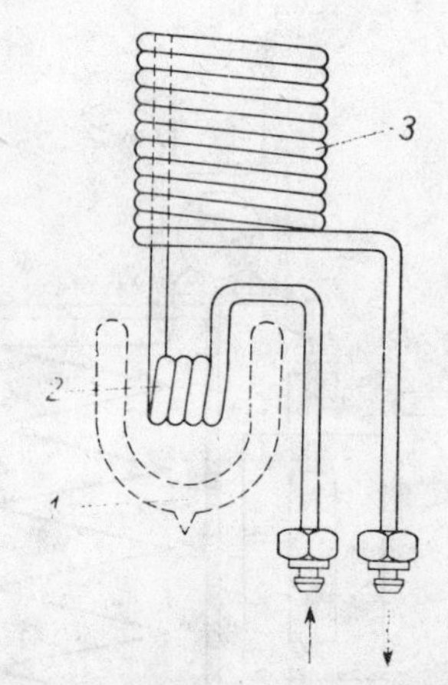

Fig. 12.2 Chromatographic column with freezer (after P. Steingaszner and H. Pines [15]): *1* — Dewar flask, *2* — freezer, *3* — column.

The microreactor can be placed directly in the thermostat or in a jacket through which the heating fluid flows. The heating fluid may be water, oils, molten salts or metals. One can also use thermostats in which the thermostatting medium is sand of a suitable particle size in a fluid state [7] (Fig. 12.3). The sand is made fluid by blowing a stream of heated air into it. This type of system has a small heat capacity and a large thermal conductivity, which facilitate a rapid change of temperature in the microreactor. This method of heating is just as efficient as metal block thermostats.

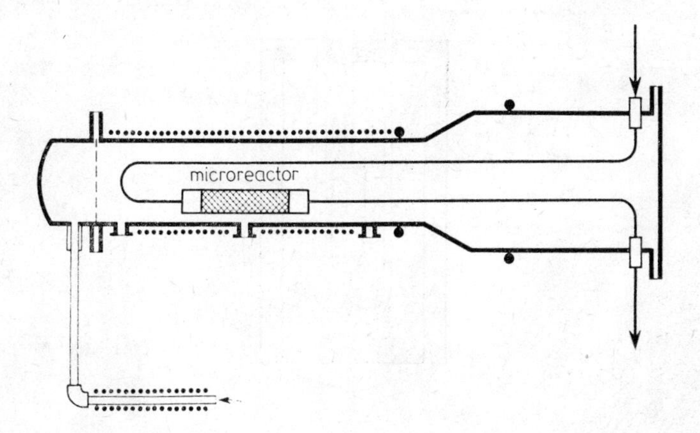

Fig. 12.3 Catalytic microreactor in a sand-bath thermostat (after D. P. Harrison *et al.* [7]).

In order to minimize chromatographic effects in the catalyst layer when using the pulse technique, the volume of the pulse should far exceed the volume of the catalyst in the microreactor [8–11]. Chromatographic separation of substances does not then take place and the pulse microreactor can be regarded as an ordinary flow reactor with a short working cycle (see Section 11.1). If conditions in the microreactor allow for good mixing of both the reaction mixture and catalyst, rates of reaction can be determined directly from experimental data. This is especially important for a non-stationary catalyst [12, 13]. Vibration is one technique that can be used to achieve catalyst mixing in the microreactor (Fig. 12.4) [14]. A microreactor with a volume of about 2 cm^3 is a glass tube with an internal diameter of 8 mm. The catalyst is placed between two filters. The carrier gas flows in from underneath, although its flow rate may be well below that needed to obtain the catalyst in a fluid state if there is no additional vibration. Vibrations (50 Hz, amplitude 1–4 mm) are provided by an electromagnetic vibrator. During vibration, the volume of an intensively mixed catalyst is almost doubled. The kinetic results obtained

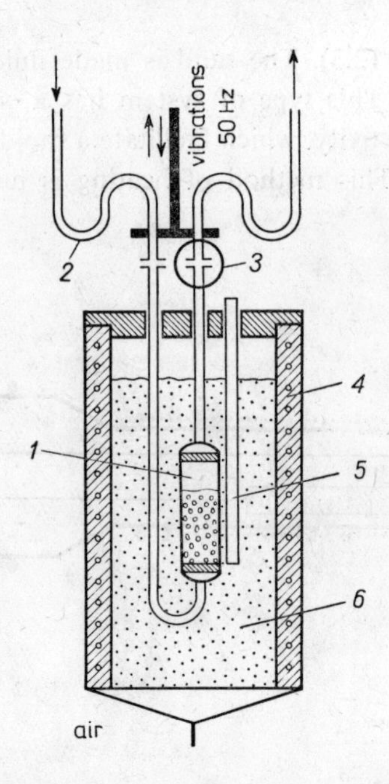

Fig. 12.4 Diagram of a microreactor with a vibrating layer of catalyst (after V. P. Schukin and S. A. Venyaminov [14]):

1 — microreactor, *2* — stainless steel tube (I.D. 2 mm), *3* — glass tube–metal tube connection, *4* — oven, *5* — thermocouple jacket, *6* — thermostatting medium — sand of particle size 0.1-0.15 mm.

in flow-circulation apparatus agreed well with those obtained in a pulse microreactor with vibrations.

Figure 12.5 shows a diagram of a simple microreactor [30]. The reactor proper is a 10 cm-long quartz tube with an internal diameter of 4 mm. The tube is located in an electrically heated copper block. The power of the oven is 350 W and is controlled by means of a transformer. The stability of the temperature was ± 3 at 873 K. The whole system was placed inside a suitably shaped block of elporite, which ensures good thermal and electrical insulation and helps to make the apparatus physically stable. This system is connected directly with the gas chromatograph. The lower part of the connection and the washers of the quartz tube are air-cooled. The temperature inside the reactor is measured with a thermocouple placed in the 0.5 mm gap between the copper block and the quartz tube. It was found that the temperature measured in this way is identical with the temperature within the quartz tube even while the carrier gas is flowing.

Another example of a simple pulse microreactor is illustrated in Fig. 12.6 [25]. It can be connected to a conventional chromatograph without the latter having to be modified in any way. The reactor and oven are made of stainless steel. The quantity of catalyst are packed into

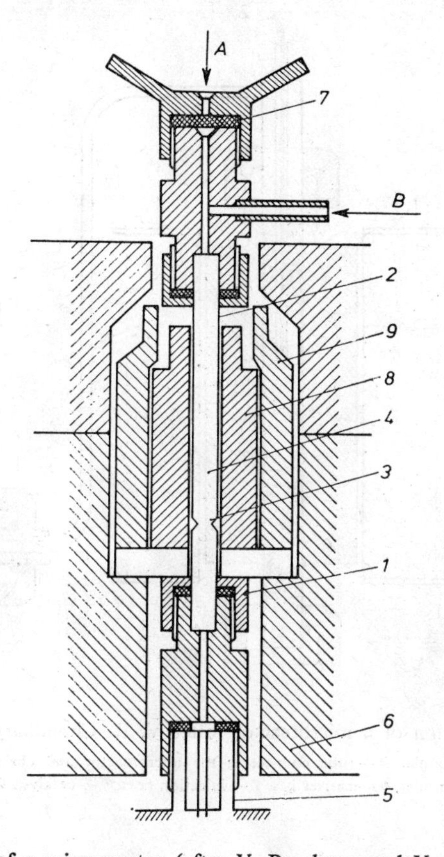

Fig. 12.5 Diagram of a microreactor (after V. Pacakova and V. Kozlik [30]):
A — sample inlet, *B* — carrier gas inlet, *1* — silicone washer, *2* — quartz tube, *3* — quartz wool, *4* — catalyst, *5* — connection to the gas chromatograph, *6* — block of elporite, *7* — membrane, *8* — copper block, *9* — heating element.

the microreactor is 0.1–0.8 cm^3. The reactor temperature may vary from the minimum — the oven temperature needed for effective separation of the reaction mixture in the column — to a maximum of around 773 K. The oven temperature is measured with a thermocouple. The microreactor has thick walls (about 10 mm), which enables a uniform temperature to be obtained throughout the catalyst layer; moreover, it ensures the stability of the reactor temperature — this is important when highly exothermic and endothermic reactions are taking place there.

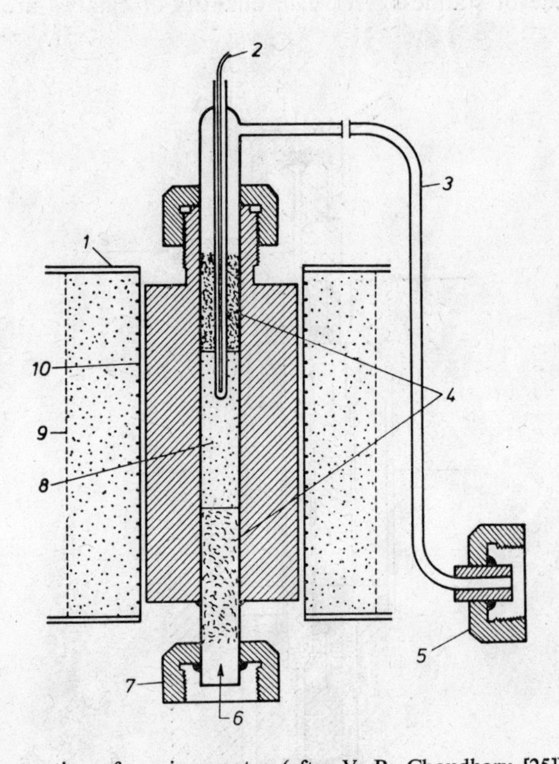

Fig. 12.6 Cross-section of a microreactor (after V. R. Choudhary [25]):

1 — oven, *2* — thermocouple, *3* — tube connecting the microreactor and chromatograph, *4* — glass or quartz wool, *5* — column inlet, *6* — carrier gas, *7* — injection port, *8* — catalyst, *9* — insulation, *10* — heating element.

The Ettre and Brenner microreactor [16] is the most commonly used type, and can be connected to any kind of gas chromatograph (a Perkin–Elmer instrument is shown in Fig. 12.7). The microreactor, a stainless steel tube (internal diameter about 1.0 cm, external diameter about 1.3 cm, length about 10 cm) is placed in an electric oven (Fig. 12.8). It is connected to one of two standard six-way taps. By turning the first feeder tap the gas sample is taken by the carrier gas to the microreactor, and then to the chromatographic column. The mixture of substrates can be analysed directly by by-passing the reactor.

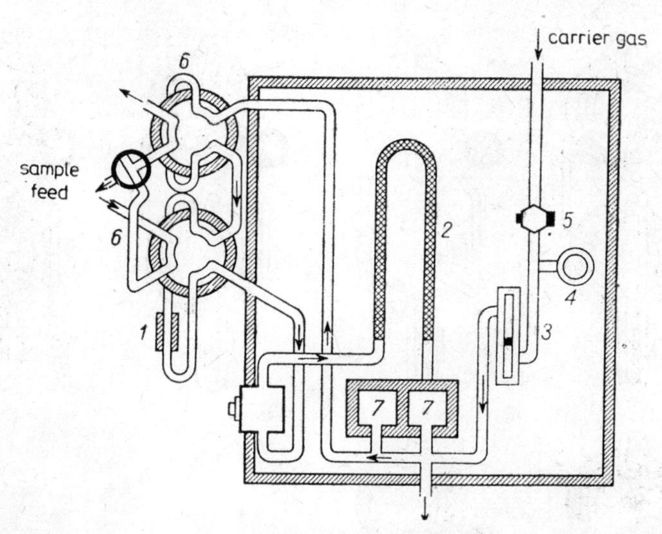

Fig. 12.7 Ettre and Brenner pulse microreactor (after L. S. Ettre and N. J. Brenner [16]):
1 — microreactor, *2* — chromatographic column, *3* — flow-meter, *4* — manometer, *5* — pressure control, *6* — six-way valves, *7* — detector.

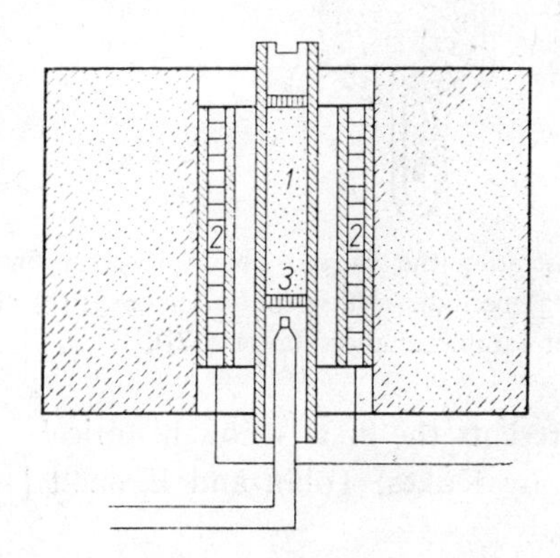

Fig. 12.8 Cross-section of the Ettre–Brenner microreactor (after [17]):
1 — catalyst, *2* — heating elements, *3* — thermocouple.

Figure 12.9 illustrates the three operating arrangements available on the Ettre and Brenner microreactor depending on the alignment of the six-way taps:

(a) periodic testing (pulse technique);
(b) continuous testing (microreactor flow method);
(c) direct analysis of samples.

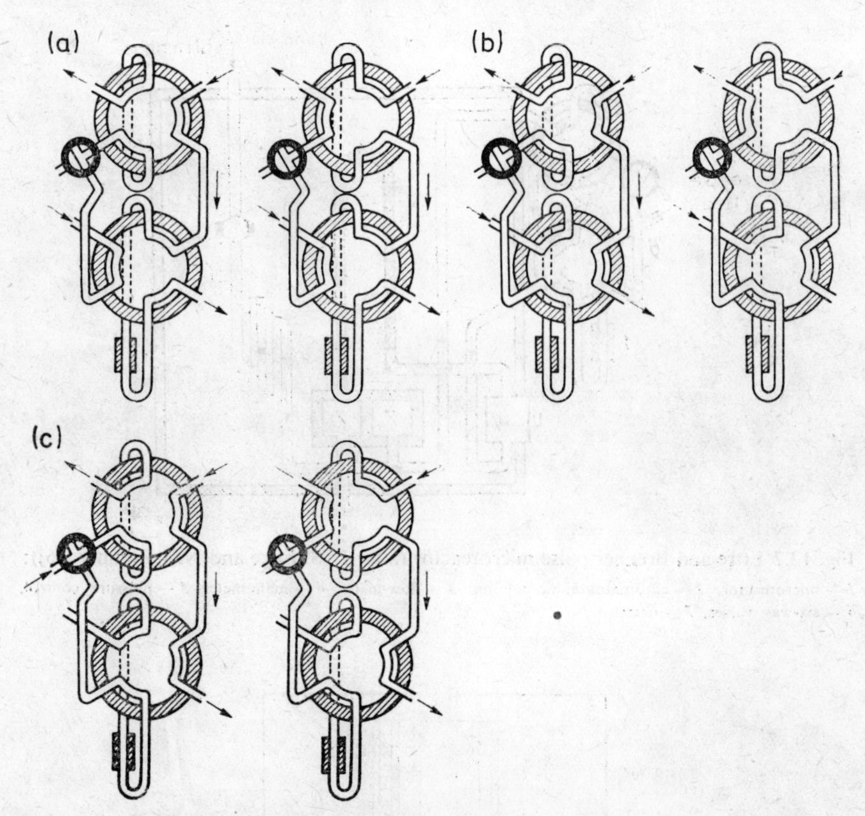

Fig. 12.9 Diagram illustrating the various operating arrangements of the Ettre and Brenner microreactor: (a) periodic testing (pulse method); (b) continuous testing (flow microreactor); (c) direct sample analysis (after [17]).

Figure 12.10 presents the first — now historical — microcatalytic apparatus constructed by Kokes, Tobin and Emmett [18] for studying the activity of catalysts.

12.3 Methods of Connecting the Microreactor to the Chromatographic Apparatus

Studies using the microreactor can be carried out pulse-wise or continuously [19]. The pulse techniques can be sub-divided into static and dynamic techniques.

In the static technique, the reactants are periodically injected into the reaction chamber and left there for a certain time (even until equi-

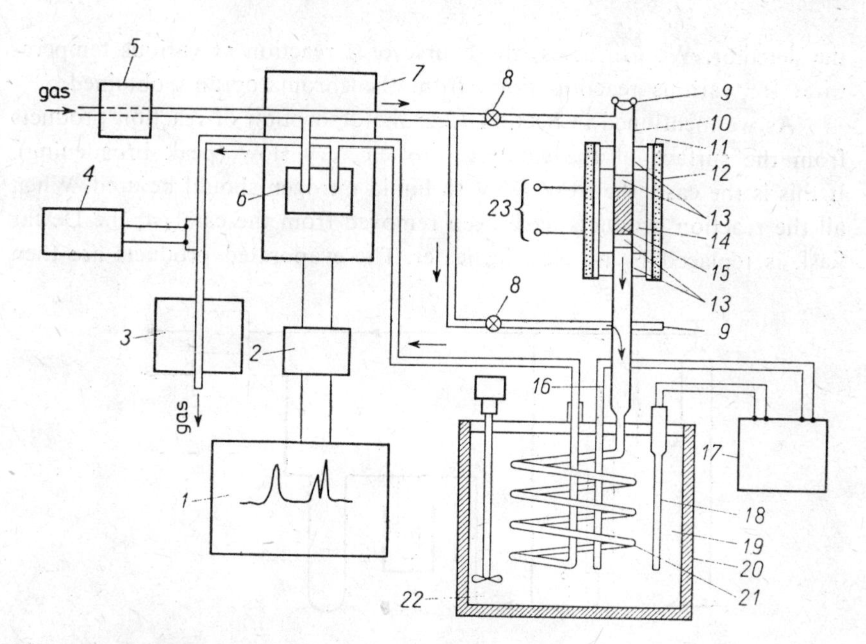

Fig. 12.10 Block diagram of microcatalytic apparatus including a radiometric instrument (after R. J. Kokes *et al.* [18]):

1 — recording device, *2* — bridge, *3* — humidity detector, *4* — Geiger counter, *5* — pressure control, *6* — thermal conductivity detector, *7* — air thermostat, *8* — tap, *9* — rubber bungs, *10* — reaction tube (E. D. 8 mm), *11* — ceramic tube (I. D. 25.4 mm), *12* — heating coil, *13* — glass wool, *14* — reactor, *15* — layer of catalyst, *16* — temperature control, *17* — electronic relay, *18* — heater, *19* — oil bath, *20* — Dewar flask, *21* — chromatographic column made from a steel tube (I.D. 4.6 mm), *22* — chromatograph thermostat, *23* — autotransformers.

librium has been reached), after which the products are analysed chromatographically. A block diagram showing how the microreactor is connected for the static technique with parallel flow of carrier gas through both detector cells is given in Fig. 12.11.

The carrier gas separates into two circuits, whose flows can be controlled precisely in order to maintain the base line. One stream of gas flows through the comparator cell of detector *10*, the other flows through the microreactor *5* containing catalyst *7*, then through the chromatographic column *9* and the measurement cell of the detector *10*. After injecting the reactants *6*, the microreactor is shut off by closing taps *2* and *3*. The carrier gas is passed through tap *4* on to the column and the measurement cell of the detector. After some time has elapsed, tap *4* is closed and taps *2* and *3* are opened. The reaction products are then eluted by the carrier gas, separated on the column and recorded by the measurement cell of the detector. We can assess the course of a reaction at various temperatures for various reaction times from the chromatograms obtained.

As we mentioned in Section 12.2, the desorption of reaction products from the surface of the catalyst is often very slow (peak broadening). If this is the case, the freezer *8* with liquid nitrogen should be used. When all the reaction products have been removed from the catalyst, the Dewar flask is replaced by an electric heater. The evaporated products are then

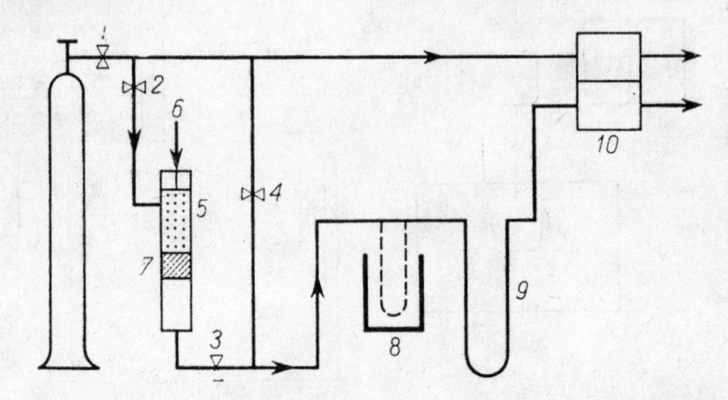

Fig. 12.11 Block diagram showing how the microreactor is connected for the pulse technique with parallel flow of carrier gas through both detector cells (after W. Celler [19]): *1, 2, 3, 4* — taps, *5* — microreactor, *6* — injection port, *7* — catalyst, *8* — freezer containing liquid nitrogen (or a small heater during evaporation), *9* — chromatographic column, *10* — detector.

analysed on the chromatograph. Figure 12.12 is a block diagram of the pulse technique apparatus with series flow of carrier gas.

The apparatus in Figs. 12.11 and 12.12 can also be used for the flow pulse technique. Tap *4* is then shut all the time while taps *2* and *3* are

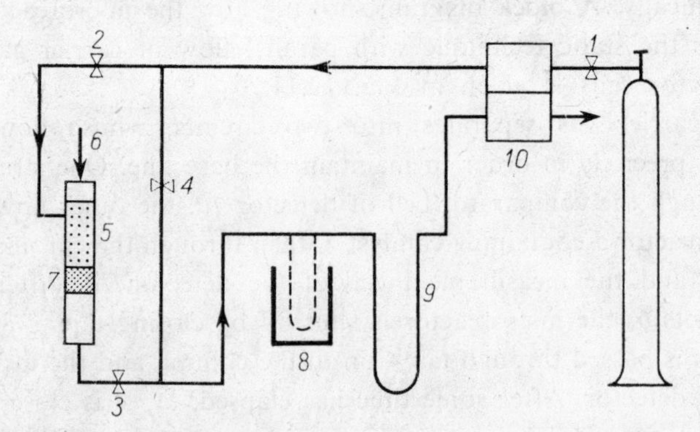

Fig. 12.12 Block diagram showing how the microreactor is connected for the pulse technique with series flow of carrier gas; details as in Fig. 12.11 (after W. Celler [19]).

open. The flow technique is used to test the catalytic activity of catalysts. Figure 12.13 is a block diagram of the apparatus used for carrying out reactions under so-called chromatographic conditions (Chapter 11).

In this method the long layer of catalyst in the reactor is at the same time the chromatographic column. As was mentioned in Chapter 11, this method is applied mainly in the study of the mechanisms of catalytic reactions.

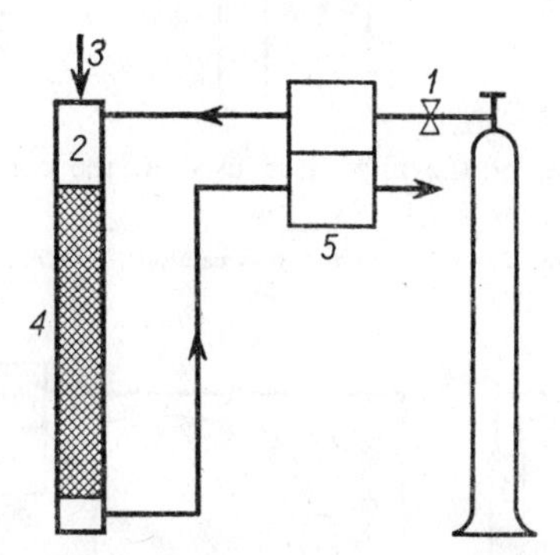

Fig. 12.13 Block diagram of the apparatus used for testing reactions under chromatographic conditions (after W. Celler [19]):
1 — tap, *2* — microreactor, *3* — injection port, *4* — catalyst, *5* — detector.

Continuous methods can be divided into continuous integral and differential methods [19]. Where reactants are continuously added in a continuous method, the reaction products are also removed continuously.

Figure 12.14 is a block diagram of the apparatus used in the continuous integral method. Reactants pass through tap *1* and into the microreactor *5*, then through tap *2* to the measurement capillary of feeder valve *4*, from where they escape into the atmosphere. To analyse the products of a reaction, the feeder valve is turned and the reaction products in the measurement capillary are swept into the chromatographic column by the carrier gas.

In continuous differential methods (flow-circulation), the reaction mixture passes through the layer of catalyst many times. The substrates in circulation are a very small part of the circulating reaction mixture; hence they do not affect the extent of conversion being established in the reactor. The removed products are also a small part of the circulating mixture. A block diagram of the apparatus used in the continuous differential method is shown in Fig. 12.15. The reaction mixture, pumped by the circulating pump *9*, passes many times through the catalyst in the

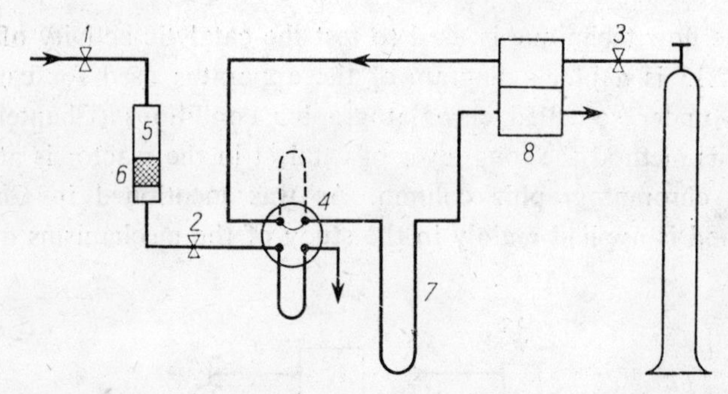

Fig. 12.14 Block diagram of the apparatus used in the continuous integral method (after W. Celler [19]):

1, 2, 3 — taps, *4* — feeder valve, *5* — microreactor, *6* — catalyst, *7* — chromatographic column, *8* — detector.

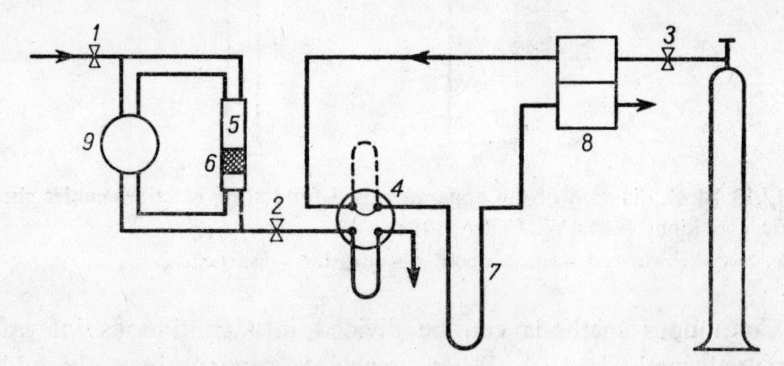

Fig. 12.15 Block diagram of microcatalytic apparatus used in the continuous differential method (flow-circulation) (after W. Celler [19]):

1-8 as in Fig. 12.14, *9* — circulation pump.

microreactor *5*. The substrates are fed in through tap *1*, while the products of the reaction are drawn off through tap *2* to the feeder valve capillary *4* from where they pass into the atmosphere. Analysis of products is performed in the same way as in the continuous integral method.

Figures 12.16 and 12.17 show block diagrams of microcatalytic apparatus for determining catalytic activity using the pulse technique and the continuous method. Such apparatus is widely used [20] in the petroleum industry. In the saturator *7*, the carrier gas becomes saturated with the vapours of the reactants.

Figures 12.18–12.21 illustrate various other sets of apparatus for studying catalytic reactions with the aid of GC.

The microcatalytic methods mentioned above have been modified in various ways, but their basic principle remains the same [21–38].

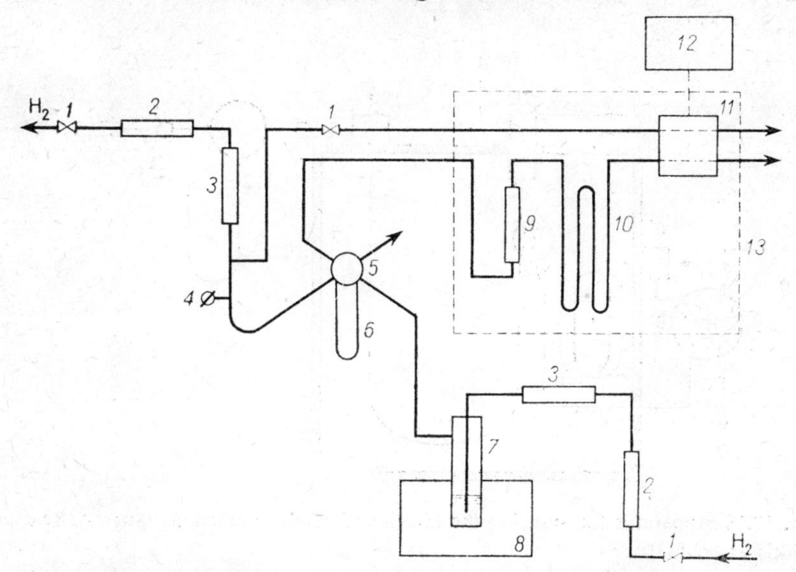

Fig. 12.16 Block diagram of the microcatalytic apparatus using the pulse technique (after M. Barbul *et al.* [20]):

1 — control vents, *2, 3* — purifier and dessicator, *4* — manometer, *5* — feeder valve, *6* — feeder capillary, *7* — saturator, *8* — ultrathermostat, *9* — microreactor, *10* — chromatographic column, *11* — katharometer, *2* — recorder, *13* — thermostat.

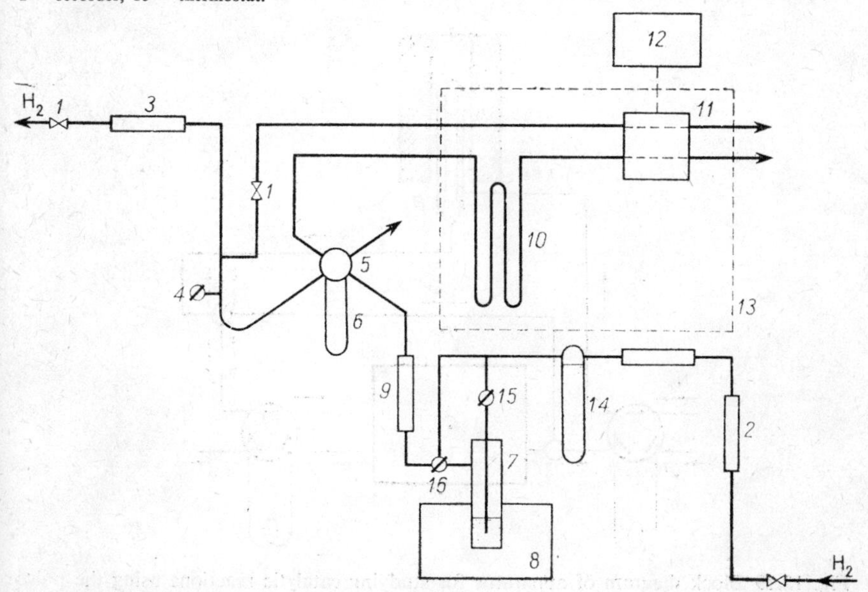

Fig. 12.17 Block diagram of microcatalytic apparatus using the continuous differential method (after M. Barbul *et al.* [20]):

1-13 as in Fig. 12.16; *14* — flow-meter, *15, 16* — taps.

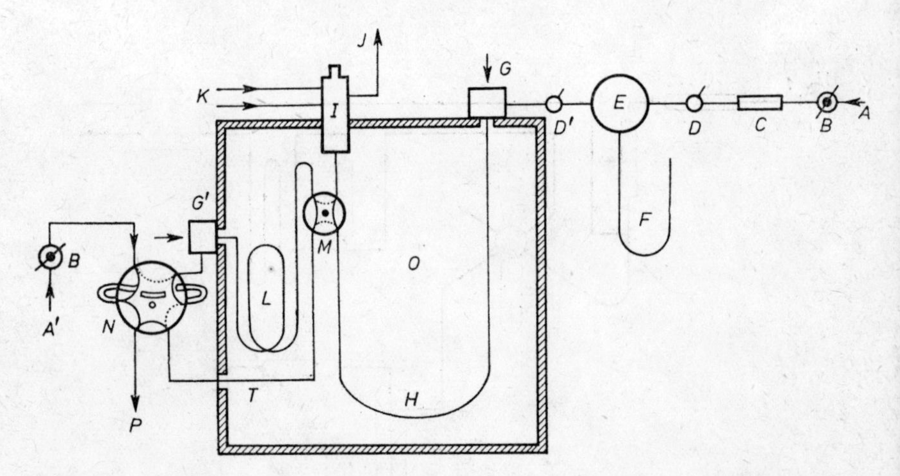

Fig. 12.18 Apparatus for studying the kinetics of catalytic reactions (after A. Lycourghiotis *et al.* [33]):

A, *A'* — carrier gas (nitrogen) for the catalytic and analytical columns, *B* — control valves, *C* — gas dessication tube, *D*, *D'* — valves, *E* — equalising tank, *F* — manometer, *G*, *G'* — injection ports to catalytic and analytical columns respectively, *H* — catalytic column, *I* — flame ionisation detector, *J* — signal to amplifier and recorder, *K* — hydrogen and air for the detector, *L* — analytical column, *M* — four-way tap, *N* — six-way tap, *O* — gas chromatograph heater, *P* — outlet to atmosphere, *T* — 2.5 mm-diameter tube.

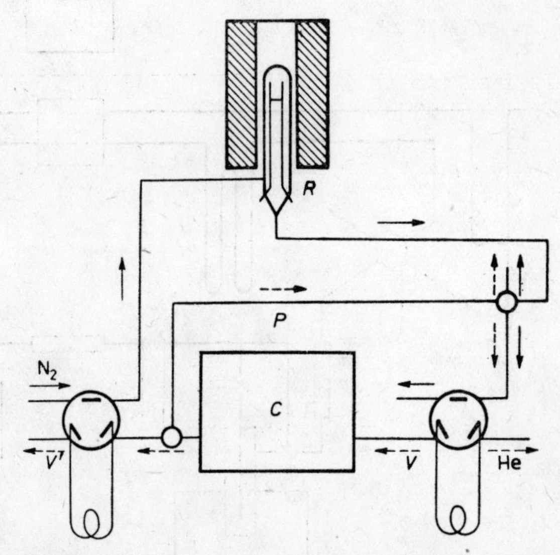

Fig. 12.19 Block diagram of apparatus for studying catalytic reactions using the pulse technique (after G. Perot *et al.* [29]):

C — chromatograph, *P* — further product purification route, *R* — reactor, *V*, *V'* — six-way connecting valves.

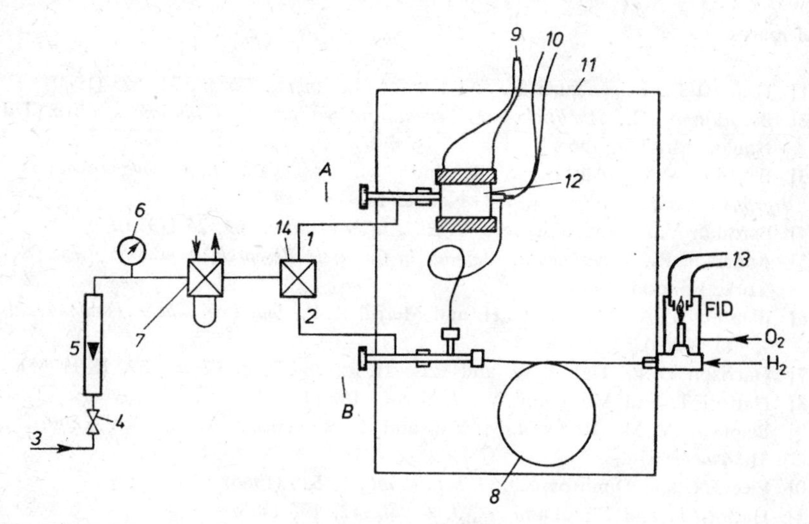

Fig. 12.20 Diagram of apparatus for studying catalytic reactions (after V. R. Choudhary [25]):

1, 2 — directions of gas flow through the selective valve, *3* — carrier gas, *4* — control valve, *5* — rotameter, *6* — manometer, *7* — feeder valve, *8* — chromatographic column, *9* — to temperature measurement, *10* — thermocouple, *11* — thermostatted part of chromatograph, *12* — microreactor, *13* — to recorder, *14* — selective valve.

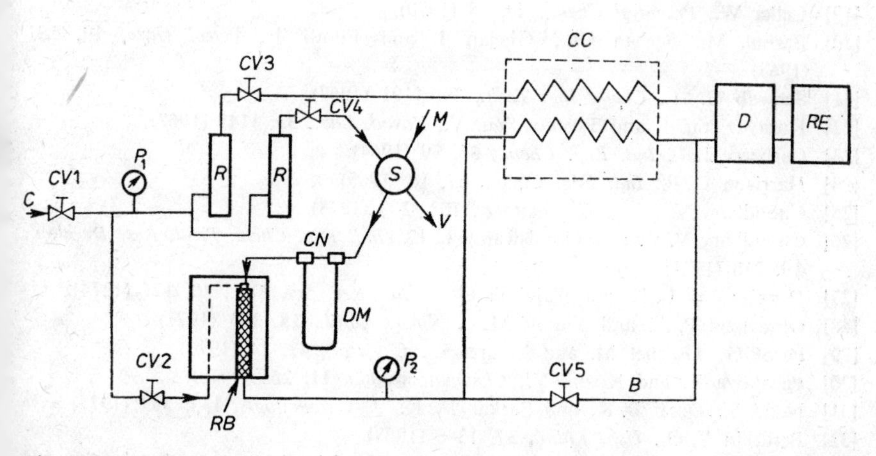

Fig. 12.21 Diagram of apparatus for studying catalytic reactions (after S. Nand *et al.* [31]):

B — tube by-passing chromatographic column, *C* — carrier gas, *CC* — chromatographic column, *D* — detector, *CN* — constriction, *CV* — control valves, *DM* — manometer, *M* — reactants, $P_1 P_2$ — manometers, *R* — rotameters, *RB* — reactor, *RE* — recorder, *S* — feeder valve, *V* — vent.

References

[1] Drawert F., Felgenhauer R. and Kupfer G., *Angew. Chem.*, **72**, 555 (1960).

[2] Berezkin V. G., *Analiticheskaya reaktsyonnaya gazovaya khromatografiya*, Izd. Nauka, Moskva, 1966.

[3] Berezkin V. G., Alishoev V. R. and Nemirovskaya I. B., *Gazovaya khromatografiya v khimi polimerov*, Izd. Nauka, Moskva, 1972.

[4] Berezkin V. G. and Shiryaeva V. E., *J. Chromatogr.*, **69**, 25 (1972).

[5] Anderson R., *Experimental Methods in Catalytic Research*, Academic Press, New York, London, 1968.

[6] Blanton W. A. Jr, Byers C. H. and Merrill R. P., *Ind. Eng. Chem. Fundamentals*, **7**, 611 (1968).

[7] Harrison D. P., Hall J. W. and Rase H. F., *Ind. Eng. Chem.*, **57**, 18 (1965).

[8] Hattori T. and Murakami Y., *J. Catal.*, **10**, 114 (1968).

[9] Belousov V. M., Rubanik M. Ya. and Gershingorina A. V., *Ukr. Khim. Zh.*, **31**, 444 (1965).

[10] Licev N. and Dimitrov Kh., *Kinet. Katal.*, **7**, 536 (1966).

[11] Hattori T. and Murakami Y., *J. Catal.*, **12**, 196 (1968).

[12] Boreskov G. K., *Kinet. Katal.*, **3**, 470 (1962).

[13] Temkin M. I., *Kinet. Katal.*, **3**, 509 (1962).

[14] Schukin V. P. and Venyaminov S. A., *Kinet. Katal.*, **12**, 533 (1971).

[15] Steingaszner P. and Pines H., *J. Catal.*, **5**, 356 (1966).

[16] Ettre L. S. and Brenner N. J., *J. Chromatogr.*, **3**, 524 (1960).

[17] Instructions to the Perkin-Elmer Microreactor.

[18] Kokes R. J., Tobin H. and Emmett P. H., *J. Am. Chem. Soc.*, **77**, 5860 (1955).

[19] Celler W., *Przemysł Chem.*, **49**, 68 (1970).

[20] Barbul M., Serban Gh., Ghejan I. and Filotti T., *Petrol Gaze*, **19**, 181 (1968).

[21] Schwab G. M., *Chem. Ing. Tech.*, **39**, 1191 (1967).

[22] Kusayev Yu. I. and Tsvekov Yu. V., *Zavod. Lab.*, **33**, 1145 (1967).

[23] Carberry J. J., *Ind. Eng. Chem.*, **56**, 39 (1964).

[24] Harrison D. P., *Ind. Eng. Chem.*, **57**, 18 (1965).

[25] Choudhary V. R., *J. Chromatogr.*, **152**, 208 (1978).

[26] Choudhary V. R. and Doraiswamy L. K., *Ind. Eng. Chem. Prod. Res. Develop.*, **10**, 218 (1971).

[27] Doraiswamy L. K. and Tajbl D. G., *Catal. Rev. Sci. Eng.*, **10**, 177 (1974).

[28] Obraztsov P. A. and Vinnik M. I., *Kinet. Katal.*, **18**, 103 (1977).

[29] Perot G., Guisnet M. and Maurel R., *J. Catal.*, **41**, 14 (1976).

[30] Pacakova V. and Kozlik V., *Chromatographia*, **11**, 266 (1978).

[31] Nand S., Desai B. K. and Sarkar M. K., *J. Chromatogr.*, **133**, 359 (1977).

[32] Berezkin V. G., *Usp. Khim.*, **37**, 1348 (1968).

[33] Lycourghiotis A., Katsanos N. A. and Hadzistelios I., *J. Catal.*, **36**, 386 (1975).

[34] Vanko A. and Repášová I., *J. Chromatogr.*, **91**, 733 (1974).

[35] Hall W. K. and Emmett P. H., *J. Am. Chem. Soc.*, **79**, 2091 (1957).

[36] Steingaszner P. in: *Ancillary Techniques of Gas Chromatography*, Eds. Ettre L. S. and McFadden W. H., Wiley-Interscience, New York, 1969, pp. 13–53.
[37] Mochida I. and Yoneda Y., *J. Catal.*, **7**, 386 (1967).
[38] McKinney R. W. in: *Ancillary Techniques of Gas Chromatography*, Eds. Ettre L. S. and McFadden W. H., Wiley-Interscience, New York, 1969, pp. 55–87.
[39] Berezkin V. G., Kruglikova V. S. and Shiryaeva V. E., *Kinet. Katal.*, **6**, 758 (1965).

Author index

Subject Index